The Refugee from Heaven

CORA EVANS

The Refugee from Heaven

Half Moon Bay
2014

The Refugee from Heaven
Cora Evans

Published by The Mystical Humanity of Christ, Inc.
CoraEvans.com
MysticalHumanity@aol.com

Book Title: *The Refugee from Heaven*—Cora Evans selected the title of the book from the clear declaration of faith by Saint Dismas, the good thief who was crucified alongside Jesus. (See Book Five, Chapter 18)

To find out more about the author and her writings, go to CoraEvans.com.

Original cover painting by JoAnne Von Zwehl, New York
Cover design by Claudine Monsour Design, Mission Viejo, California
Interior design by Sherry Russell Design, Pasadena, California

Library of Congress Cataloging-in-Publication Data
Evans, Cora
The Refugee from Heaven

ISBN 978-0-9910506-2-8 Hardback
ISBN 978-0-9910506-0-4 Paperback
ISBN 978-0-9910506-1-1 Electronic book text

Printed in the United States of America

PUBLISHER'S STATEMENT

The Refugee from Heaven is based on the private revelations of Cora Evans.

Public Revelation—Sacred Scripture

The Catholic Church recognizes the clear distinction between public and private revelation. Public revelation, meaning the Old and New Testaments, ended with the death of the last apostle. It is complete; the age of public revelation is closed and there will be no new public revelation.

It is no longer public revelation [Sacred Scripture] that grows, but we grow in our comprehension of it.

Private Revelation—A Possible Means To Growth And Understanding

The purpose of private revelation is to help a particular soul grow in faith and to develop a greater love of God.

For even though public revelation is already complete, it has not been made completely explicit; it remains for Christian faithful gradually to grasp its full significance over the course of centuries. Throughout the ages, there have been so-called private revelations, some of which have been recognized by the authority of the Church [Saint Bernadette of Lourdes, Saint Catherine of Siena, Saint Margaret Mary, Saint Faustina]. It is not the role of private revelation to improve or complete Christ's definitive Revelation, but to help live more fully by it in a certain period of history.[1]

---

1 *Catechism of the Catholic Church* (65,66): Second Edition, revised in accordance with the official Latin text promulgated by Pope John Paul II in 1997.

RECOGNITION

The Mystical Humanity of Christ, Inc.,
Gratefully acknowledges the Extraordinary Generosity
of the
Theresa and Edward O'Toole Foundation
Bert Degheri, Co-Trustee

PUBLISHER'S ACKNOWLEDGEMENTS

The mission entrusted to Cora Evans continues and we wish to express appreciation to Dorothy Evans, daughter of Cora Evans, Bob Spaulding, nephew of Cora Evans, Irene and Mark Montgomery, June Haver MacMurray (deceased), Kate MacMurray, Al Marsella, Msgr. Padraic Loftus, Joe Berberich, Don Ryan, Rob Smith, Michael McEntee, Peter Marlow and Peter Marlow Jr., Jennifer Martin, Gabrielle Lien, and her late husband, Warren. Thank you Patrice Bennett for printing support, and Christine Bellefontaine for her generosity. Special appreciation is expressed to the Jesuits of the California province, Fr. Vito Perrone, COSJ, and Fr. Gary Thomas for their spiritual support and advice, Richard Beemer for editing, Rob Bussell (deceased) for his inspiration and participation, Michael Huston, advisor, retreat leader and board member, and Pamela McDevitt, for her encouragement and guidance. Thank you Joanne Von Zwehl for the cover painting of Jesus inspired by this book.

DEDICATION

The publisher appreciates the role of Fr. Frank Parrish, S.J., who entrusted us with the writings of Cora Evans and the responsibility to promulgate the Mystical Humanity of Christ.

Our Lord Jesus Christ said,

"WATCH AND PRAY WITH ME."

This is an answer to that invitation.

Contents

BOOK ONE

The First Retreat

1. The Nazarene 17
2. The Nazarene Is Loved by the Crew 23
3. John Baptizes Simon 31
4. The Baptism of Jesus. 35
5. The Island 43
6. John's Temple 49
7. The First Retreat: Part One 55
8. The First Retreat: Part Two 61

BOOK TWO

John

1. Jesus Returns to the Mainland 69
2. The Fires of the Sacred Heart. 75
3. Nazareth 81
4. Magdala. 87
5. The Birth of Jesus 93
6. Visit of the Magi 99
7. Joseph 105
8. Rachel and the Mother of Mary Magdala. 113
9. The Dungeon 121

10. Herod . . . 129
11. Salome . . . 133
12. The Burial . . . 139

BOOK THREE

The Last Mass

1. Dismas . . . 149
2. The Little Children . . . 157
3. The Brother of Rachel . . . 165
4. The Storm on the Lake . . . 171
5. The Last Hour . . . 179
6. The Last Mass . . . 187

BOOK FOUR

Mary of Magdala

1. Jesus Comes to Bethany . . . 197
2. The Eyes of a Little Boy . . . 201
3. The Preparation . . . 209
4. The Meeting . . . 215

BOOK FIVE

The Cross

1. The First Holy Sacrifice . . . 225
2. Consecration of the Wine . . . 233
3. Peter's Hands . . . 241

4. The Exchange of Hearts 245
5. Peter's Enthronement 253
6. The Beginning of the Agony: The Holy Grave 259
7. Watch and Pray 267
8. Jesus Prays Alone 277
9. The Sword 287
10. The White Rose of Consolation 297
11. The Sanhedrin 307
12. Pilate 311
13. Death of Judas 319
14. The Scourging 327
15. Jesus Carries the Cross 337
16. Jesus Is Nailed to the Cross 345
17. Peter's Ecstasy 353
18. Jesus Dies 361

BOOK SIX

The Resurrection

1. Fear 373
2. Jesus Is Taken down from the Cross 381
3. The Burial 389
4. The First Love Feast: The Sealing of the Sepulcher 399
5. The Resurrection: Inside the Sepulcher 411
6. The Resurrection: Jesus Comes through the Sepulcher 419
7. Jesus Appears in the Dungeon 427

Epilogue 433

BOOK ONE

The First Retreat

CHAPTER 1

The Nazarene

AN ATTRACTIVE, MIDDLE-AGED woman and her small grandson walked slowly along the shores of Mount Carmel Bay, and looked out anxiously across the rough waters of the Mediterranean Sea. Gently, yet firmly, the woman held fast to the boy's small, chubby hand as he tried to free himself to run with the receding surf that creamed white just beyond his feet. They were waiting and watching for the appearance of fishing ships on the far-distant horizon.

The boy tried to wrest his hand from hers, and the woman said with a trace of sternness in her voice, "Not now, son. Another day you may chase the seabirds and race the surf. Now, we must watch and pray for your grandfather's safe return with his men and ships."

The boy asked, "How long will that be?"

"He should arrive before sundown," his grandmother answered. "Come, let us watch."

Within an hour several other women and children, as well as many aged and poor, assembled on the beach. Carefully they scanned the watery horizon for the waving banners of Simon's fishing fleet.

Simon was known throughout this land as the greatest captain of the sea. Although self-skilled in navigation, it was claimed he had never lost a ship. Nor had he ever turned away the poor when they asked for fish as he lay anchored in the bay. He always listened kindly to the oppressed and the afflicted and offered them words of counsel on faith and loyalty to God above and beyond their thoughts of self. He was strong, courageous, just, and charitable.

A faithful worshiper, he often prayed in the synagogues with his brother, Andrew. It was not at all uncommon to hear Simon praise Andrew's charitable prayers and sacrifices, for he believed those prayers to be direct channels of his good fortune in finding the best schools of fish in the rivers of the sea. Many people believed him wealthy, for he owned the largest fishing fleet in that district. However, he was not, because of his excessive charity for the poor.

Suddenly, a joyous cry arose from the crowd. Black specks, tiny on that great waste of water, were Simon's fleet and they grew taller, inch by inch, as they slowly climbed the steps of the sea toward the dry land.

Presently one ship could be seen ahead of the others. It was Simon's and its great banners of crimson and gold waved high on the ocean's breeze. Eagerly those on shore listened to the deep tones of its great bell, which told them that all was well. Faintly its sound carried to them above the crashing roar of the breakers.

Two hours later the ships anchored. Simon immediately leaped overboard and swam toward the shore where his wife and his grandson, hand in hand, stood ankle-deep in the frothing surf. He greeted them with most tender affection and together they waded to the dry land. All about them others were greeting their men as they swam in from the ships.

As Simon dried the sea water from his powerful arms and shoulders, Rosa Maria told him the news of the village. It was all very commonplace and uninteresting, except for the fact that he was expected to appear, even at this late hour, before the local council of the Sanhedrin.

Simon's deep voice growled above the pounding of the waves and then subsided as he learned that he must defend one of his own fishermen. He was content then. Who else would protect his men if he, Simon, did not?

Sending his wife and his grandson on ahead to the village, Simon shouted orders to his fishermen and to the sailors still aboard the ships. Almost immediately great copper kettles, measuring some four feet across, appeared over the sides and were floated shoreward. As they drew nearer, other sailors grasped them and dragged them up on the beach. They were filled to the brim with fish—Simon's present to the aged and the poor. He smiled contentedly as he watched them push forward, thanksgiving upon their lips.

As Simon started for Mount Carmel and the Sanhedrin, he noticed a tall, well-built Stranger reclining on the beach watching the scene with great interest. He seemed intrigued with the quick obedience given Simon by his men and by the calmness and the order with which the people emptied the great kettles.

As Simon approached, the Stranger arose and stood watching him. Simon wondered who He was and from where He might have come, for he was quite sure he had never seen Him before. Then his interest quickened and deepened beneath the impact of the calm dignity of this Man. As he drew nearer he could see His beautiful eyes quite clearly and that He was not a sailor, for His magnificent hands were not thick and calloused. Yet he seemed intensely interested in the laborious work of the crew and in their care of the poor.

The Stranger smiled at Simon's expression of puzzlement. "Good evening, Captain of the Sea," He said quietly. "I have long looked forward to meeting you, for I have heard much that is good about you. Your countrymen praise you highly for the discipline with which you govern your men. I must also praise them for their obedience to your least command. Such cheerfulness can only be the result of the justice and the charity of the man who captains them."

Simon stood quite still as though stunned. Never had he heard such a voice, nor had he ever been so praised before. Most men remained silent in his presence, for was he not the captain, and did not men out of respect wait for him to speak first? He asked, "Who are you, sir? Thank you for what you have said, but I am sure I do not deserve your praise."

The Stranger's voice was even more quiet than before as He answered, "I am Jesus of Nazareth. It is an honor, Captain, to speak with you."

As Simon opened his mouth to make reply, he was interrupted by shouts and commotion on board his ship. As he peered through the rays of the golden sun he could see two men lashing at each other with long, silver fish, using them as though they were swords.

Silent indignation flashed from Simon's eyes as he shouted a command to cease. The men did not hear him. Angrily, he then strode through the surf and swam quickly to the ship.

Grasping a low hanging, knotted rope, he swung himself over the bow. Without questioning either fighter, he picked up one from the deck and hurled him into the sea. The other he ordered back to work. It was too bad the Stranger from Nazareth had seen that breach of discipline, but then he had handled it well enough.

Once more on shore Simon brushed sand and water from his feet and said, "I'm sorry about that disturbance, but it was easily taken care of. However, now I shall have to be going, for there is a matter in town that demands my attention. Good day, sir. I hope I shall see you again."

He started away. He was filled with satisfaction over the way he had handled the fight and in the kind nod the Nazarene had given him. He was glad his countrymen respected him for his many virtues of justice and charity. It gave him a nice, warm feeling.

"Captain," the Nazarene said, "I know you are a man in favor of strict justice, and I was just wondering whether or not you threw the right man overboard?"

Simon came to a sudden stop. Had he been just? He hadn't allowed either man to explain what had happened. He suddenly became uneasily aware of rash judgment.

Without a glance at Jesus, Simon crossed the beach and once more plunged into the sea. When he reached his ship he climbed aboard, hand-over-hand. Finding the other offender, he quietly and without a word threw him over the side.

His crew looked at him in amazement. They had never before seen their captain in such hasty action, nor was he usually so easily angered. What in the world was the matter with him?

In answer to their questions Simon said, "I was profoundly disturbed with the thought that I had acted unwisely and unjustly toward the first offender by throwing him overboard, while the second offender merely resumed his work. Now, I have treated them with equal justice."

He buffeted his way to shore. Once there he nodded cheerfully to Jesus as if to say, Sir, justice has now been carried out. You need worry no more about it.

"Are you sure, captain," Jesus asked, as Simon once more started away, "that it was a fight, or was it simply boisterous fun among happy men?"

Simon froze as though brought abruptly to attention by a commanding officer. His pride now hurt, he began to wonder why he should be so questioned and disturbed by a Stranger. Turning to Jesus he asked in a tone of agitation, "Why are You, a Nazarene, concerned with what I do? And why do You ask about my men?"

Jesus answered calmly, "A man of justice is disturbed only when he feels guilty of an unjust act pertaining to a question involved at the moment. A just man has a fine conscience—so fine it cuts his soul with the fierceness of a flaming sword when justice is bruised. No one escapes it, for it wounds each man's soul according to the depth of his love for God."

He then extended His arms in blessing. "Simon," He continued, "be absorbed in God. His blessedness of joy, love, and charity are yours. Pray to be a fisherman of souls."

This strange blessing frightened Simon. Suddenly, however, he became aware of an interior feeling of subjection toward the Nazarene where before he had felt a growing animosity. He relaxed his fists at his sides and wondered what kind of power this Man had.

Without speaking, Simon returned again to his ship. He found the two offenders and demanded the reason for their fight. To his surprise he learned it had not been a fight at all, but a mimic duel in which the men had used fish instead of swords. When Simon heard this, he swallowed a little and then apologized as he gave them permission to continue their sport.

This time he was not quick of step when he returned to shore. He was thinking deeply about what had happened and about the holy words of wisdom that the Stranger had spoken. He looked around quickly and discovered Jesus had left the shore and was walking along the path toward the village. He hurried to overtake Him.

When he reached Him and fell into step beside Him he said, "Jesus of Nazareth, are You a tradesman of spice and fine linen? If you are not, perhaps You are a master of wisdom and knowledge?"

"I am not a tradesman," Jesus answered. "In fact, I am a poor man. However, I am a teacher of the philosophy behind the New Law, which is to teach you and everyone else on earth about the love of God."

Simon tried to hide his surprise. Surely this powerful-looking Man could not be a philosopher. Such men were usually frail and hidden in prayer in the synagogues.

He exclaimed, "You're joking with me! I need men like You with good physiques and great knowledge to man my ships. What do You say now? Be here tomorrow before dawn and I'll hire You as my assistant."

Jesus said nothing, so Simon continued, "I would like to learn more of Your wisdom concerning the new way of love for God, for we all expect the Messiah to arrive and dwell with us during this age, as You no doubt well know. However, we don't know just exactly when that will be."

Still Jesus did not say anything. Simon went on, "Work on my ship will be a good change for You. Perhaps You need to get away from the quiet life You must be accustomed to in Nazareth. In fact, if You come with me, You will get an enlightened view of the world and of the people who live about You. In mixing with them, You will realize that the question uppermost in their minds is, when will the Messiah come? Your philosophy should be very useful to all of us after He has arrived. Do you happen to possess facts or figures as to when we might expect Him?"

Jesus smiled slightly as He answered, "I am not seeking work, but I thank you very much for your kind offer. I choose to continue My search for wounded souls, for I can give them hope through the love of God and His mercy. His ways are those of merciful consolation, love, and hope for eternal life after death, since this life soon ends for all of us. I find great joy in doing this, for it makes Me a physician of souls."

Simon marveled at this Man's words. More than ever he wished he could persuade Him to work on his ship. However, if He would not do that, perhaps He would tell his crew just what He had told him. Jesus promised to do as Simon wished the following evening.

The two men parted, and as Simon hurried on into town he thought over what the Nazarene had taught him—especially about guarding against rash judgment, a fault he had failed to see in himself before.

He would have to tell Rosa Marie and Andrew, who lived with them, about this Jesus of Nazareth. He and Andrew had often discussed the coming of the Messiah (as indeed, who had not?), and they had often hoped they might be among the fortunate ones to live on earth when He did come. Anything new concerning Him was of great interest to both of them. Yes, he could hardly wait to tell Andrew about Jesus and about what He had said concerning God.

But first he would have to appear before the Sanhedrin on behalf of the man who needed him. He stepped forward cheerfully into the approaching darkness and was soon lost to sight.

CHAPTER 2

The Nazarene Is Loved by the Crew

ROSA MARIA WAS PREPARING DINNER for Simon and Andrew. She was a small, dark woman with large brown eyes that reflected the gentleness of a lovely culture, and she wore her straight, black hair in two long braids heavily ornamented with strands of pearls. Because she was happy, she laughed with Andrew at her grandson, who was romping with her dog. Yet she knew her brother-in-law was troubled, for she could not help but see how anxiously he watched down the night-filled pathway for the coming of Simon.

She asked quietly, "Are you still wondering whether or not to tell Simon about John?"

"It has been tremendously interesting watching him baptize hundreds of persons, Rosa," Andrew answered somberly, "and to listen to his teachings that his baptism is an outward penance for their sins—a penance that will make their souls pure in the eyes of God before the coming of the Messiah. Did you ever hear anything like that before?"

Rosa shook her head.

"That's just the trouble," Andrew went on. "Neither did anyone else that I know of. And that isn't all. From what he said, you might think the Messiah is already here on earth with us right now!"

Rosa gave a little gasp and stood very still. She asked, "Are you sure, Andrew? There have been so many impostors lately. Even though his actions are ceremonial and seemingly motivated by the most charitable principles, it is still possible that he is not what he seems . . ."

"That's why I'm reluctant to tell Simon about him," Andrew answered quickly. "Why, only a month ago Simon spoke with deep emotion of his soul's loneliness and his longing for the day when God would be with us. It would be cruel to raise his hopes by telling him what the baptizer says if it is false."

Rosa asked, "Isn't there some way you can make sure?"

"I will pray and make inquiries," Andrew answered simply. "I may even question him, directly. Beyond that . . ."

For a few moments there was a deep silence in the room, broken only by the sound of the boy playing with the dog. The Messiah already on earth? Where? Could such a tremendous gift be possible? Wasn't it being presumptuous even to hope for it? Simon had said something like that once.

A bright, gentle light appeared in the depths of Rosa's eyes. She said at length, "I will pray with you, Andrew. What is the other name the baptizer gives to the Messiah?"

Andrew answered softly, "You mean, the Bridegroom?"

"It is a beautiful name," Rosa said slowly. "How could a man who speaks like that be very wrong in what he says?"

Simon came home triumphant, at last, from his appearance before the Sanhedrin, and as the four ate their dinner, he told them about his meeting with the Stranger on the beach that afternoon and of the episode on board his ship. They chuckled over his embarrassment and listened with interest as he even reenacted the mimic duel and confessed his humiliation when he realized his need for God's help and for self-control.

He intended telling them, also, the Nazarene's name and something of His philosophy, but he hesitated for, face-to-face with Andrew, he remembered how unbending he was in his respect for the old laws of Moses. He would have nothing at all to do with these self-styled teachers and preachers that seemed to be springing up everywhere these days. Yet, if one did not listen to them now and then, and sift the evidence of their remarks carefully, how was one to know the truth?

Simon decided not to tell Andrew any more than he had already. For that reason he did not ask him to attend the speech scheduled for the next night.

On his part, Andrew was surprised that Simon had paid the least attention to the Stranger. Could He have been John the Baptizer? If so, He must not have said anything about His doctrine of cleansing souls. For a moment, Andrew toyed with the idea and discarded it as being unlikely. However, John was an orator as well as a man of great wisdom. Andrew determined to listen closely to him the next time he spoke for any word that might correspond with what the Stranger on the beach had said.

The next night Andrew prayed silently in the synagogue for the grace of knowledge and wisdom to analyze John's statements correctly. From whom, and from where did he receive the original principles that he taught?

Andrew felt that he must be a holy man, for it was claimed that he knew loneliness and hunger and had kept long vigils of prayer in the desert. It was also voiced through the land that he was alone in the world, that his relatives were as strangers to him, and that he cared little for current events. People said that his constant companions were pain, fasting, and penance. From all this it would seem that the unction of God must be upon his work, but in spite of it all Andrew still felt the need for further investigation.

On the beach, Simon, with forty of his men, awaited the arrival of the Nazarene. Driftwood fires were ablaze and towering peaks of fire, like golden tongues, cast a copper glow over the black, lapping waves as they rose and fell near the waiting men. Gone from the earth were the last rays of twilight, and all was quiet except for the sound of the sea. Simon caught his breath in wonderment, as the magnificence of a pale moon clothed the restless water in a majestic, shimmering gown of silver blackness that stretched as far as the eye could see beyond the glow of the fires. Even the crew was caught and held in this great shroud of beauty.

Suddenly, Simon jumped to his feet. His quick ear had caught the sound of a footfall. Cupping his hands to his mouth he shouted, "Hello! Are You Jesus of Nazareth?"

The clear, calm answer came back to him, "Yes I am He. I am glad to be here with you, Captain."

Slowly, Jesus emerged from the shadows, and approaching the fires He said kindly, "Simon, may the same measure of peace and symbolic beauty that is in the evening world attain for you, through the Eternal Father, the grace to understand the unchanging truths of love and charity that souls have one for the other."

Simon felt the same awe before this Man that he had experienced the previous afternoon, and again he was at a loss to understand it. Quietly, he introduced Jesus as a philosopher and a carrier of good news concerning the Messiah's reign.

Jesus faced the semi-circle of curious men. With the sighing of the sea in His ears and the fire casting flickering shadows across His face, He spoke to them.

"The ancient prophets," He said, "saw the God-Man in vision, and in this deep prayer of union they were taken up into God's light where there is no time, and in that wisdom where everything is present, they walked and talked with Him."

He told them that the prophets had been deeply grieved when they learned how the Messiah would die on a cross because He was believed to be an impostor. He urged them to study the Scriptures and the words of the prophets so that they would know the Messiah when He came, and thus not have a hand in putting Him to death.

He told them of God's Heart on earth and how that Heart symbolized all truth and infinite love.

"The Sacred Flesh of the Messiah," He said, "will be the castle of the Eternal Father, and the God-Man will say, 'He who sees Me, sees the Father. He and I are One.'"

Jesus continued: "In all things except sin, the Messiah will be like you. Watch and pray so as to recognize Him, for He could be your closest friend. His Heart of fire, like this blazing fire before you, will win eternal life for you if you pray, study, and listen to His words, which are given to you through the prophets.

"Through penance and prayer you will know Him, and the spiritual fire within you will become His other indwelling. Keep that fire burning, don't let it die—as this driftwood fire burns away. You are as worthless pieces of driftwood without the effects of penance, and you are cast out upon a sea of pain and of strife. Your life here on earth is but a means of winning the reward of life everlasting. Win this life everlasting through penance and the love of one for another.

"The God-Man cannot die and His word is truth. Down through the ages and even to this hour He whispers, 'Come to Me!' When you finally know Him you will be symbolically washed ashore and He will enkindle you into the likeness of His Father. Driftwood either becomes waterlogged in the sea, which represents sin, or it washes ashore, there to dry in order to become another transformation. You will be a transformation without sin, which will make you clothed in transfiguration.

"Become brave in the goodness and the likeness of God while you live on earth. All of these things the Messiah will teach you in a greater way when you know Him. He will need brave men—men who are not afraid to expound to the world the brightness of His fire within them."

Jesus told them more, but it all concerned eternal life and God's personal love for each and every one in the world. The driftwood fires at length smoldered into black ashes, and those rough men of the sea wished only one thing above all else on earth—namely, to find the God-Man and to follow Him. None of them had ever heard a man talk as Jesus had, nor say the things He said. From that hour on their lives were changed.

In their new love for God they pledged allegiance to their Creator to be as one in mind and to go in search of the Messiah no matter where He might be. Somehow, they now believed Him to be on earth.

Some of them thought Jesus an inspired prophet filled with wisdom and a gift of speech. Others wondered whether or not He might even be the Messiah, for He was to them as they would want the Messiah to be, a Man filled with understanding, kindness, and cheerfulness. Yet they did not dare ask Him. How they wished they were scholars of Scripture for then they would know, as He had told them. They at length contented themselves by pleading with Him to visit them again and to tell them where they might begin their search for the Messiah and into what far lands they must travel.

Jesus answered by bowing His head and praying silently for them to receive the grace of faith. It was not yet time for Him to tell them who He was, for He wanted them first to have greater merit by searching for Him.

When He had gone, Simon dropped to his knees in the sand. One by one his men followed suit. They prayed that God would accept their pledge to search for the Messiah, and they pleaded with Him to make them His bodyguard, His providers, and the worshipers of His love. Eager to begin their search, they hoped God would chart their course so that success might at last be theirs.

Simon at length returned home. In answer to the question in Rosa's dark eyes, he took her into his confidence and enthusiastically told her of the wonderful talk Jesus had given, and how he and his men had pledged themselves to leave all earthly possessions and careers and go in search of the Messiah.

Icy fingers plunged deep into Rosa's heart and then just as suddenly vanished. At that instant she was drawn into the same loving grace that God had given to Simon. She begged to be allowed to see and hear Jesus, too, the next time He spoke. Simon readily gave his permission, but asked her to stay back out of sight. Rosa promised happily.

But, what to tell Andrew? For the time being, Simon did not know, and he asked Rosa not to say anything to him about the incidents and the decisions of that night. Andrew was certain not to approve.

Rosa kept the secrets of both men deeply within her heart. She prayed constantly during the days that followed, for God's guidance over them, for surely both could not be right.

A strange restlessness, coupled with a loneliness they did not understand, descended upon Simon and his men during the following week. They agreed that they missed the company of Jesus. But why should this be true of a man they had known for only such a short time?

Simon decided to go in search of Him. He found Him in Mount Carmel talking to a group of men, explaining the views of the prophets on earthquakes, floods, and the end of the world. None of these questions and answers were of the slightest interest to Simon. All he wanted to hear, and to learn, was the New Law of Love, and how he could begin his search for the Messiah. He firmly believed that such a man of wisdom and oratorical powers, as Jesus was, must be a great prophet of God.

Jesus recognized him almost at once in the crowd and waved a welcome to him, "Simon, come nearer! I hoped you would come in search of Me. I have missed you. Rest here on this bench while I finish with the question just presented to Me."

It was dark by the time Jesus and Simon, arm in arm, reached the beach once more. The driftwood fires were lighted and the men huddled about them, for the night was cold. To a man, they greeted Jesus enthusiastically.

This time the Nazarene's sermon treated of obedience to the Messiah. "Each individual soul," He said, "must rise to a state of interior peace above the anxious bodily interests of intemperance, lust, impatience, and avarice. Self-sacrifice and self-restraint are easy when God's love is the motive that absorbs a soul for its eternal gain."

As Jesus talked, Rosa Maria made her way quietly through the darkness to a position just beyond the crowd of holy listeners. There she knelt, in the shadows, listening intensely to the Nazarene's voice, which blended with the hum of the inky black waves that splashed near her feet. She believed what He said and she instantly loved His voice and His calm kindness. But above all these virtues, she loved the assurance He gave her soul, the assurance not to fear God but to love Him. As she listened, she understood why Simon was willing to sell all of his possessions and leave her alone. She, too, would like to leave all cares and go in search of the living Messiah.

At last the sermon was over, and as Simon walked slowly home he was joined by Rosa. Both were filled with gladness and peace; both felt the new birth of God's love within their souls.

As they entered their home they saw Andrew on his knees caught up in the deepest prayer of quiet. Silently, they knelt beside him. Andrew prayed for wisdom in regard to John's teaching, while Simon prayed for the grace with which to find the Messiah. Rosa prayed for the intentions of both men and for the hidden desires that they kept from each other. Was it possible, she asked herself, as she looked from one to the other, that both could be right?

CHAPTER 3

John Baptizes Simon

SEVERAL WEEKS LATER, Simon, his wife, Andrew, and the crew left Mount Carmel and traveled to Lake Galilee. This was their custom, for Simon's inland fishing fleet was the greatest on the southern part of the lake as well as on the Jordan River as far south as the Dead Sea. But no matter how busy they became, mending nets or fishing, they again felt the great loneliness for their friend, Jesus.

At length, Simon dispatched a man back to Mount Carmel with an invitation for the Nazarene to return with him and remain a while as their guest.

As this sailor traveled through a certain mountain pass, he chanced upon John the Baptizer, who had recently journeyed inland for the winter months, teaching his doctrine of penance and baptism.

Simon's man stood in wonderment at the sight of hundreds of people wading in single file in the waters of the Jordan. As each one passed John and received his penitential baptism, he loudly professed his belief that the Messiah's reign would be in this generation.

The sailor had never heard of John, nor did he know anything of his doctrine, but he was quick enough to notice how closely it corresponded with the teachings of the Nazarene. A trifle breathlessly he listened as John proclaimed the coming of the Messiah. Possibly this strange man might know where the Messiah could be found!

Instead of going on to Mount Carmel, the sailor returned quickly to Simon. Andrew was absent as the sailor related what he had seen.

With great concern, Simon and his crew discussed this new turn of events, for it seemed to them all that the crusade for the God-Man was about to begin. By an overwhelming vote they decided to seek out this John the Baptizer and investigate his teachings. If they found them sound, they would be baptized at once lest they meet the Messiah unworthily.

The next morning, Simon and his men made their way through the pass until they came upon the multitudes standing on the banks of the Jordan. They had been standing there patiently, in single file, from an early hour waiting for John to appear. When they saw Simon they hailed and cheered him, for he was known to them all. With growing excitement, Simon began to question everyone within earshot as to their reasons for being there.

Then a great cry went up and John, a tall, thin man, his feet bare, browned and calloused from his penitential life in the deserts, and wearing a loose-fitting goat-skin cape over a long, coarse, camel-hair shirt, waded toward the center of the river. Once there he turned, ready to begin his tremendous task of changing dark souls into dazzling light. His voice rang through the mists of that mountain pass as he pleaded with all present to act now for the Living God by making straight the way of their souls.

Simon and his men watched and listened, awestruck, as the ceremony began. A man's gruff, jeering voice broke in upon it. He shouted, "John, why do you wear a camel-hair shirt? Did God tell you to wear skins?"

"I wear these penitential clothes," John answered, "as a continuous petition to God in reparation for His chosen people. They are also a constant offering of humility and mortification in penance for my country. You see, I do not like to wear them!"

The jeering voice became silent.

As the single file of people approached John, he asked each one to bend forward three times, immersing their forehead in the river each time. As this was being done, he prayed and blessed them.

Hours passed. John, at length, rested on the warm bank and Simon and his men drew near. With rapidly beating heart, Simon asked if he knew whether or not the Messiah was then on earth. John regarded them for a moment and answered simply that the Messiah was indeed on earth at that very moment, and added humbly that he, John, was not even worthy to untie the Master's sandal.

Simon and his men exchanged glances and then Simon asked with trepidation, "Have you, then, seen the Messiah?"

"I have not seen Him with the eyes of the world," John answered kindly, "but with the eyes of my spirit, in prayer, I have seen Him many times. I have walked and talked with Him often in the different deserts that are my penitential homes. I cannot tell you exactly where He is, or where He lives, but I do know He is on earth!"

In numbed wonderment Simon and his men knelt in prayer. They thanked God for the privilege of living in such an age—the age that the ancients and the prophets had only dared dream and talk about. Now, it was upon them. They trembled in fear and wondered how they would approach their Creator when they found Him.

They asked one another to whom they might go for instruction in ecclesiastical wisdom and knowledge. Would John be good enough to teach them? In what manner should they speak and act when they meet the Messiah? So fearful they were now, since John had expressed his own uneasiness, in the thought of actually seeing the Master. Hadn't John said that he was not worthy even to untie the Master's sandal, after he had seen and talked with Him? What, then, should they do?

John stood up and asked, "Are you ready to be baptized unto penance for your sins? Come, I will clothe you for Him whom you seek."

Silently, Simon and his crew followed him into the Jordan and were baptized, one by one.

The people on the banks cheered, for Simon was a great man among them and they were proud of him. Hundreds who had doubted before, now followed him into the penitential waters.

By the time the shadows of night filled the mountains, all were baptized. Campfires began to blaze against the chill of the air, and the sound of happy men's voices could be heard as they prepared their meals. Later, a celebration was held for Simon and his crew.

The next morning Simon began his actual search for the Messiah. Through cities and towns he looked. He asked, "Have you heard at any time of the Messiah's birth? It would seem that all the people in the world should know about Him. Do you have any record of a story about

Him that was treated with indifference? Do you know of any man in prison who claims to be Him? If you have, I would like to talk to him."

Not once did Simon receive a satisfactory answer. The scribes and the wise men in each city were as much interested as he in the Messiah, but they became fearful and asked many questions when they learned he had accepted John's baptism. Many then berated him and turned a deaf ear to any further questions. Others laughed him to scorn.

The news of Simon's search and his questions traveled far, and even in Jerusalem people began to ask, "Where is the Messiah whom John the Prophet talks about? Why doesn't He show Himself? We could use some of His wealth and power!"

That sort of talk angered Simon. Somehow, he did not want either wealth or power. He wanted only to serve. That, alone, would be an honor.

Disheartened, he retired at last into a synagogue in Jerusalem to pray. During meditation, he came to the conclusion that he should return to Mount Carmel and seek out the Nazarene. He would like to discuss with Him the mystery of John's seeing the Messiah through prayer. That corresponded with the way Jesus said the prophets of old had seen Him. More than that, though, he resolved to ask Him to accept baptism at the hands of John and then come with him to search for the Messiah. He wondered why he hadn't asked Him to do that before.

Weary and tired, Simon returned to Rosa in their Galilee home. She greeted him tenderly and then listened eagerly to his experiences. When she learned he was going to Mount Carmel she begged to accompany him. Simon agreed, and she requested a second favor. Would he please take her to John that very night and ask him to baptize her? Simon bowed his head.

Andrew, who was second in command of Simon's fleet and who had been away on business and thus did not know of Simon's baptism or of his search, regarded them curiously as they prepared to leave. Simon told him they were going to take a walk in the coolness of the evening air, which of course was true enough. Andrew simply nodded.

Together, Simon and Rosa made their way to John, who was living in a cave near where Simon had last seen him. Then, in the peace of the night and alone in the waters of the Jordan, Rosa was baptized, as Simon watched and prayed on the silent bank of the quiet river.

CHAPTER 4

The Baptism of Jesus

THE FOLLOWING EVENING, Simon and his men were mending their nets on the shore of Lake Galilee. As they worked, Simon told them of his plans. To his gratification they all signified their desire, not only to accompany him to Mount Carmel, but to sail with him when he left the harbor with the Nazarene—assuming, of course, that Jesus would go with them.

First, however, Simon must dispose of his fishing fleet. He could not leave just anyone in charge, for he wanted to make certain the poor people would continue to be furnished with as much fish as they needed. Once that was taken care of, they could go.

As they reached their decision, Simon glanced up, and there, approaching them across the sand, was the Nazarene.

Simon scrambled to his feet and shouted, "Hello, Jesus!"

The Master waved, and Simon ran to meet Him. "We were just talking about You," he said. "Did You just arrive?"

Jesus smiled at the pleasure in Simon's voice and manner. "It is My great happiness to find you, Simon," He answered. "I have been visiting My mother in Nazareth and came this way hoping to see you. It is wonderful for the poor that you have a fishing fleet here as well as on the sea. You are doing a great work of charity."

"We want to talk to You about that," Simon said. "But first, we want to tell You our good fortune in coming across John the Baptizer. We have accepted his doctrine of penance!"

Encouraged by the Master's nod of approval, Simon professed his belief that the Messiah was at that moment on earth, as John had said. Now that they were baptized, they could meet Him in an honorable manner.

"I know about John," Jesus said quietly. "He is certainly very close to God."

Simon was surprised. "Are You baptized, then?" he asked.

Jesus shook His head. "No," He answered, "I am not."

"Well, then," Simon said, "if You know of him and approve his teachings, why do You hesitate?"

"I will have him baptize Me in the morning," Jesus promised.

Simon was satisfied and happy. He embraced Jesus and told Him what their plans were. He begged the Master to accompany them, and hoped their endeavors would be known in history as the first crusade to go in search of the Messiah.

Jesus did not answer this request directly. Instead, He prayed silently to His Eternal Father that when Simon and his men found Him with John, and learned that He was the Messiah, God's grace of understanding would spare them great shock. He implored that God's grace would lead them to understand that He had converted them to a Baptism of Love through John's Baptism of Penance. Then they would understand that it was not they who had converted Him, for all these gifts of grace were made possible only through Him.

Jesus spent that night by Himself, and in the early morning He found John, still in the mountains, with thousands of new followers, each waiting his turn to be baptized.

Jesus joined the long line and presently a man came and stood behind Him. It was the great, shy, Andrew.

Silently and prayerfully, unaware that the Messiah was directly in front of him, Andrew moved slowly toward John. He was trembling in anticipation. At the same time, he was worried about what Simon would think, and he wondered how he could ever tell him he had been baptized.

At length, Jesus stepped into place in front of John. Instantly, John recognized Him and backed away. This was the first time his natural eyes had ever seen the Master.

Humbly, and without noticeable gestures, he adored Jesus. He said softly, "Jesus, the Living God! Why have You come here to me? I cannot take this privilege. I am not worthy to untie Your sandal, therefore, how can I touch Your hands, or ask You to bow so that Your forehead touches the running water?"

Quietly, Jesus answered, "John of the Wilderness—he who was sent to make straight the paths of souls for My coming, remember I am the teacher of humility. My request to receive baptism is just another step in the way of perfection for you. I am the Way for My friends to follow. Even in humility they must follow Me into baptism. The baptism that I will teach them will take away Original Sin, whereas, John, your penitential baptism is the means of grace to help them receive My way. My way of baptism will be as a new, invisible fire enkindled upon souls, for haven't I come to cast My fire upon the earth, and what would I, but that everyone in the world become enkindled. My Father's Light, or fire, is within Me for My Father and I are One. Come now, baptize Me and you will receive the greater gift of humility for all eternity."

In trepidation and trembling, John stepped forward and placed his hand on Jesus as He bent forward.

As the Master straightened up, the heavens were opened and John and Andrew were enlightened in the hidden delights of sudden ecstatic rapture wherein they beheld a magnificent vision. Heaven's golden fire whirled toward them and there resounded the glories of triumphant music heard through the words of the Father, "THIS IS MY BELOVED SON IN WHOM I AM WELL PLEASED!"

Through the great whirling light there seemed to be a white flame of fire, which raced toward the earth. Then it slowed and lingered near Jesus, lowering itself to His shoulder where it assumed the appearance of a white dove.

Quickly, then, the vision vanished.

Jesus stepped aside so that Andrew could confront the trembling John. Both were still in the effects of ecstatic rapture. As the radiance of the intellectual vision faded from their souls, John whispered to Andrew, "Did you see the heavens open? Did you hear the voice of God? Did you see the transcending fire of God assume the form of a dove?"

Overcome with joy because someone else had seen the vision with him, Andrew simply nodded. Rapture was not new to him, but he marveled and wondered who the wonderful Man beside them could be, Who had been so blessed with the mystery of God's hidden love that He could share His vision and gift with them.

Excited voices came from the riverbanks. People pointed heavenward and exclaimed with mixed expressions of joy and fear that they had seen an unusual light. Because of this, John and Andrew agreed that many, especially small children, had seen the holy vision.

During the excitement, Jesus withdrew quietly.

On his way home, Andrew could not stop thinking of that wonderful Man. He pondered over and over the words of heaven's language, "This is My Beloved Son in Whom I am well pleased." The expression baffled him. Could He have been the Messiah? Andrew had never dreamed the Messiah would be publicly announced in this manner, or that He would be called Son.

Enthralled with these thoughts, and with the joy that he had just been baptized, he wondered if he actually had heard the voice of God. Fear seized him. He walked faster so that he might ask Rosa what she thought. He always trusted in her judgment.

It took him an hour to return home, and in that time he noticed that the cloud, or the immediate effects of ecstasy, had left his body. Again he was in the world and he found it difficult to recall the minute events of the vision. This apparent loss of memory, or interior cloudiness, added to his fear.[2]

Once home, he did his best to tell Rosa what had happened, but he could not remember Heaven's exact message. Yet he did tell her that he was resolved in God's holy wisdom, to believe with complete trust that John's baptism and his teachings were the way and the means of truth for souls to accept in order to meet the Messiah in a worthy manner.

He resolved to talk to Simon that very night, come what may. He also intended to beg Simon to follow him and be clothed in the gown of penitential love as he was.

Later, when she was alone, God's grace pierced her soul and Rosa

---

2 The people of the Old Law, not having received the Living Bread and the Gifts of the Holy Spirit, did not have the faculties of retaining the higher contemplative memory.

wondered, could this holy Man who stood in front of Andrew be that great orator, the Nazarene? Andrew's description tallied with the way she remembered Him.

Fearful and excited over such a thought, she breathlessly waited for Simon's return. Now she, as well as Andrew, wanted to talk to him.

As silent questions and answers rose and fell in her mind, she became more and more convinced that she had already seen the Messiah. He could be nobody else but the Nazarene.

But, in spite of her excitement, she was tired, and she finally fell asleep before Simon came home.

Toward morning, Simon awakened her and he was radiant with happiness. He had had a long talk with Andrew and each had told the other his secret. Now, they both wondered whether or not the Nazarene could possibly be the Messiah. And if He were—why had He kept His identity hidden from them?

Simon could no longer hold back his tears. He wept as he prayed for guidance. This Nazarene—was He God? Rosa prayed with him but said nothing of her personal convictions in the matter. Simon must find out for himself.

When it was daylight, Simon and Andrew hurried to the crew on the beach and Andrew told them his wonderful news. Then, with Andrew leading the way, all hurried to find Jesus and John in order to talk to them about the miracle and to ask Jesus if He really was the Messiah.

They found thousands of people assembling on the slopes of a low mountain ravine, for John had announced that the Nazarene was going to speak. Baptized and unbaptized alike hurried from far into Galilee to hear Him.

Simon and his friends pressed forward and froze in their tracks, for Jesus was just beginning His sermon as they entered the ravine. His voice was like deep thunder as it poured down the mountain passes, even more eloquent and powerful than when they had last heard it on the shores of Mount Carmel Bay.

With one accord, they fell upon their knees.

"I am the Way," Jesus said, "and I am the Truth. He who believes in My words hears the Eternal Father, for I am the Son of God. He who hears Me hears the Father, for We are One!"

Here was Simon's answer.

Great drops of perspiration dripped from Simon's face as he recalled how boldly he had talked to Jesus a number of times, especially that first day on the beach.

Andrew wept uncontrollably. Now he could remember similar words used when the Voice from Heaven said, "This is My Beloved Son in whom I am well pleased." He realized for the first time that the word "Son" meant God-with-us-on-earth—God as Man in flesh. He had actually heard the Living God announced to the world on the day of His baptism.

While they knelt transfixed, Jesus walked down the slope toward them. Tenderly, He lifted the trembling Simon to his feet and embraced him as the multitudes shouted, "He is the Christ! He is the Living Messiah! O, God-among-us, forgive us our sins!"

Jesus raised Simon's face from its bowed position of prayer and shame and He said, "Simon, I'm glad you found Me. Do you remember the day we met on the beach? I asked you to consider becoming a fisherman of souls. You did not fully understand Me then, but now you are able to grasp the meaning of My words a little better. Later I will teach you a great deal more as I call upon you to serve in My plan for the redemption of men."

Simon's eyes glistened as he answered, "Jesus, My God, how can I think clearly now that I have just found You? I know You will help me understand all things."

Jesus turned to Andrew and the crew and embraced each one. "Come," He said, "follow Me, as you wanted to do. In the next few months we have many things to accomplish together."

At that moment, Rosa came from the crowd and stood beside Simon. Shyly, she said, "Jesus, I give You my will and I accept all denials—such as worldly separation from Simon when he goes with You as Your bodyguard. You have come to give us life everlasting, just as the prophets promised. How would I dare stand in the way of such happiness?"

Jesus answered, "Rosa, your faith and joy are very great. Simon will come with Me, but you must stay within the shelter of your own home and follow Me by means of hidden works and prayers."

As John the Baptizer came toward them, Simon asked, "Jesus, who is this man? Is he Elias, whom the prophets foretold would come into the world?"

Jesus answered, "He is John, the greatest man born of woman. He makes straight the crooked paths of souls, the better for My indwelling, which I will teach you later.

"It is My delight to be with the children of men, and it is possible for Me to be in all men's souls when they have made themselves ready for Me through the penitential life that John teaches. His penances and love for Me have endeared him to all the ancient prophets and to the angels in Paradise.

"He is greatly loved by Elias, who finds his heavenly pleasure on earth through actually directing his soul and guiding him in his mission of penance. Many times when he speaks, Elias speaks through him. This gift of Heaven's laws is seldom given to the world. It is a moment of possession by My saints and angels when a person is in ecstasy or rapture. It is part of the gift of the Communion of Saints. It is the mystery of love through Me, in and through My saints in Heaven and on earth."

When Jesus retired in Simon's room that night it was decided that the Master, Simon, Andrew, and the crew would sail for a retreat on foreign soil in about six weeks. This would take them away for a time from all worldly attractions and strife.

First, however, Jesus and Simon had individual actions to perform. Simon must make a final effort to dispose of his ships, and the Master wished to go on a forty-day retreat, by Himself, in the desert near Nazareth. At the conclusion of this, they all planned to meet in Mount Carmel.

In speaking of His retreat in the desert, Jesus told them that before He started His public life, He had made at least one other forty-day retreat in the same locality, and He asked them to pray for Him because He knew while He was there He would be tempted often by the devil, who would assume the form of man.

"Aren't You ever frightened by his presence?" Simon asked. "Does he perplex You with new temptations?"

Jesus answered, "No, I am not frightened by any form of evil. Because I want to practice patience and suffer all things that man suffers in this life, I must allow Myself to hear temptations and suggestions. Rather than being new each time, they are repetitious. The devil tries to follow the plan of a man's life with ordinary temptations, repeated over and over. Nothing is so fatal to man's patience as the constant repetition of suggestions on the same subject.

"No doubt the devil will try to make Me perform miracles when I become hungry and thirsty. You see, he does not know for a certainty that I am the God-Man, and will take this means of trying to find out. The devils, like people on earth, wonder when I'll appear according to the prophets' views and visions.

"When you travel south, pray for Me."

Before daybreak the next day, Jesus told them goodbye. Simon, Andrew, and the crew took John with them through Lake Galilee into the Jordan River, where John wished to resume his work of baptism. Following this, Simon hired new sailors to operate his inland fleet, which took care of all his holdings in Lake Galilee and the Jordan. When this was concluded to his satisfaction, he and Andrew and the crew traveled on to Jerusalem and from there to the coast.

South of Mount Carmel, Simon had a small fleet operated by fishermen who lived in that locality. He gave them those ships on the one condition that they continue to feed the poor. This left him with only his main fleet in Mount Carmel Bay. Some of these, of course, he would use when they sailed for their retreat.

As they resumed their journey north, they met Jesus, Who by that time had finished His forty days in the desert. Traveling together, they heard the Master speak several times to the people along the way and saw Him heal their sick.

At night, as they sat about their fires, Jesus taught them many things. It was during one of these talks they learned the necessity of being fortified with the armor of prayer, penance, and mortification before He would allow them to reach out for other souls and endeavor to bring them into His Kingdom. From that moment on, they offered their weariness, pain, and loneliness for their families, as preparation for their retreat.

CHAPTER 5

The Island

BEFORE DAYLIGHT ONE MORNING, almost two months after their return to Mount Carmel, Jesus, Simon, and Andrew walked slowly toward the bay, where their ships were at anchor and ready for sailing. As they walked, they listened to the petulant moods of the sea, and were awed with the black water's slow moving fretfulness beneath the first streaks of dawn.

Jesus spoke quietly, His eyes on the breakers. "Listen to the music in the breaking waves as they splash at our feet," He said. "How beautifully each one tries to tell us, in tones of its original, but now dimmed music, of the fall of Adam, which caused the sea ever since to moan and to rise in terrible storms to terrify man with its awful power. It is continually engaged in a sad struggle for victory over apparent defeat, evident by the rise and fall of its tide.

"Listen for the hidden symphonic poem each wave tells while you mystically watch it, for in each rolling breaker there is a fountain of wisdom. Picture in your minds silver steeds pulling chariots to the shore—chariots filled with precious cargoes. These precious cargoes are the angels in charge of the sea. In this piteous turmoil of law without perfect order, they cry out through the waves as they break along the shores, 'We want the joys of our former peace. See what you have done to our playground of pleasure in God's creation!'

"Listen to the twitter of the awakening seabirds. Last evening they were lulled to sleep by the rhythmical hum of the waves—this morning, God's noiseless rising sun in the eastern sky awakens them.

"This I tell you to remind you that My Father's graces are as silent as the rising sun. They resemble invisible dart-like arrows, which awaken souls into the knowledge of eternal life. As these sea-birds are awakened by the silence of the dawn and are drawn in flight to the rising sun, so too I draw souls to Me that they may become one with the Father and Me. Watch the happiness of these birds as they wing their way upward—for that is the way men must delight in Me.

"But how much greater than the flight of birds is the phenomena of grace in living souls when they soar to God through prayer. How beautiful they are as they rise above the glamour of the world and its sins. Their music arises like the faithful tones of the sea, reverberating into the perceiving heavens as one continual symphonious sound of love. Let us pray to make the symphony of your souls greater in the mastery of faith and love."

Simon and Andrew thanked Jesus for this morning meditation, and then caught sight of John the Baptizer as he hurried to meet them. Kneeling at the Master's feet, John thanked Him quietly for the privilege of serving Him and of seeing Him in real life.

Tenderly, Jesus lifted John from his knees and embraced him. In that second of holy embrace, Jesus gave him the greater gifts of union in the silent realm of perfect love. Also, He whispered into John's soul His love, devotion, and gratitude for the gift of baptismal penance made possible for the world through John's cooperation with grace in self-willingness, penance, and self-denials for the whole human race. At that moment John, through intuitive knowledge, knew all the events of his future life. He understood even his martyrdom, but not the means by which he would die, nor when.

"I know You are going on a retreat," John said, gazing into the eyes of his Master, "but where are You going?"

"Across the Mediterranean and into the Arabian desert," Jesus answered. "Simon, Andrew, and forty of his crew are going with Me. It will be of new interest, for I have never been on retreat there, nor have I ever had companions before. Pray for us."

"Master," John begged hopefully, "use one of my desert homes! It is on an island north of Arabia. Simon, with his great skill in navigation, can find it easily when I tell him how to set his course. Please go there."

Jesus nodded His approval.

Before they left, at the suggestion of Jesus, John told them all something of his life. "When I was ten," he began, "I left home, friends, and the comforts of the world for the hidden life of prayer. Through the many paths of God's contemplative knowledge, I learned I was to introduce my penitential philosophy to the people. I instinctively realized I must be fortified with the armor of prayer and its reciprocal gifts, which would come to me through mortifications before I would dare venture forth to teach.

"My last lingering memory of the world is one that is still most dear to my heart. It concerns the simple kindness of my aunt, who took me to daily prayers in the synagogue. I loved to watch the high priests as they offered incense, and I marveled at the solemnity and the grace with which they wore the royal temple robes. But most of all I loved being aware of God's special nearness, which would come over me as I prayed and watched incense rising heavenward. To leave all of that was indeed a sacrifice."

John hesitated, finding it difficult to continue. Tears filled his eyes as he whispered, "Oh, Jesus, God-among-us, those things were as nothing compared to the joys of Your visitations to me in the deserts. How I hope that these new followers of Yours will rise above the realities of their lives, and find Your Kingdom on earth within them. They will gain a new light of understanding, which will, in turn, lead them to the higher principles of Your indwelling. May the ever growing light of their penitential lives burn before You as a sanctuary lamp on earth. And Jesus, may Your path of living prayers on earth, from one kingdom[3] to another, ever be ablaze with Your children's gifts of fervency and zeal."

John turned back to the men. "Jesus and I were never together in our infancy, nor in our childhood. However, as I told you, Simon, we often walked and talked together in my desert homes while I was in the hidden life of the spirit.[4] Perhaps Jesus will one day show you where we had our visitations. You may well guess it was indeed a surprise for me to see

---

3 Person.

4 Ecstasy.

Him in the Jordan that day, and it was the humiliation of my life to be His baptizer.

"The first two years in the Jordan desert," John continued, "were a challenge to my faith, courage, and fortitude. I was unspeakably lonely and a great many times I wept until I shook with sorrow. Many times, too, the world and its attractions called loudly, as if pleading with me to return to its pleasures, comforts, and friends. Those years seemed very slow in passing, and I was about to question God's desires and designs when Your holy grace, Jesus, caught and pierced my heart with the deeper knowledge of Your will and Your mystical, personal nearness. It was then, through God's will, that I understood that I was to cross the sea to a desert island and there build another home of solitude.

"Through the effects of God's personal love I suddenly realized I was quite grown up, even though I was still a small boy, and that God had given me the tremendous grace of detachment.

"I came here, built a raft, and set sail. God's goodness helped to guide me safely to my destination, the island to which you are now going.

"After I reached there I planned my daily life as if each day were my last on earth, and I disciplined it into regular hours. I had certain hours for prayer, work, and rest. Through grace and the effects of the governing laws of discipline, I found my life, from that moment on, most delightful and joyous. I was engaged in the fascinating game of working and loving God.

"Would you believe it, I even began building a synagogue out of the natural red sandstone from the hills? With flint implements that I made myself, I chiseled the stone blocks and cemented them together with clay. Many times angels came to help me. They lifted the heavy stones to the top of the rising wall and to the tower."

John hesitated. "I've often wondered," he said, "whether they were amused, or troubled, by my pets. I had a goat, a lion, and a wildcat, and they were constantly in the way."

Jesus laughed. "No," He said, "they weren't troubled. Rather, they marveled at your patience when you tripped over them in their eagerness to be petted."

John heaved a sigh of relief. "You have no idea how much better that makes me feel," he answered, and then laughed as he remembered how many times his pets had scattered when he stumbled with a block of weighty sandstone in his arms.

"Did you finish the synagogue?" Simon asked, much interested in the account.

John shook his head. "The tower is completed," he answered, "and the walls reach upward to a height of about twenty feet, but there is no roof. Nevertheless, I am sure you will find comfort, peace, and solitude within those cool walls, which are so dear to me.

"I had planned chiseling a few stone benches for the front, but time did not permit. Nor did I have the pleasure of finishing a fireplace in one side wall. Perhaps when you need relaxation you will finish it for the glory of God."

His eyes then grew soft with gentle memory. "I hope that while you are at prayer, God will permit His angels to visit you as they visited me so many times. Often their cloud-like, assumed forms of men would entirely fill the roofless temple, and they would chant the symphonic prayers of Heaven with me. Try singing the psalms of David, for the glory of God, and in this way you may coax them to you."

Then John looked at Jesus wistfully. "I know that my mission here on earth is about finished," he said. "I must now diminish the love and admiration my people have for me so that their love for You may increase. I have learned and accepted the call to be the victim of reparation for my country. And, Master," he concluded, "I hope You have a joyous journey. Take me with You in Your heart, for I, too, long for life alone with Thee!"

CHAPTER 6

John's Temple

JESUS, SIMON, and the men waded and swam to the ships anchored in the bay. The churning, gray sea reflected the silver dawn back to John as he stood on the shore waving a farewell and a blessing to them.

Three days later, Simon sighted the island and anchored offshore. It took but a moment to reach the beach and start inland.

After a half-day's search, they found a cave that John had used as a home at the base of a hill on a great plateau that was permeated with an awesome silence. The earth's natural richness of red sandstone and the echoing breeze from the distant hills breathed a welcome from the Baptizer.

Hand-hewn from the natural rock, its walls covered with wonderful etchings, the cave told only too clearly of John's infinite patience to do all things well for God. Knee-hollows in the kneeler of a rock prie-dieu spoke to them of his hours of penance and prayer.

Leaving the cave, they hurried along a well-kept pathway of smooth, white sea-stones. Presently, the sight of the temple burst upon them, and they stood aghast at its tremendous size and magnificence. Two hundred feet in length it was, and seventy in width, and its red sandstone walls were twenty feet high as John had said. A pyramid-shaped tower that rose forty feet from the ground was in the center of the front wall, over a great arch, and its tapering top ended in a square platform of stone, six feet across. Upon this platform John had built a stone bench that faced south toward the sea.

Slowly, they entered through the arch. It was like stepping from the present world into the infinite. Smooth, red stones formed the temple floor, and in the center there was inlaid a huge cross of black rock, its foot toward the arch. At the front of the temple, where ordinarily an altar would stand, was a magnificent, low hand-carved rock platform, the height of a step, with an inscription cut in the riser that read, "FOR THE GOD-MAN, THE MESSIAH."

A stone incense table, or platform, also hewn from rock and strewn with gray-black ashes, stood in the right rear corner. The Baptizer had left the natural floor of earth about it in a semi-circle of some fifteen feet in diameter. In this semi-circle he had planted many wild shrubs and trees, and at the back of the platform were date palms that served as a canopy.

Simon and his men fell to their knees. Jesus walked to the central platform and faced His friends. He began to speak on the true greatness of John—and it was His first sermon on earth delivered in His own temple built especially for Him.

As He talked, He drew attention to the walls, which were covered with carvings of scriptural quotations and pictures. The long side walls bore excerpts from the Book of Isaiah, which had been given to John in the knowledge of ecstasy and wisdom, and a large etching of the Messiah carrying the cross to Calvary as Isaiah had seen Him in a vision, hundreds of years before His birth.

From this, the men learned, in the fullness of knowledge and appreciation, that this great Man, Jesus, standing before them, was indeed the Messiah Who would actually be crucified. Some of them wept, while others gazed into space in sheer wonderment, as they realized their nearness to the Man whom Isaiah had been permitted to see only in vision.

The low, gentle voice of Jesus awakened them to earth's realities as He drew their attention to the carvings in which John had depicted the coming ages—even to that very time. Some of these drawings showed the Messiah bringing power and law for the Clean Oblation Sacrifice to the world, and in these, bread and wine were depicted as Living Fire. It was the Living Bread because the Messiah had set the laws and had given them to the world. The Sacrifice of Calvary—Jesus on the Cross in death—would end the bloody sacrifice according to the old law of Moses.

The great drama of Transubstantiation was portrayed in high relief work over the incense table. Pictured there were multitudes of people standing in the rays of the Living Bread, a symbolic way of showing them receiving Holy Communion. Another tablet presented the God-Man reaching into His heart, and from there bringing forth the living fires of His Father, in order that man—while yet on earth—might become enkindled in the fires of His love.

Yes, John was a great man to have done all this.

Finished with His eulogy, Jesus turned to other matters. Within the hour He would leave them and travel alone into the depths of the desert there to pray for the conversion of souls for the entire time of their stay. He promised, however, to return the evening of each seventh day to instruct them further on the ideals and the management of their retreat.

"Pray for the gift of faith while I am away," He begged. "Through faith the armor of humility will come into your lives and its shield of strength will guide you to the higher gifts of wisdom. One of these higher gifts, purity of intention, can be gained in your souls if you will make daily willing sacrifices to please God above all transitory things. As an example, look at the sacrifice and the supernatural intentions John put into the building of this temple. The world would consider his work a useless gesture of love, and certainly a waste of time. But God did not consider it so. God accepts hidden, selfless work—work that appears foolish to the world—as one of the highest forms of prayer and adoration."

Jesus continued: "Spend the hours of the day as John did. Set aside certain hours for prayer, actual work, and recreation." He turned to Simon and said, "From now on you are the acting retreat master. Your retreatants will gain great merit for the higher ways of faith by following you in obedience. The first law that leads to personal holiness is built upon the foundation of obedience to a superior. Spiritual character is formed by the willingness of a soul to be tried in the hands of a superior as gold is refined in a furnace."

Jesus concluded by suggesting that they finish the big, half-completed fireplace, and chisel new benches from stones they could roll down the mountainside.

Then He yielded His place on the platform to Simon, and with some trepidation the big fisherman asked for suggestions from the men and assigned them to duties.

He asked several to make the stone benches as Jesus had suggested. Some, he appointed to complete the fireplace. Two others were given a seemingly useless task—that of gathering large, dry leaves, stacking and tying them into bundles of a hundred leaves each, as penitential offerings for their sins. These bundles would be burned in the new fireplace in a great celebration at the end of the forty days. To the remaining men were delegated the tasks of fishing, cooking, and the general care of the temple.

Simon next completed the laws of their retreat. The first four hours after sunrise would be spent in prayer and the singing of psalms; the next four hours would be given to God in work and silence; and the following four hours would be taken up by recreation and rest. After the evening meal the rule of silence would be observed, the better for them to learn God's way and life of meditation.

When the men had all accepted the plan, Jesus said, "This way of obedience you have chosen is living a life of kindness, understanding, patience, and charity toward one another. It is the way of merit through which you can save your souls and rise to great spiritual heights in the paths of meditation. Through the intention of one's will to pray and do supernaturalizing work lies the greatest way to perfection.

"These degrees of perfection are the same as the many mansions in My Father's house in Heaven. These mansions, or thrones, were lost forever by the fallen angels because they rebelled against God. It is My desire that you have the thrones for your eternal happiness. You may rise into them according to your selflessness and charity toward other souls."

He turned to Simon. "Even though I placed you in charge of this retreat you, too, must come under certain orders and obligations. I want you to show perfection in your actions and charity toward these men. You will be judged severely in the eyes of justice on the results of your example through your obedience to Me. Watch and pray, little-Master-in-the-world, lest you forget the grace of humility and how to keep yourself holy.

"Also, Simon, you must show a willingness to cooperate in carrying out monotonous and useless work as well as following set rules and orders. I suggest that you sit on the bench on top of the tower and from there watch and pray for the men who work beneath you. You will see their faults and imperfections, which you are to correct. Call each man before you and correct him firmly but with great gentleness.

Simon bowed his head in willing submission. As Jesus was about to leave for the darkness of the desert, He blessed each man and spoke comfortingly to them. "My friends," He said, "learn to sanctify your work, sufferings, prayers, and joys in the thought that all you do must be perfect in the eyes of My Father. Through faith you can change each hour's work, pain, or joy into golden grace for your eternal life. This is a bond of perfect trust between My Father and you. Keep alive within you the knowledge of the silent, invisible, eternal reward of Heaven's mansions, which may be yours through obedience motivated by the love of God and doing all for Him. Let that eternal reward be your sunlight—ever visible to the soul as your treasure in Heaven. Let your soul follow the habit of the birds, for they are without care as they fly to greet the morning sun. Fly hourly into My heart for your reward of warmth, which is just another way of saying come to Me for consolation."

Outside the temple on the white stone pathway, the men knelt at the feet of Jesus as He blessed them. Turning, he walked into the desert darkness. Their eyes closed in a prayer of adoration and thanksgiving; they listened to the sound of His steady footsteps on the temple path. Ah, what a singular privilege. They were actually listening to God's footsteps—God's footsteps echoing in the paths of time!

In that moment of rapturous understanding, several men fell prostrate upon the ground in order to hear the receding footsteps just a little longer. Finally, when the sound was entirely gone, they hurried into the temple to pray, lest they give way entirely to sadness and tears. There, in the quiet of meditation, they tried to recapture, in memory, the words Jesus had spoken, particularly His kind blessing of love to them.

Their retreat was under way. They all agreed that this first day would be a spiritual treasure for all eternity—they knew God in His humanity.

CHAPTER 7

The First Retreat: Part One

THE SIXTH DAY OF THE FIRST WEEK was drawing to a close. The last shades of twilight lingered over the island and deepened into night. The retreatants were restless and peered continually down the shadowed desert paths, hoping that Jesus would return a day early. When there was no sign of Him they spent the night in the temple, praying, waiting, and listening for His footsteps.

Dawn came slowly with all its adornments of quiet beauty as they assembled before the low, stone platform in the temple for their first four hours of singing and prayer. Their hearts and their voices ascended together toward the heavens with the rising of the sun.

The Master entered through the arch at the end of the first hour. Majestically, devotedly, and ceremoniously He walked toward them, a tall, roughly-hewn shepherd's staff in one hand.

Stepping up on the platform, He smiled a greeting, and suddenly they found themselves listening to sweet, celestial music that filled the whole temple, just as John had predicted it might. The angels were singing psalms of praise to the hidden God on earth, Who stood before them. In a dazzling demonstration of Heaven's artistry, the angels, in assumed forms, unrolled a scroll showing the ages to come and how the Messiah's followers would adore Him in His gift of the Eucharist, the Living Bread.

The heavenly music gradually died away and the arch of angels that had formed a roof for the temple slowly disappeared. Jesus led the men in prayer. They had all been in rapture but they did not realize the transition, nor the intuitive knowledge they received, because they were not yet gifted with the Holy Spirit. All of it would return to them vividly at the time of His descent upon them after the Resurrection.[5]

Jesus blessed them and they crowded about Him. Each at the same time tried to tell Him how joyful the past week had been and how the wearisomeness of silence and prayer had not been a burden to them.

One asked, "Jesus, did You pray continually while You were gone?" Another asked, "Did You eat and sleep? Were You cold at night? Did You build a fire?"

Jesus answered, "I prayed most of the time and enjoyed long walks through the desert night in the beauty of My Father's glory. Many times I blessed you and the earth, the better for the earth to show My Father's power and glory through men, and for men, in the coming generations.

"All science and industry have My blessing in a most special way through this retreat. Our prayers and works are united—in numbers there is power. Science and the arts will take on a new degree of progress because men's intellects will be enlightened by our blessings here. People, everywhere, will now enjoy leisure, pleasure, joy, and the lessening of pain so that all may see the hidden miracles brought about by the power of My Father, in and through the men who discover them. From now until the end of time men will have more time to adorn themselves in gifts of great graces for their eternal lives by loving My Father through Me. He who sees Me, sees the Father.

"No, I did not eat, but I did drink water once a day and I slept a few hours each night. I would have been very chilly, but mother always finds a way to make Me comfortable. She asked her angels to send a flock of swallows to keep Me warm. They flew over Me in slow flight and then descended upon Me, nestling close together, covering Me as warmly as though they were a blanket. With the warmth of those four hundred swallows over Me I didn't even need a fire.

5 See Andrew's reaction to the voice from Heaven, Book One, Chapter 4.

"I would have sent them away, because I was there to practice denials, but I remembered that even I must honor My mother and her wishes. Mother watches over My every need, and unless I ask her not to perform her deeds of mercy for Me, I never find a way of practicing denials and mortifications."

Jesus sat down on a newly chiseled bench, and the men came to Him one by one with their problems, either good or bad, and He advised them according to their needs. How they loved His gentle kindness, and in reverence they kissed His hands and feet as they left His knee. Smiles and tears of joy were theirs.

The day drew to an end and it became time for Jesus to return to the desert. The shadows were growing tall when Simon walked slowly a little way from the temple with Him. As they kept step together, Jesus gave him new suggestions for the retreat. At the moment of final departure, Simon knelt at the Master's feet and apologetically confessed his sins of weakness during the week, for he had several times doubted the strict orders Jesus had given them. The Master admonished him kindly and praised him for his truthfulness. Then He analyzed his problems, and when Simon realized his stupidity he began to chuckle.

With a smile and a wave of His hand, Jesus walked away into the darkness.

The men were all waiting at the temple entrance when Simon returned. When they sighted him they ran to meet him. Like children, they asked, "What did Jesus say to you, Simon? What were His last words? How did He look—was He sad? Lonesome? Was He happy with us—have we pleased Him?

Simon answered, "You have more than pleased Him." They walked back inside the temple and Simon went on: "Sit down, for I want to tell you my own failings and how the Master corrected them. Several times during the past week, while I watched you from the tower, I was tempted with misgivings and I even mistrusted the ideals of John in building this temple in such a desert. The more I thought about it the more it seemed such a lot of wasted work, for neither the world, nor the people in it, would ever enjoy its beauty and meaning.

"I also became convinced that my work of leisurely watching over you from the ease of a bench was a waste of time, too. Frequently, I resolved to tell the Master about it when He returned—to let Him know that I would much rather do something worthwhile—something that had a purpose and a meaning. I reasoned that none of us were doing anything to benefit mankind. But then, when I saw Jesus, I completely forgot my complaints and felt only sorrow for having had such thoughts. Just seeing Him filled me with devotion, and I understood that my desire was only to do what He asked of me without question, and that nothing He wanted would, or could, ever be a waste of time.

"You see, I was ambitious to a degree of great stupidity. I had conveniently forgotten the Master's teaching that little things done well, and the doing of that which seemed to be nothing, under the advice of a superior, is great in the eyes of God.

"To make matters worse, I tried to hide this guilt when I confessed my other troubles. But in His kind way, the Master reminded me of my neglect and my questioning moods and asked me to tell Him everything without fear. He already knew I had questioned His judgment and yet He wasn't angry!

"With great gentleness He even told me of each time I questioned Him—even the exact expressions I had used mentally. I was mortified to the dust and wished above everything else that I had not spoken so loudly in my thoughts, for I guess our thoughts are as loud as spoken words to Him. No wonder He asks us to be careful of them.

"I confessed my interior misgivings fully. In answer, He told me that through confession we earn the grace of humility, for in admitting faults we grow strong in our infirmities. It is also a lesson that we are nothing without His sustaining care."

Simon was filled with a deep, interior peace when he had finished speaking. Now he was eager to begin the penance the Master had requested of him—the first penance He had ever imposed on any of His followers. Simon was to stand on the tower and pretend that he was casting a fishing line into an invisible sea from where he was to catch invisible fish. These would symbolize souls on earth who would be brought to Jesus through the merit of obedience. Simon was eager to learn the sublime truth that doing nothing, under obedience, was to save souls for God, even to the end of time.

As Simon finished telling of his coming chastisement, he and his men laughed heartily, yet they believed and understood its depths of knowledge, wisdom and merit. Even though it was dark, Simon sent one of his men to get a long palm frond. He stripped it of its leaves and fashioned a nine-foot fishing rod from its main stem. He was used to fishing only with a net, but he accepted his penance with a smile. As he climbed the tower stairs, several men begged to be remembered in his penance.

The second week passed in perfect peace and tranquility. The men all felt the reciprocating gift of God's love coming hourly into their souls. Together they embraced the unity of their unique spiritual love and felt the essence of oneness among themselves. Because of this unity of love, new benches were made, the fireplace was completed, and hundreds of bundles of dry leaves were stacked in readiness for the celebration to come.

Simon was an example of humility and obedience as he stood for hours each day catching invisible fish from the imaginary sea beneath him. The rhythmical motion of his fishing rod often brought songs to the lips of the men, and Simon sang with them. The psalms of David were many times heard on that desert island. Then all would be silent again.

As all things must, the retreat finally neared its completion. The days were glorious and happy, and several of the men asked Simon whether or not they could remain on the island for the rest of their lives. The world failed to call them from this hidden peace and deep beauty of prayer. If Simon would only grant them permission, they would vow to give their lives as an offering for the God-Man's successful reign on earth. They wanted all souls to know and love Him as they did. No sacrifice was too great to achieve that end.

Simon asked them to wait and ask Jesus. The decision should be His. However, he felt certain the Master would give His permission, and in anticipation of that, he prayed courage would be theirs in the months and years to come.

He sounded a note of caution, though, by saying, "While you foster this noble idea of self-sacrifice, question yourselves whether or not you fully realize that you are nothing, and are deserving of nothing in life. And yet your very nothingness is able to praise God. For when your soul burns with love for Him, His grace speaks lofty desires into your mind. All good thoughts come from Him. Do not forget to thank Him for every one. If you think only of the beauty and the peace and the quiet of this place, you seek escape from a sordid world. That is self-pleasure. But if you can honestly say that you want to stay here only for the glory of God and your own sanctification, then His grace has touched you.

"Your constant prayer must be, 'God is all! God is everything! God's will is mine!'" The men bowed in humble subjection to Simon's words. Then they went to their favorite places of quiet and prayed far into the night.

CHAPTER 8

The First Retreat: Part Two

THE THIRTY-NINTH DAY of the retreat was over, and the desert silence was like a lingering hand of kindness over the little community of men. Eagerly they scanned the horizon—as they had the seventh day of each week—hoping by the moment to see Jesus appear. They were concerned and sad because the Master had shown signs of great fatigue the last time they saw Him, and they were afraid He was hungry and ill.

Simon walked up and down the white, stone path, listening attentively for any sound of the Master's footsteps. Suddenly aware of a nearness to Jesus, he stopped his pacing. Putting his ear close to the ground, he began to smile. Jesus was indeed coming! Then far down the path, almost hidden in the somber glow of the evening twilight, Jesus came into view slowly and waved to them.

The men ran happily to meet Him and stopped short in shock. Jesus was staggering—He was ill! Simon jumped forward and caught Him in his strong arms just before He fell to the ground, so great was His weakness from fatigue and hunger.

With great care the men cradled His limp body on their shoulders and carried Him carefully through the temple arch. They laid Him gently on a bench, and Simon stroked His tangled hair tenderly while his tears moistened His fevered brow. Simon's love and pity for Jesus was so great he could only weep and touch Him as He lay in an exhausted sleep.

After an hour's rest, and having sipped a cup of water, Jesus felt much better. He walked to the platform and extended His arms in blessing over the crew as they hurried to kneel before Him. They exchanged glances of relief, for this was the Master as they had always known Him.

Jesus' expression alone was a sermon of love. Then His enthusiasm broke into words as He told them His joy over the twelve men who wanted to stay on the island and thus take up the way of life John had followed.

The men looked at one another. How did Jesus know about that? No one had told Him!

One sailor exclaimed, "God knows everything!"

Jesus smiled at the twelve and said, "You will be permitted to remain here if you wish. Your prayers, works, sufferings, and joy will make up My first treasure chest on earth, and I will often dip into it for the graces necessary for future conversions."

He turned to all and said, "Are you ready to accept My baptism, which will be the New Law's government of spirit within you and which will remove all darkness of Original Sin?"

Most of the men answered joyously that they were ready to do anything He asked without question, but several others were puzzled, for they had assumed that the baptism of John was all that was necessary. Why then should it be repeated?

Jesus explained to them the difference between His baptism and John's baptism—as He had explained it to the Baptizer that day in the Jordan. "John's baptism," He said, "was an outward sign that you were willing to do penance, or to perform an actual act of sorrow for sin, which made your soul brighter for My coming. However, My baptism is one of invisible fire, emanating from My Father's throne. This fire will clothe you in a brightness comparable to Adam's likeness before he fell from grace and lost the supernatural life for the whole human race. This is the only way you can receive a gift directly from God, which will lift you up to a state of transfiguration while you yet live on earth. He will even give a foretaste of the joys of Heaven to a few on earth who abide in grace."

When the men heard this, they followed Jesus eagerly to the sea and waded in after Him, for this baptism was to be performed the same way as John's. The Master beckoned to Simon, who was the first to be baptized in the New Law by Jesus, Himself. Andrew was second, and the rest followed in line. Boisterously and joyfully the men then picked Jesus up and carried Him on their shoulders back to the temple. They knelt around Him as little children. At first they were silent, but because they were so filled with joy they broke into cheers.

Later that evening, the twelve men who were going to stay on the island grouped themselves close to the Master's feet and studied Him silently. Tomorrow He would leave them and this would be the last time on earth they would see Him. They tried to memorize His expression, His gestures and His words, for they wanted to be able to remember Him later in their hours of loneliness.

It was hard to realize this was their last evening with Him. Many of them wept as they kissed His feet. They shuddered at the thought that sin could separate them from Him for all eternity. Oh how they feared sin and its awful penalty! They prayed their memory would never forget this living picture of Jesus before them. Would that they could never forget how He smiled and talked and how His eyes drew them into the deeper love of His humanity!

At midnight Jesus asked for the fires of celebration to be kindled in the new fireplace. Bundle after bundle of carefully counted penitential leaves were thrown joyfully into the flames, there symbolically to burn away the sins of the little community.

Songs of praise to the Living Messiah rose and fell as the men feasted on broiled fish, wild berries, and honey. They took delight in giving the Master favorite bits of fish from their portions, and even tossed the choicest berries at Him. Some of these He caught in His mouth. How they laughed with Him in His happiness—just as they had wept with Him a few hours earlier in His awful fatigue.

One man knelt before Jesus in an exuberance of faith. Gazing steadily into the Master's eyes he said, "Jesus, You are the real living Messiah whom we have waited for and hoped to see. Jesus, You are God hidden in this clay form which resembles us. How can we thank You? Your humanity in clay is hard to believe, yet I firmly believe it and I adore You. I would have You as You are and no one else. Jesus, to think our sins made You choose this clay body in which to live as our prisoner! Let those of us who are going to remain on this island become Your pillars of gratitude in Your heavenly Kingdom."

One by one the men fell asleep at the Master's feet as the lantern moon swung higher and higher into the great dome of the night. Quietly and alone, Jesus climbed the narrow stairs to the temple tower. He pretended to fish from Simon's bench as He cast the line for invisible fish into the imaginary sea. He smiled as He imitated Simon's gestures, and He marveled at the big fisherman's patience in continuing this tiresome game for forty days instead of for the one week He had suggested.

While Jesus mused and cast the line, one of the devil's demons, assuming the appearance of man, came and stood before Him on the temple tower. He tempted Jesus scornfully with the same words he had used on other forty-day desert retreats. He showed Him a vision of all the earth's riches and kingdoms from the highest pinnacle in the world, and he said he would give all this to Him if only He would bow down and greet him as a power of God.

When Jesus did not answer, the devil tempted Him again and said, "I dare You to prove Yourself to be the Son of God and not an impostor. If You are the hidden God in this mask of clay, You could cast Yourself down on the rocks below and not suffer. If You are hungry for bread, these stones will turn into bread at Your command. Prove to me You can turn stone into bread. Remember only tonight You and Your men were wishing for it. If You can perform miracles, why do You hunger?"

Receiving only silence as an answer, the devil cried out in a rage, "Why do You hesitate to show me You are the Son of God? Are you ashamed to admit it?"

Jesus stood up in silence, with an expression of utter scorn on His face. Towering above the assumed form of the devil, He struck him with the fishing rod. The devil instantly returned into hell, but he did not realize the spiritual power that put him there nor from Whom it came. He was dejected and scoffed at by his henchmen for his stupidity in not discovering whether or not that Man was the Son of God.

When morning came, Jesus awakened the men, for they would be leaving soon for the mainland. He blessed, consoled, and encouraged the twelve who were staying, and gave them advice that would help them battle the devil when he made his appearance, or when he whispered thoughts to tempt them against faith or purity. He told them how He had cast the tempter back into hell during the hours of darkness just past, and how He had blessed Simon's fishing rod for just such occasions. It thus became a sacramental of great power. He explained that devils cannot understand sacramentals that do not have the usual visible appearance of holy objects.

He told them to go alone to the tower when they felt the devil's nearness and to scourge themselves with the fishing rod according to the magnitude of their temptations. The devil would leave. He promised that the rod would last until all on the island were dead.

Jesus called the twelve aside again when they reached the seashore, and in secret told them that in the near future He would choose Simon to head the New Law and upon him He would build His Church on earth.

"As yet," Jesus said, "Simon does not realize his calling and he is still one with you as you have always known him. At the time when the New Law is established, Simon will be known as Peter, the symbol of immovable rock—the firm foundation for the new Church. Pray for Simon Peter and his successors."

Jesus promised the twelve He would send John to visit them before many days. Through him they could send word to the mainland if they still desired to live this hidden life on the island. Then, He and the men who were leaving entered the water and began their swim to the ships.

The twelve remained on their knees as the ships moved out to sea. Jesus waved His farewell to them. Never would they forget His expression of joy when He told them Simon would be chosen to succeed Him.

BOOK TWO

John

CHAPTER 1

Jesus Returns to the Mainland

IT WAS A CRISP, STARLIT NIGHT when Simon's ships approached the mainland, and the surface of Mount Carmel Bay looked like smooth, black ice. On the beach blazed a golden driftwood fire.

The ships cast anchor, and as the men waded ashore a lone figure on the beach came to meet them. It was John the Baptizer, who had been waiting since dawn for Simon's red and gold banners to appear on the horizon.

Jesus called out immediately, "John, I stood enthroned and completely captivated on the platform you built for Me!"

"Were You happy there?" John asked, simply.

An avalanche of praise caused John to beg the men to eulogize only the Master and to remember that without God's help he could have done nothing.

Many of the men were shivering in the cold night air, and John urged them to sit close to the fire so that their clothes might dry. As they looked on gratefully, he served them with broiled fish and a hot brew made from wine and boiled honey.

When all had been served, and another beam of driftwood cast upon the fire, John knelt at the God-Man's knee. "I missed You, Master," he whispered.

Jesus touched his shaggy head and asked, "Would you like to return to your island for a visit? Twelve of the crew are waiting for you. They are going to live there all their lives—so you see, your temple toil was not in vain."

John's broad smile was his only answer, but in his eyes could be seen his loneliness for the solitude of his cave home and the stillness of his temple.

Jesus went on: "Teach wisdom to those twelve holy men, John. Tell them of faith and of the ways of silent prayer." John nodded and the Master concluded, "I'll arrange with Simon to have two of his crew take you there next week."

John's expression was one of extreme gratitude, even though he suddenly understood through intuitive knowledge that this would be his last visit to his home and to his temple. Also, he realized that his death was near—that his life could be counted in days. He was going home on earth to his island—but he was going home to God for all eternity. His look at Jesus was one of perfect resignation and it conveyed an unspeakable "Thank You" from his heart.

The stillness of ecstatic union between Jesus and John cast a quiet sleepiness over the crew, and one by one they left for their homes. Jesus, Simon, and John, arm in arm, walked toward Simon's home and Rosa Maria.

Bright was the path as Rosa, lantern in hand, came to meet them. Andrew had hurried ahead to tell her they were coming. Her whole body trembled at the sight of Jesus, and she flung herself into His outstretched arms as He extended them in welcome to her.

When they reached home, Rosa and Simon left Jesus and John alone to talk.

The next morning Jesus walked with John to the edge of town. A dense fog was settling over Mount Carmel as John hesitated before setting out on his path into the desert, where he planned to stay until leaving for the island. As he and the Master looked into the broad stretches of the valley before them, John was caught up into rapture.

In that instant of wisdom, he learned that this would be the last time on earth that he would be with Jesus. This had been their first actual walk together in real life, and now it was to be their last on earth. Tears were in both their eyes as John knelt to kiss his Master's feet. Then, as he said goodbye, he felt the emptiness of the world about him, for he had quietly emerged from his rapture. He straightened up to discover Jesus was gone.

Two weeks later, before the quiet, silver fingers of morning touched the earth, John and two of Simon's crew unfolded the canvas wings of a small fishing boat, and were almost instantly cradled in the dawn's sweeping breeze, which sped them across the sea.

John's enthusiasm was childlike as hour after hour he scanned the horizon for a cloudy haze, which would tell him they were approaching his island. At last he could see its faint outline far in the distance, flat against the water. How he wished the Master could be with him.

Some time later, drenched with sea and mist, John and his two companions knelt on the warm sands of the island. Hungrily, he embraced the goodness of the earth as he let the sands sift slowly through his fingers. He was home.

Awed with the beauty of the sun's rays, which spread like a huge fan over the island, the three men climbed the hill that led to the plateau. And then, ahead of them were the massive temple walls, which seemed to shimmer in vast beams of incense smoke as the sunlight played across their colored stones. It was as though the misty light of the sun was the fringe of the Master's gown as it threw a thousand caressing colors over the temple walls. Each stone cast its reflection into one great brilliance, which resembled a huge candelabra aglow with ceremonial light to greet John and his friends.

The two men were awed by these adornments of God's goodness in the mystery of light and color about them. Silently, they gazed upon the temple from the cobblestone pathway that led to the great arch.

John knelt beside a mound of earth that resembled a grave beside the path. Neither sailor had noticed this particular mound as being any different from the hundreds of others scattered over the desert when they had been there on the retreat. Because of John's emotion and great reverence, they asked him about it.

John straightened up slowly as he answered, "It is indeed a grave," he said, "and the resting place of a Melchizedek priest of the Old Law."

The men knew little about Melchizedek's order of priests and said so.

John explained: "He was here with me for one year before he died in the embrace of God's holy slumber.[6] I buried him just one year ago this season. He came six thousand miles in a handmade raft in

6 Prayer of ecstasy.

obedience to God's command that he find me and ordain me a Melchizedek priest. I am now the last of the line and the priest who links the Old Law with the New by introducing the real Messiah to the world. He taught me the incomprehensible ways of God in the mystery of the Sacrifice of the Clean Oblation as given through intuitive knowledge, and the mystery of the real Oblation, which will be instituted when Jesus forms His Church on earth.

"It was a great joy for the Melchizedek priests to live in the realm of ecstatic gifts and to realize that with God there is no time. Past, present, and future seemed to them as only one hour, and in that knowledge they understood the ages of the present and the golden ones to come. By the power of God, and through His will, they offered the Clean Oblation Sacrifice in anticipation of the real Sacrifice. In their prayers they lived the life of the Messiah in the foreknowledge of His birth, His death, His Resurrection, and His personal gift to the world—the Living Bread.

"They understood that God's new order of priests in the New Law, after the death of the Messiah, the High Priest, would follow Melchizedek's methods at the altar by offering wine and bread, and this bread and wine would be turned into the Living Body and Blood of Christ. Great would be the number of priests in the New Law, where heretofore in the Old Law it was not uncommon for a generation to have but one living Melchizedek priest at a time in the world. Yet never was the chain broken, nor will it ever be severed until the end of time.

"The Old Law's Melchizedek priests actually saw the Golden Light of God, or the reflection of the Divine Nature, when they offered the Clean Oblation Sacrifice. That Golden Light of God was always before them at the altar and when they lifted the bread into that Light it was consumed and reduced to ashes in their hands, thus foretelling the death of the Messiah for the redemption of man. But now in the New Law, when the Master gives the word to begin the real Clean Oblation Sacrifice, He will speak these words through His priests at every Sacrifice, 'This is My Body and This is My Blood!' Jesus, whom you know, is the High Priest."

John gazed wistfully at the grave. "We had many wonderful days together," he went on, "talking about the mysteries of God in the New Law, which you men will actually have the opportunity of seeing.

There will be no other Melchizedek priest to follow me in the designs of the Old Law. I will be the last on earth to offer sacrifice in the Old Law's power. My days are numbered—I will soon die. The Old Law must diminish that the Messiah and His New Law may increase, for God in His priests will never die."

In silence, the two men followed John into the coolness of the temple walls.

CHAPTER 2

The Fires of the Sacred Heart

THE MEETING BETWEEN JOHN and the twelve was long and joyous. When it was over, John sent a man to the boat to bring back a cup of wine and a small loaf of unleavened bread. He placed these on the incense table and then lit a pitch-covered torch to symbolize the prayers of those assembled there. The men knelt on the floor as John began the celebration of the Clean Oblation Sacrifice of the Old Law. As he ended each psalm, he sprinkled natural-herb incense into the torch fire. While its sweet, balm-pungent aroma ascended heavenward, the men sang their praises and thanksgiving.

From out of the heavens, God's Pillar of Golden Fire appeared, the same Fire—God's Divine Nature—that had become visible to the wandering Israelites in the desert. John slowly lifted the unleavened loaf into it. As he lowered it, the God-graced bread had been changed into ashes, a prefigure of Christ's death on the Cross, and of the future gift of Transubstantiation.

As he let the crumbling mass of ashes sift through his fingers, his soul breathed this prayer, "O Emmanuel, Emmanuel, Emmanuel, grace Your people with the wisdom to know You as the Everlasting Truth when You come to give Yourself as the Living Bread in the real

Clean Oblation Sacrifice. Bless Thy children with the gift of faith with which to believe in Thy true Presence."

John continued with other psalms and prayers, and as he did so he sprinkled the holy ashes into the cup of wine. The wine now became the symbol of Christ's life on earth—the mingling of the supernatural with the natural.

The men's faces were rapturous with holy wonder as John invited them to take part in the sublime sacrifice by tasting the wine. They knelt before him and were privileged to receive a type of Holy Communion in anticipation of God's goodness through the laws of Melchizedek.

In trepidation they sipped this tremendous phenomena, which allowed them to view both the Old and the New Law. Here was John before them offering the Old Clean Oblation Sacrifice while at the same time the Messiah, the High Priest, was on earth making preparations for the New Clean Oblation Sacrifice, which would continue daily until the end of the world.

All these thoughts and events left them quite dazed until John told them they were favored, that rarely had this type of Communion been allowed in past ages as a gift to the people.

They knelt in a prayer of thanksgiving and were caught up into the rapturous phenomena of ecstatic union. There, one man understood the holy wisdom of God, as though Jesus said to him, "You are to baptize John as you, yourself, were baptized to show forth the greater gifts of humility. John will understand." At the same time, John was listening to the Master speak these words within him, "John, return in the morning to the mainland. Go and admonish Herod for his sinfulness and his laxity in the laws of Moses concerning divorce and the sin of adultery. You will die as a result of this obedience. Herod will have you put to death."

The brightness of God's Pillar of Fire dimmed slowly as the flaming torch bent to shower a path of black, scattered ashes across the incense table. Gradually, they all awakened from their meditation's slumber in God, and were frightened when the man who had received God's instructions to baptize John whispered what the Master had said to him. None of them felt worthy even to approach the subject to John.

John understood their hesitation, however, and humbly, as a little child, told them he already knew the Master's wishes and begged to receive the gift from their hands. Thus the situation was resolved easily, and with light hearts the men followed John to the beach and found the exact spot in the cove where they had been emblematically gowned by Jesus.

Thus was John baptized in the invisible Fire of God.

That night John told them he was going to his death at Herod's hands. The men were startled and amazed at his courage, humility, faith, and fearless obedience. John said quietly, "When principles of God are attacked we fear neither friend nor foe, and for God we die, that we may live again.

"Before coming here I had heard that several thousand of God's former friends were following Herod's views on divorce and adultery. It seems that he has set himself up as a maker of Divine laws, as well as a destroyer of them. The world will have many like him, and for this reason countless martyrs will gain glorious crowns in Heaven.

"It is only natural for good men to turn with loathing and repugnance from such persons, but when these good people realize how God loves everyone and that He will die for each one personally, they find themselves willing to become martyrs because of His way of redemption. Be saviors of men through Christ, not necessarily for men alone, but to restore all things to God.

"It appears in this age of little faith that Herod is placing his judgment ahead of the laws that Moses received from God, and the people are following him all too readily. I must admonish him and then take my punishment in order to share in the redemption, or reparation, for those he has led into sin. All because I know God loves us. O God, make me worthy to perform Your will!"

One of the crew asked, "Tell us how you prayed when you were here alone. How did you send blessings to people all over the earth? Teach us your way of prayer so that we can follow it to God."

John answered, "Many times when I was lifted out of my body into God's embrace, or closeness, and while we walked and talked together, Jesus taught me how to bless the world and my friends. His simple pattern was to take His crosier-staff and draw a picture in the sand of the All-Seeing Eye, the symbol of God everywhere watching and listening to His creatures. Then I walked around that symbolical eye and asked Him to bless the people of the earth. This All-Seeing Eye will not be used after He dies. In its stead you will use the Sign of the Cross—Jesus outstretched on the wooden cross."

Another man asked, "How many times has Jesus made a solemn retreat of forty days?"

"The Master has told me of six other such retreats into the desert. Each time the devils tempted Him in the same way, daring Him to prove that He was God, for they are not sure He is the Messiah. This is not surprising for we have had many impostors, and even the people of the earth will find His identity hard to believe. For that reason we can understand the confusion and doubt of the demons. It is well that they will not realize the truth until after He is dead."

They were still talking when the eastern sky opened its silver valleys of dawn before them the next morning. In farewell, John said, "Pretend that this silver dawn is the awakening of your new life. Bask in its interior warmth and beauty, for it is the symbol of quiet prayer. Meditate that you are in the vastness of that dawn, playing in the delights of God's immensities. You will find no attachments there—all is yours in the freedom of prayer. Would you mar its beauty with unkind thoughts, evil expressions, or loudness of voice?

"God has two natures, Divine and Human. While you live on earth you must try finding both. You will feel the majesty and power of His Divine Nature in the vastness and quietness of creations like this dawn, and you will find His Human Nature in the simple little things of earth, such as a rose, a blade of grass, a chalice, gold, or gems.

"Find Him in everything—He is your companion. And while you walk and talk with Him, remember He is quiet and speaks only to a quiet friend. Always think calmly while the artist in you muses, for words are deeds in His mind. Watch the dawn; it is noiseless, and yet it is the most powerful force on earth. So also watch your silent prayers—they, too, are the most powerful force on earth."

Tears blurred John's vision as he, shortly afterward, looked toward the shore from the small boat that was taking him from the island back to the mainland. Then he faced the open sea resolutely and did not look back again.

To the men who manned the boat he said, "Please do not mention to anyone that I am the last Melchizedek priest. Nor do I want anyone to know of my pending death. I am not afraid and I do not want sympathy.

No honor or fame must be taken from the Living Messiah, Who will suffer for all. However, tell Simon that I was baptized according to the way of the Master. He will be glad."

The return trip was long, for the little boat encountered a bad storm, and it was a happy moment when they sighted the mainland with its mountains and narrow canyons. Towering breakers crashed along the shore as they landed.

After resting, the three men walked to a mountain pass through which John planned to go to Nazareth, which was the first leg of his journey to Capernaum and Herod. For years he had longed for the opportunity and privilege of visiting Mary, the mother of Jesus. Through prayer he knew about her graces and how she had been preserved from the darkness of Original Sin. Now through the prayer of ecstatic union with Jesus, he knew it was in the Divine Plan that he visit her.

Saying goodbye, he went on alone. Just before he passed out of sight, he turned and waved his last farewell. Smiles and silent tears were the men's parting gifts to him.

Alone now, the two sailors vividly understood sin and its penalty, sin which could separate them from Jesus and from John. To avoid sin was to see them again. They resolved to shun it at all costs, and they pledged help to one another in the discipline of their spiritual growth.

CHAPTER 3

Nazareth

NAZARETH CAME INTO SIGHT AT LAST, and as he approached Mary's humble house John quickened his steps. He was breathless with excitement—he was going to see the mother of God!

As he turned into the pathway shaded by a huge olive tree, Mary came to meet him, a smile of welcome on her face. John fell to his knees. He had never seen such a beautiful woman, and her gentle greeting warmed his heart.

"Mother of God—mother of Jesus!" he exclaimed, kissing the hem of her gown reverently.

"Dear John," Mary said, "it is so good of you to come to see me."

They walked side by side into the shaded patio. Mary was a magnificent gem of dignity, and her speech was an ornament of rhythmical thought as she spoke of Jesus. Quietly she asked of Him.

John told her happily about the retreat the Master had made with Simon and his men. A smile played across Mary's face as she asked, "Did He tell you whether or not He liked the swallows I sent to keep Him warm? My angels told me it was cold there and together we planned the surprise. And did He happen to tell you that each time He started to step over a thorn, or a stone, the angels quickly removed it? They reported He had many a laugh over their efforts, for they wore the assumed forms of men and were a little clumsy. He just said, 'Mother always finds a way!'"

"I know," John answered. "He told the men all about it and I remember they said He laughed as He told them. What a joy it would have been to see Him. What a joy for all Heaven to witness! But how He misses your particular nearness and personal attention.

"Mother Mary, I have good news for you. Jesus will be here before many days. He said He was going to take you to Jerusalem, where He has been with Simon and his crew while I visited my island home."

Incomprehensible was Mary's smile—an expression of mingled gladness and sorrow. She did not speak for a moment, and John wondered as he watched whether or not she knew of her Son's approaching death. Could it be sooner than he expected? He did not know the time nor the hour, though in vision's ecstatic union it seemed that it was far away. A shudder chilled him, for he wanted to be the last person in the world to bring news to her of the nearness of that dreadful time.

Through her virtue of great composure, Mary said, "I have known for a long time that I would journey to Jerusalem to witness the death of my Son—but it will not be on this trip, John. Thank you for His message."

Quickly her voice changed to a more cheerful tone as she asked, "Did He say when I could expect Him? It has been such a long time since we traveled together. How wonderful that we can be coworkers with Him in the plan of redemption!"

John's eyes filled with tears as he relived the vision that told him of his own death and he hoped he would be able to face it bravely. Then he answered, "No, Mother Mary, Jesus did not tell me the day nor the hour that you could expect Him."

Knowing John's thoughts about Capernaum, Mary hurried to change the subject by asking, "Would you like to see the Master's room? His toys and trinkets are still there—just as He left them when He was a child. Perhaps you would like to rest for a few hours in His bed."

John was almost speechless with happiness. To rest in His bed!

Mary went on, "Later tonight I am going to Cana for Vow Day Exercises in one of the Schools of David. I would like you to go with me."

"With all my heart!" John answered simply.

Mary smiled her gratitude. "Here is Jesus' room," she said.

John looked around slowly, his heart full. There were the Master's toys, as His mother had said, and on the wall hung a collection of canes and crutches. At John's puzzled expression, Mary explained that Jesus had collected them from the crippled and the paralytic. Often Joseph had made new and better ones and offered them in exchange for the old ones. Jesus had then taken them, polished them, and hung them on the wall. It had been His hobby.

There was an empty cage that had once housed Twitchy Ears, His trained mouse. Mother Mary laughed as she told John about him. And outside the window was a larger cage in which Bobin, a pet rabbit, had once lived.

On another wall were chalk drawings of sunsets, stars, trees, and even horses. These were the little Christ Child's first attempts at drawing, and Mary had preserved them.

For an hour Mary talked, and then John lay down in Jesus' bed and dozed in meditation's sleep in this wonderful room of memories. Mary tucked a tapestry cover over him.

As John slept, Mary prepared a lunch and otherwise made ready for their trip to Cana. She planned to take John to the School of David, where Jesus had attended classes two months out of each year, or whenever He was home.

She smiled as she worked and mused about the Messiah in school. Only one professor, a high priest of the Old Law, had known his little Scholar. He was the one to whom she had confided her secret when the angel announced to her that she was to be the mother of God. He believed her and gave her permission to take the swaddling clothes for the Messiah's holy infancy.

Her mind turned to the holy women,[7] teachers in the Schools, or Houses of David, whose duty it was to weave and embroider these swaddling clothes for the kings who were to be born through the lineage of David. One special set was put aside every twenty-five years for the birth of the Messiah, whom they believed would be born to a virgin in the House of David.

The parents, the holy women, and the high priests were the only ones who were allowed to see the king's linens before they were carefully wrapped and sealed in a gold casket at a solemn celebration. No

---

7 Anna, the prophetess who had recognized the Messiah when He was presented in the Temple, was one of these.

one but kings were allowed to wear swaddling clothes, so they were not in common use.

As the other high priests and holy women did not know the Messiah had been born, the custom of secrecy concerning the king's clothes was still kept.

Vow Day Exercises took place two days later in the School of David in Cana. The scene was one of brilliant color and movement as the high priest and the boys and girls, the firstborn of the local families, appeared wearing gold and red. Relatives and friends were dressed in purple and chanted prayers, which symbolized the denials of the young people and were as bright fires to coax the Messiah to begin His reign on earth.

Mary and John listened as the young men and women professed and renewed their perpetual vows of virginity for the spiritual heritage of David. Through these mortifications, the pathway would be made straight for the coming of the Messiah.

When night came, these dedicated virgins changed into dull, bluish-gray, or brown-colored robes. They were to wear these throughout their lives as a singular blessing and reminder that they were dead to self for a glorious reason. They regarded themselves as helpers in the great plan of redemption.[8]

John and Mary stayed in Cana for more than a week, and during that time John met the high priest who shared Mary's secret and was shown a set of swaddling clothes, which were an exact duplicate of the linens Jesus had worn.

Then one evening, in the sifting rays of a purple twilight, John knelt before Mary to say goodbye. She asked God's blessing upon him and kissed him on the back of the neck, whispering, "When you were born I took care of you. I was the first person to caress and embrace you. My wish then was the same as now—that in your martyrdom you will not feel the pain that ordinarily a sword would inflict. Jesus and I love you, John, and my heart will follow you. Go now, and God's blessings on you."

---

8 It was on Mary's Vow Day that the angel Gabriel announced that she was to be the mother of the Messiah. Both she and Joseph, being the firstborn of their parents, had attended respective Schools of David and had taken the perpetual vows of virginity.

With smiles and tears they turned from each other to follow separate paths to the heart of God. John understood now that his martyrdom would consist in being beheaded by a sword. Fear crept through him and then he remembered Mary's promise, "My heart will follow you."

That promise helped to make him fearless and steady in his path toward death.

CHAPTER 4

Magdala

JESUS HAD TOLD JOHN about His boyhood days in Magdala and had invited him to visit there, as well as to meet His grandmother, Granny Mary, the mother of Joseph. John was almost as anxious to talk to her as he had been to speak to Mother Mary. He wanted to ask her about Joseph—about his life, his moods, his death, for he knew very little about him.

Granny Mary, a frail, quick little woman, received him kindly and drew him into the cool interior of her house. Knowing him to be hot and tired from his journey, she made him lie down on soft cushions and gave him a cool drink and cookies to nibble—the kind Jesus liked, she explained quickly. Poor John! How really uncomfortable he looked—and he was!

Owlishly, John struggled with all his might to tolerate this ease of the world when austerities were his real joy. His nervousness and misery caused him to itch under his camel's hair and goatskin robes. He squirmed and tried to sit up, but Granny Mary pushed him down again, gently. In doing this, she perceived a fine mist of perspiration upon his forehead. Quickly dipping a cloth into cool, scented water, she bathed his face and hands.

This was too much for John. He scrambled to his feet awkwardly. Granny Mary said, "I'm sorry you don't like my attempts to make you comfortable. Jesus is far more obedient and obliging when He visits here. He's a much better actor than you are!"

John lay back down on his couch again. He chuckled to himself as he thought of Jesus accepting all this. It was a mortification, that's what it was! He thought, "If Jesus can bear it, so can I, even though it's the greatest penance of my life!" He relaxed and tried to lie still.

This was certainly a new, hard way to follow the Master, but John was not surprised at anything. In spite of all his good intentions, however, he cringed as he heard Granny Mary splashing more cool rosewater into the basin, and his muscles tensed as she again bathed his forehead and wrists. As she did so, she whispered, "Poor John, you are so tired!"

For an hour John endured this hospitable, kindly torture, even allowing a beautiful tapestry to be placed over him. There were more cookies, more cool drinks. In desperation, John finally asked, "Won't you tell me something about your son, Granny Mary? He must have been a wonderful man to have been chosen the foster father of God."

Granny Mary nodded, and her mind began to reach back through the many years. "Joseph was an honor student in his School of David," she began. "He was considered its most brilliant scholar and was most meticulous in his deportment.

"As he grew older, he became proficient in the art of mapmaking. He knew every river, mountain, and path in Palestine and in the surrounding country. Everyone loved him—and particularly elderly people, for he was quiet and reserved.

"His hobby was carpentry, and it was time well spent for charity. He made crutches, benches, staffs, canes, and smooth wood-sliders for the aged and the crippled.

"He loved to pray, and through prayer he seemed to reach a great horizon of hidden knowledge and wisdom.

"He was a good swimmer and an excellent diver. Many times he went deep-sea diving for pearls." She removed a necklace she was wearing and handed it to John. "This is a gift from him. He gathered each pearl for me."

Taking the pearls back after John had looked at them, Granny Mary kissed them reverently and let them fall into the folds of her gown. "The original strand," she continued, "was much longer than this. I divided it with the innkeeper's wife in return for her kindness and hospitality the night Jesus was born."

John forgot his discomfort in his quickened interest. "Tell me about that!" he begged. "Were you there?"

Granny Mary made herself comfortable on the couch beside him. "It's a long story, John," she said, "but I'll try to remember it as best I can. I'll begin with Joseph and Mary getting ready to go to Bethlehem for the census. They asked Jacob and me to go with them—Jacob was my husband, Joseph's father—as well as other relatives and friends, as we all came from the same vicinity and had to register. We ended up about fifteen in all.

"Around midnight one night, after several days of traveling, Mary called to Joseph who was walking ahead of our caravan. He dropped the leather bridle of the donkey he was leading and hurried to her.

"Mary said, 'Joseph, listen to my heart.'

"Joseph listened for a moment and then called me. John, as I leaned toward Mary I heard the most beautiful music. I was speechless!

"Mary said, 'I've known for quite a while that when I hear this the hour of the Messiah's birth is near.'

"Joseph and I called the others quickly, and Mary allowed each of them to hear the heavenly music. We formed a semi-circle of worshipers around her and the little donkey upon which she rode. I remember Joseph saying, 'The little King will soon be born then.'

"The music began to fade and Mary asked us to find a place for her to stay.

"As we were near Bethlehem, we split up, thinking we might find lodging more quickly that way. Thus, Joseph and Mary were alone when they stopped at the inn.

"It was the providence of God that there was no room there, for it would have offered them no privacy at all. It was a huge, oblong building with very high walls. In the enclosure of the walls were long porches where travelers slept and rested while their animals were tied to the porch pillars. The dirt and mud in this patio was overrun with all sorts of beasts of burden moving here and there as the innkeeper tried to find room for each new lodger as he arrived. Joseph said the stench was worse than a pigpen, and certainly no place for the King of Kings to be born.

"While Joseph was looking the place over, the innkeeper's wife, Rachel—a short, heavy, very unkempt woman who must have weighed nearly two hundred pounds, came outside carrying a lantern and talked to Mary, who was waiting on her donkey. She had been drinking and was not too steady on her feet, but she took pity on Mary and suggested she stay in a stable on a nearby hillside. She assured Mary she would do everything possible to make her comfortable.

"Joseph came out of the inn at that moment and he and Mary agreed to adopt Rachel's suggestion.

"Rachel picked up the reins of the donkey and led the way slowly up the hill to an enlarged natural cave about two hundred yards away on the outskirts of Bethlehem. Once there, she loosened the tapestry bundles from the donkey's carrying straps and Joseph hurried them inside. She and Mary followed.

"They entered through a large door into a small storage room—only a part of the whole stable—where grain and hay were kept. Rachel hung her lantern on a peg and chased out several squawking geese and chickens. Then she climbed a short ladder to a loft and from there pulled down clean fresh hay with which to make Mary comfortable.

"Across the back of the room there was a low, rock wall, and fastened into this were upright wooden beams, or bars, through which food could be pushed to animals from a manger directly in front. The flickering lantern light showed the heads of cows, oxen, donkeys, and goats looking curiously through the bars. The room was warm because of the heat from their bodies.

"Rachel smoothed the hay and then, not wanting to leave, began to feed the animals, her eyes fastened with a curious expression upon Mary. She even tried to get as close to her as she could. Joseph smiled as he told me about it, for both he and Mary knew she could hear the music from Mary's heart and could not understand it. No doubt she thought her over-indulgence in wine was responsible. They couldn't tell her the truth.

"At any rate, she suddenly became frightened and hurried from the stable, calling over her shoulder that she would be back with bedding.

"Apparently, she thought the fresh air would clear her head as she hurried to her room in the inn. In a little while she returned, and after arranging the straw and blankets for Mary, she stood looking at her.

It was quite clear there was something strange about Mary that she could not understand.

"Mary smiled and said, 'Don't be afraid, and thank you for your great kindness.'

"Hesitantly, Rachel answered, 'You are beautiful! I've never seen anyone like you and—and I don't understand the way I feel.'

"Mary asked, 'How is that, Rachel?'

"'There seems to be music in your voice, and when I look at you I don't want to have anything more to do with my life at the inn, or any more to drink. If I gave it all up, could I become like you?'

"Mary answered, 'You could become beautiful and enjoy the richness of God's peace if you would only love all your friends. That peace would give you the poise and refinement God desires all women to possess. Try raising your standards of womanhood to a more lovely state. Other women will follow. I'll ask God to help you.'

"Rachel said slowly, 'You speak as though you knew God. Is it possible the Messiah is here and you have seen Him?' When Mary did not answer, Rachel went on, 'I believe He will come someday, for the prophecies say so, but how will I know Him? There are impostors through here nearly every day.'

"Mary answered, 'I haven't seen the true living Messiah, but I am certain that before many hours pass the world will both see and hear of Him.'

"Poor Rachel, she could not understand these words, so to change the subject Joseph excused himself and came in search of Jacob and me.

"Rachel was about to ask Mary another question when she heard her husband's booming voice shouting for her. Reluctantly, she left, saying she would be back in the morning. A few moment's later, as Mary knelt in prayer for her, she heard the innkeeper's whip crack as he used it on Rachel for lingering so long to talk."

Granny Mary bowed her head and tears were in her eyes. Quietly she asked, "John, will you have a cup of tea with me?"

John nodded yes.

CHAPTER 5

The Birth of Jesus

GRANNY MARY CONTINUED. "Mary told us that as she prayed for Rachel's protection (she could still hear the lashing of the whip and the poor woman's cries), the stable was suddenly filled with Heaven's transcending light. There before her stood Michael, the Archangel. His greeting to her was, 'Fear not, Mary. I have come to be with you until Christ is born.'

"Mary answered, 'Incomprehensible are God's ways! I am glad you are here, but I wish Joseph would hurry back, for I would like to have him here, too. And won't you please bless our good friend Rachel in a special way? She has been very kind to us.'

"Michael bowed and said, 'Joseph will find his mother and father and bring them here very shortly. Fear not, Mary, and in peace recollect yourself into God's way of deeper prayer. The angels are already assembling to honor His birth and to be the first to sing His praises in His holy Humanity as He begins His sojourn on earth. As for Rachel, she will have my blessing. She will play a great part as a victim of love to the Master's divine plan on earth.'"

Granny Mary's eyes grew soft and filled with happiness over the mystery she was relating. "As Mary prayed, she watched Michael unfold the bundle in which were rolled the swaddling clothes. He took from it the tapestry, which was about twenty feet in length and six or seven feet in width. Its fringe was a luxurious depth of eighteen inches.

"Standing on the low, rock wall, he tied the fringe on one end to the rafter poles above, allowing the tapestry to hang down as a curtain between the animals and Mary. Then he smoothed it over the manger and across the straw-earth floor as a carpet, arranging the fringe on the other end in a beautiful swirling design.

"Mary was joyous, for now she was hidden completely from the animals. The only evidence she had of their nearness was their warmth in the stable and their heavy breathing against the tapestry curtain.

"The beautiful golden design woven into the tapestry delighted her. She could find more stories for meditation in them than we could when we saw them later. However, I did remember a huge sunburst design that brightened the stable with its reflected golden light as the candle before it bobbed and flickered. It was woven of the brightest golden threads on a background of purple and black. That part of the tapestry, which hung below the manger, was aglow with white clouds and doves, which were flying toward and into the center of the great sunburst above.

"As Mary examined the tapestry, Michael placed the swaddling bandages on the rock ledge in the order in which he would use them. Then he said to Mary, 'I'll teach you how to wrap these around the little Jesus when the time comes.'

"Mary told us how she vaguely remembered, after that, rising in the unitive way of prayer in God. Michael continued from there. In that ecstasy of joy where the human senses are as though dead, and the spirit races to God, Mary was suddenly encased in a tremulous and unspeakably bright light. That light, rising through her as a tower of ivory into the heavens as seen by the spiritual eye, was too bright even for the gaze of the angels, who hid themselves outside the sanctuary of God's mother. Michael was the only one who dared approach her. He seemed to walk into this heavenly mist and lifted from it the Christ Child as if he were lifting Him from a cradle.

"Tenderly he caressed the Infant God as he carried Him to the manger. He placed Him inside, and kneeling to adore Him he called Mary.

"In perfect obedience she arose from her divine ecstasy, and after walking to the manger knelt beside Michael in adoration. Then she picked up the little Jesus and kissed His sleeping eyelids, which fluttered and opened slowly to the world. The first thing He saw was the image of His own mother before Him. His baby eyes held fast to her gaze while she laid Him back in the manger of beautiful tapestry padded with straw. Michael had arisen and was busy unfolding the swaddling bandages with which to dress his King."

Granny smiled at John. "You know," she said, "that birth was the most miraculous because the little Infant Body was not even damp nor did it have any of the effects of a natural birth. It was as though He had been in the world about ten days. Mary told us that the nakedness of His manhood was clothed in an ethereal mist of light like a tight-fitting cloth close to His Body, so dense in natural-colored light that no mortal eye could penetrate it.

"But let me get back to Michael's account. He said, 'Jesus will never be completely exposed to the eyes of the world, for this shield of cloth-like mist will always protect Him. It will always be before you, Mary, for you are His bride as well as His mother, and He wishes to save you and His friends any embarrassment due to your knowledge of His divinity and His majesty. Only at one time will His nakedness be exposed, and then only to one man in the temple on the day of His circumcision.

"'He will not be nursed as a natural child of the world. Eating in any form is one of humanity's crosses because of Adam's transgression. Original Sin has never cast its shadow across your purity, Mary, and hence you do not share in any of its effects, just as you did not suffer pain when Jesus was born. Any eating you have done has been under the laws of obedience and the same thing will be true of the Messiah. He will willingly suffer the effects of sin but not sin, itself.

"'Throughout His life He will purposely forget His divinity, from time to time, in order to suffer all things, except sin, in His true humanity. If at any time He wishes to mortify His Body I will care for His every need. There will be times when you will be allowed to give Him a little cow's milk, for this will protect you from questioning about His care. I will advise you on those occasions, as it will be necessary to keep His identity hidden from the world for many years.'"

Granny Mary settled herself a little more comfortably and continued. "Michael taught Mary the mystery of how to wrap the swaddling clothes around the tiny Body of Jesus. They were majestically happy in the unique privilege that was theirs—that of dressing the King in His royal robes for the first time on earth.

"At that moment Joseph and his father and I hurried into the stable, and for the first time we saw the Infant God-Man and the actual visible appearance of Michael.

"We fell to our knees and I was afraid of Michael until he spoke and invited me to hold the Holy Infant. While I held Him, Joseph and Jacob continued to kneel transfixed. Neither man seemed to have the courage to touch little Jesus.

"Then Michael said, 'God is showering great gifts upon the earth. At this moment He is showing us visibly how He will choose the lowly people of ignorance and sin, the outcasts of nations, and those of the highest culture and education, into the ways of His grace. This providence will continue from now until the end of time.

"'As we stand here, God is allowing a band of angels to be seen visibly by shepherds on the eastern hills. Since they are the outcasts of the Jews, people will question why they should be allowed to see such signs and wonders. All favors are gifts from God, and He gives to sinners as well as to the good. The good will then stay closer to God and often the sinners will abandon their evil ways. The angels have assumed the forms of young men and are telling the shepherds that this night a King is born unto them, and that He is lying here in this manger dressed in swaddling clothes.

"'Swaddling clothes are a contradiction to these men, for they have heard the unique history of these garments and how they belong to the kings who follow in the royal line of David. They are asking, 'How can this be? A king from Heaven, the Messiah, dressed in swaddling clothes and lying in a manger that tells of poverty? The king we look for would not be born in a stable where animals are kept!'

"'Others are saying, "Come, let us search for this miracle of which the angels have spoken. We would like to see swaddling clothes which only kings may wear. It would be worth traveling a hundred miles just to see them for tradition tells us they are most beautiful and costly. How did such poor people happen to get them?"

"'The swaddling clothes will be a contradiction to the people of the earth until the end of time. They are a figure of beauty that will be symbolized in all His churches the world over—for beauty and magnificence will often attract countless people to the understanding of God.

"'Tomorrow the shepherds will come to this cave as though it were a church. They will admire the swaddling clothes and yet not realize the God-Man's personal, invisible blessing while they are near Him. That blessing, however, will be the means of their future conversions.

"'There will be over fifteen hundred people here, Joseph, their curiosity aroused by the shepherds having seen the vision of angels. Hurry them in and out in small groups to keep Mary from being questioned. The majority will be here only to catch a glimpse of the swaddling linens anyway. Don't worry about the high priests sending for you because of these clothes, for you will move from here in two days to a house in Jerusalem, where you will be kept hidden until you are told to move again.

"'Now I shall tell you about God's plan for people of great culture and intelligence. The symbolism of this type of person will follow a certain plan until the end of time. At this moment a great Melchizedek priest is caught up into his accustomed ecstatic way of prayer. He is spiritually watching the world and its people. In this state people resemble great towering beacon lights reaching upward toward the heavens as they pray. Even now he is aware of a great new light—a beacon light so powerful that it brings these holy words to his lips. Ah, at last the Tower of Ivory is here. Heaven's Mystical Rose is blossoming on earth. This Light is the mother of God! She is God's House of Gold. Where these treasures of light are, there is the Messiah. He is the Star of the East—she the Morning Star. Oh, Morning Star, I am at once beginning my search for thee and for my God on earth. Seat of Wisdom, pray for me, and help me to find thee in the shadows of the East!

"'Now, an angel of God is telling this Melchizedek priest, who will be known as the head of the Magi, that he is allowed to see this great phenomena so that the Book of Numbers may be fulfilled, A star shall rise out of Jacob, and a scepter shall spring up from Israel.[9]

"'Mary, that great star is your immaculate, spiritual fire within your body. It is rising up into the heavens to form an indestructible bridge of light—God's Light in you between Heaven and earth.

"'The Melchizedek priest will leave this night in his search for you and will be joined by two other priests of his order along the way. They, too, will see your light and know where you are when God captures them into ecstatic prayer.

---

9 Num. 24:17.

"'During their long nights of the spirit they will wander far from the right course, but in God's mercy they will see your light again and continue on. Through trials, fasting, thirst, disappointment, and dismay they will find you and Joseph south of Bethany two years from now. They will bring many gifts and jewels. You are to accept these gems because from time to time in the Messiah's life you will be obliged to sell them as a means of livelihood, for Joseph will be forced to travel at great distances in order to keep the identity of Jesus hidden.'"

Granny Mary suggested they take a little rest, after which she would continue with the story.

CHAPTER 6

Visit of the Magi

JOHN WATCHED QUIETLY, with a little smile, as Granny Mary fed and cared for a pet parrot. When she finished, she came back and sat down once more on the couch beside him.

"Now I shall tell you the story of the Magi," she said, and memories once again began to crowd into her eyes. "Joseph and Mary and the Infant Jesus stayed in the stable two days, and then we departed at dusk one evening for a little house nearer Jerusalem, as Michael had instructed.

"Rachel saw us go and hurried after us. She had been away the past two days and had missed the crowds. She knew nothing of the extraordinary events that had taken place.

"When she caught up with us, she admired Baby Jesus only as she would an ordinary child. She couldn't see the swaddling clothes, for we had wrapped Him in a tapestry shawl.

"She couldn't keep her eyes off of Mary, and her expression was certainly one of great admiration. Timidly, she begged, 'Please give me something that you have worn, for I would dearly love to have a keepsake. You are the most beautiful woman I have ever seen and you haven't turned away from my ugliness and poverty. I am sure your good husband provides well for you and that you would not have stayed in the stable if the inn had not been crowded. I am sorry about that, but I am grateful that I met you because I am trying to imitate you.'

"Rachel leaned toward Mary, and the perplexed expression appeared upon her face once more. 'It seems I hear music whenever I come near you,' she said. 'I heard it the night you came here, but I had been drinking and I thought that was the reason. But now I haven't had a drink—and I will never take one again—and I still hear the music. You must be a very holy person. Are you a prophetess? I have heard of music and heavenly fragrances coming to them, but I never dreamed I would be close to such a favored one.'"

Granny Mary sighed as she continued. "We often heard music coming from Mary's heart, even after the birth of Jesus, and so could appreciate Rachel's amazement. She hadn't the faintest idea, of course, that she was talking to the mother of God.

"Mary wore no ornamentation of any kind, so I offered Rachel part of my pearl necklace. I broke the string and took off ten pearls and ten tiny gold nuggets, which I tied into a bracelet. Mary toyed with and admired it on her own wrist before she placed it on Rachel's and kissed her.

"As we said good-bye, Rachel hoped fervently that we would meet again. Then she turned and hurried to the inn. A soft sigh escaped Mary and she said, 'We are visibly seeing and hearing God's blessings given to the world as sacramentals. Rachel's pearls, for instance, are especially blessed. She can actually hear Heaven's music when she holds them to her heart. Many people will be drawn in this manner to Jesus, all through time, and not to the crib as we would imagine.'"

Granny looked at her necklace thoughtfully. "I didn't understand Mary then," she continued, "and someday I hope I see Rachel again, for I would like to ask her whether she kept the pearls and if she heard the music more than once. I also think I'd ask her to trade just one of her beads for one of these. I've listened and listened to these pearls but I have never heard a thing."

John said, "God often manifests Himself through sacramentals. He has allowed me several of those occasions of joy and they are wonderful! I believe it's His way of playing a game with us, and we should reciprocate by our simple faith and joy in searching His ways through prayer. I feel sure you will see Rachel again, Granny Mary. I wonder if she has kept her resolution and continued following the ideals of Mary?"

They talked at some length about Mary and her ideals, and then Granny resumed her story of Jesus. "The following two years were interesting, John," she said. "Joseph and Mary traveled from one town to another, as Michael advised, to keep the Little Master's identity hidden, but Jacob and I did not go with them. Shortly after they moved to Jerusalem we came back here to Galilee with our relatives. We were all given the grace to keep the wonderful secret—until such time as Jesus is ready to tell the world who He is.

"The Holy Family visited us here several times, and then for about a year we did not see them at all. We hoped and prayed they were safe, for we heard that all infants two years and younger were ordered killed. We didn't learn the whole story in connection with that until Jesus was about three years old and Mary and Joseph came again to visit us. You can imagine how glad we were to see them!

"One evening Joseph told about the visit of the Magi. Apparently he and Mary were living in a little cottage somewhat south of Bethany when that great event took place.

"Jesus was tumbling and romping on the floor with Joseph when Mary called the little Messiah to her. She had heard an approaching caravan, and she knew that it was the Magi of whom Michael had spoken. Quickly, she smoothed Jesus' tumbled locks and straightened His tunic.

"Joseph went outside into the roadway to meet and direct the great kings with their slaves and animals. Jesus and Mary stood in the doorway watching, the little Master's hand held tightly in His mother's. His eyes were very big and round at sight of all the pomp and majesty and all the people and the animals and the noise and disturbance they made, but He wanted to see only the camels and the dogs.

"The Magi dismounted and were led by a procession of slaves toward the cottage. This evidently frightened Jesus, for He turned and ran from the door and sat on a small, red footstool that faced the entrance.

"However, He smiled as the trembling kings entered the room with Joseph. They stopped short, awestruck and bewildered when they saw Jesus as a small child before them. Never had they thought, even in vision life, that they would see the Messiah like this! They looked at one another as though to ask, 'How are we going to address Him?' In their lives of sanctity they had never practiced this type of humility and meekness—that of becoming as a little child and of speaking as one.

"They knelt before the Blessed Infant and stuttered a few phrases clumsily, and then one of them turned to Mary and pleaded, 'Tell us what to say. We are lost for words with which to express our gratitude and belief to such a little child. We realize He is the Messiah and thus has all knowledge, so is it proper for us to address Him in a childish manner? Or should we speak to Him as an adult? It's very puzzling!

"'We have often seen Him in the hidden realms of prayer and even talked to Him, just as Isaiah both saw and walked with Him in His humanity, but to actually see Him in His childhood is another phase and a mystery for us. Teach us how to say the things we want to say!'

"One of the Magi begged, 'Mother of God, may we have your permission to offer incense before Him? Many times we have done that to His Majesty as the God of Mystery, but we have certainly neglected His childhood in our meditations and how to conduct ourselves accordingly.'

"Mary answered, 'Yes, you may offer incense before Him.'

"Thus put more at ease, the Magi actually chuckled as Jesus watched the flickering lights of the green and red gems in their crowns, and bent His head this way and that trying to capture the beauty of each one.

"Then His sharp, brown eyes caught sight of the Magi's dogs, outside the door, as they strained at the end of their ropes trying to get away from the slaves who held them. To everyone's surprise, the little Master called one of them by name and tried to coax him into the room!

"Joseph said the great kings were shocked, but when they discovered neither Joseph nor Mary were dismayed they broke into chuckles once more and told the slave to let loose the dog. The animal came into the room quietly and laid his head across the tiny knees of Jesus and stayed in that position as the kings lit their incense in miniature golden gondolas at the Master's feet.

"While the incense rose into the air, Jesus patted the hound and His baby eyes followed the thin, wavering streams of smoke rising higher and higher until they reached the ceiling, there to billow out into clouds of wonderful fragrance that spread throughout the room. And again Jesus peered at the beautiful crowns of the Magi, this time through a curtain of golden vapor, and allowed His eyes to feast on the shimmering fires in the gems that were made brighter by the charcoal embers at His feet.

"As the incense burned away, the kings asked Mary's permission to bless Jesus. Mary smiled at Jesus, but He had other plans. He rose quickly to His feet, and extending His chubby hands He blessed the Magi, saying, 'My holy priests, you must not return to Herod as he commanded. Go back to your own country by another route. Be on your way.'

"Throwing His arms around each one, He kissed them on their cheeks. Each fell instantly to his knees and kissed the Master's feet in return. Each had seen for an instant in His childhood eyes the same expression he had often witnessed, in vision, in His manhood eyes.

"Suddenly they were caught up into ecstasy, and there before them stood the God-Man. He said, 'I have a special mission for you, the oldest Melchizedek. One day I will call for you to go in search of a certain man by the name of John, whom you must ordain to the Order of Priests. He will then become the last Melchizedek priest to offer the sacrifice of Clean Oblation in the Old Law and also the last to offer the sacrifice of anticipation of My dying for men. I am the High Priest who will make the sacrifice live, and for that reason I have come into the world that My friends may always have Me with them. You are to keep My identity hidden until I speak to you again through the illumination of great prayer.'"

Granny sighed heavily, for she was almost carried away into the depths of meditation. John reached over, and patting her hand, said, "Granny, you have known the ordained mission of my life and death all these years and yet, during the time I have been here, you have humbly kept all this knowledge within the depths of your soul. You are wonderful, and just continue to be your natural, simple self, for that alone is a great vocation of love to God.

"You have made me realize in a much greater way the sublime position I hold and I am grateful. And Granny Mary, whether you know it or not, you are a master of self for having kept humble throughout all these years, even though you stood on the threshold of knowledge and wisdom that is seldom given to women."

Granny answered, "I have tried to practice humility, John, but at times I have failed, and I'll have to admit that I was frightened in your presence, for I know of your greatness in the providence of God.

"Now I recall a beautiful expression Jesus once used. He said, 'Granny, remember Me in My Humanity. Don't be afraid of Me. I am here with you to find joy in your customs, manners, and the simple pleasures of the world. Treat Me as any grandmother would treat a grandson and you will be sure to please Me. I love your human touch and the gentleness with which you coax Me to have cookies and to rest on your down cushions.'"

Granny continued, smiling at John, "So you see, to spoil you with kindness is to serve my Jesus within you, for that great indwelling that you possess in your soul is God. I have only to look at your simple humanity and I marvel at the goodness of God, who esteems man so highly that He places you in the grace of your sublime position. You wouldn't want me to be frightened of you—and neither would Jesus."

CHAPTER 7

Joseph

FAR INTO THE NIGHT Granny Mary and John pursued their conversation. Then pensively, Granny said, "John, it was so wonderful to hear Joseph say, 'Mother, to have Mary near is always to have a masterpiece of loveliness within reach. God has spoiled me.'

"Joseph died in this room—upon this same couch and pillows upon which you are reclining. Jesus and Mary were with him. I was sitting in the patio doorway and so could overhear their holy conversation.

"Jesus asked, 'Father Joseph, I know you realize that you are a very sick man—would you like to receive the spiritual gift of My Father as fire from the hands of an angel? I am aware that you remember the story of My Father's nearness to Isaiah when He appeared to him in the form of fire, which depicted to the world the Divine Nature, and how an angel brought that fire to the prophet because of his constant yearning to receive God just as all people will soon have the privilege of receiving the Living Bread. Likewise, you believe that I came into the world to cast My Father's fire from within Me upon the earth, hoping that souls will be enkindled with His love. My earthly body is but a means of tempering the awesome majesty of My Father. Through My humanity, My friends will not be afraid to approach the Eternal Father, for they will no longer feel the shriveling bodily burns that Isaiah felt when the angel granted his desire to receive My Father.'

"Joseph smiled and answered, 'Jesus, I am not worthy to receive God in this manner. However, I have longed for the fulfillment of the great promise and have dreamed of receiving the Living Bread, which I understand will follow the manner of manna from Heaven. But why should I be so privileged? The greatest of men have actually died of broken hearts because they could not receive it. Perhaps it would be better that I die as a man of desires and follow David in his longing for You, the Living Promise.'"

Granny dried a tear as she continued. "I hurried to kneel beside Joseph for I, too, had prayed to live long enough to have one glimpse of Heaven's Living Bread. Perhaps I would be privileged to see the angel with the fire.

"Then I heard Jesus whisper these words: 'I'll kiss you on the lips, Father Joseph, and then the Gift will not burn you. No one in the flesh shall see God the Father and live, yet as I have just said, I have come to bring My friends closer to Him through My tempering flesh. Through Me, as God-Man, I'll cast My Father's fires, through the symbol of My Heart, over the earth hoping to enkindle souls to a greater depth of love in Him.

"'Mortal flesh could not stand the effects of the Beatific Vision—the body would crumble to ashes. Therefore, My mercy overshadows justice. A foretaste of My Father's glory on earth will be given to a few souls while they live in the flesh. This extravagance of My Father, through My humanity and through My Heart, to souls will not consume them nor will they receive bodily burns from it. Father Joseph, are you ready to receive God now?'

"Joseph's smile was his answer. Suddenly, the room filled with the light of angels, who had assumed the forms of young men and who knelt around Jesus and Joseph. Then Michael, in all his glory, pomp, and color brought in his assumed hands the living flames of God's Holy Presence. It reminded me of the story of the burning bush and how its flames were not consuming. The glowing fires appeared to enter into Joseph's very heart, and for a moment he seemed to be part of that great fire. Then, once more his outline became clear.

"As he breathed his thanksgiving, he whispered, 'My Little Foster Son, my Jesus and my God all in One. I am leaving You, now.'"

"With these last words of Joseph lingering in their hearts, Granny and John relived, for a few minutes, the phantasmal thoughts about God's goodness to men.

After an hour's reflection, John again began to squirm in his unwanted ease of down cushions and golden tapestries. Poor John! Now he knew the piteous penitential call of obedience to a grandmother, and so he snuggled deeper into the pillows and nibbled faster on the cookies. This was the hardest penance he had ever performed, but he wanted to follow Jesus even in the obedience to a granny's womanly whims and ministrations.

A little later, Granny knelt at the side of John's couch and whispered a sad petition as she looked into his steel-blue eyes. "John, while you are in this city I beg of you to talk to the people. Many are turning away from the laws of Moses in order to follow Herod and his ways. It is rumored that our people are blaming a certain Arabian family for this evil that is among us.

"A story is told that a few years ago an Arabian prince, his wife, two daughters, and a son joined the faith of our fathers. So severe was their persecution in Arabia that they migrated to Magdala and tried changing their identity and customs. The eldest daughter, Mary, was a beautiful girl. She was truly an Arabian—fiery and persistent in following the joys of her native culture and life.

"At first, she graced many of our social anniversaries, for she was very talented in singing and dancing. Then Herod heard of her and offered her a career in his court. She accepted the invitation—overriding the opposition of her parents.

"From that time on she began to disregard her faith. Publicly she announced that she did not see any evil in Herod for marrying his brother's wife, and she does not try to hide her contempt of our charitable principles and the love with which we esteem the Law of Moses.

"This beautiful dancer was given the name of Mary of Magdala because we were proud of her. Since she had the courage to offer opposition to a foreign god we held her in high esteem. Because she was of royal blood we thought it honorable to call her Mary of Magdala. However, it is now to our sorrow, for many young girls are following her ways and her attitude toward our law and order.

"Just a few days ago I heard her father died, and the mourners gather daily at his tomb, as is the custom. It is claimed he died of a broken heart because of Mary's actions. Please, John, speak to the people!"

John arose from the couch and began to pace back and forth across the room and patio. "Granny," he answered, "I will act and pray according to your wishes. But do you know, this Mary of Magdala must be a chosen soul of God to be tempted in this manner so soon after her conversion. Sometimes there are souls whom God has chosen for great works who find themselves tempted with the worst of evils, and frequently travel to the very depths of sin before grace finally enlightens them. And then when they are recaptured by God it is His triumph over evil, for a returning soul of this nature often brings back other souls to God with it. God often permits evil so that good may come of it. Granny, watch this girl, for I think she will prove herself to be a great soul and a lover of God.

"Now, Granny, it is time for me to retire, for I must rise before dawn and be on my way. Earlier in the evening you mentioned that you would like to receive the Baptism of Penance. I'll baptize you at dawn if you will meet me on the lake shore at the end of the patio footpath."

Granny was elated—she knelt through the entire night in prayer, asking God to bless her coming act of penance.

After the ceremony in the morning, John went on his way to the city. As he moved along with his quick, hurried stride, he allowed a smile to play across his face as he thought of Jesus letting Himself be pampered by the little old lady, and he chuckled at the mental picture of the Master resting on down cushions eating cookies. "Poor Jesus!" he breathed aloud.

As John entered the city, people turned to look at him for he was a stranger, and their eyes opened wide at sight of his hermit clothes. They were awed, for this was the first time they had seen a hermit in camel and goatskin clothes. Within a few minutes a great crowd followed him. As he paused to return their friendly gaze, they pushed closer to stare at him. He sat down and smiled. They drew nearer and sat down beside him. Finally, an elderly man ventured to ask, "Are you a hermit because you love God, or because you hate people and the things of the world?"

This was the opening John desired. Stifling a chuckle, he answered, "I am a hermit because I love God and the Commandments. And now since you have asked me about my life I'll tell you why I am here. I have come to warn you of the necessity of keeping the Commandments that God gave through Moses.

"I understand you have been listening to a false philosophy taught you by Herod. Does he think he is God, for only God can change the

Commandments! Abraham didn't dare change one word—then why does Herod attempt to make divine laws as if they had the seal of God?

"Who is this Herod? I'll tell you who he is. He is a man in great ignorance in regard to the laws of Scripture, and in his stupidity he is leading you astray. For you to accept his views is to bow before him as though he were God. If you follow him you are actually stealing from God!

"But I am here to tell you how you may return to your Creator. You must do penance because your sin is deadly. Only in that way will you once again find favor with God. Penance is actually doing something that will take its toll upon the body's senses, for through the senses you have turned away from God. Many of you are so covered with sin that you need a thorough cleansing. Suppose then, since you experience trepidation of body even at the thought of entering into a stream of water, that we use that as a means of penance—baptism of water over your body to show God you are sorry for your sins."

Several others joined the old man as he went through the streets shouting joyfully, "Come, listen to the hermit-man who is brave enough to take a stand against Herod. What will our king do to such an opponent? Will he cast a hermit of God into a dungeon? Come, listen to him, he has news for you!"

Hundreds of people hurried to the center of town, where John now stood on a high porch from where he could view the sea of faces forming beneath him. His thundering words concerning the laws of God dislodged the darkness of spiritual characters from many human souls, and he watched the devils depart for their caverns of hell. One by one the people realized the cleansing of their darkened minds and they wept tears of joy as the true meaning of God's Commandments returned to them.

John loudly told the people who cheered for Herod that they were no better than the golden calf worshipers, and he demanded, "What would Moses do with you if he were here? I know. In his righteous indignation he would assail you with plagues, famine, and pestilence. He was a prophet of God and could command those things as law because he was an ambassador. I, too, am a prophet of God!"

A great cry of fear arose from the people. John continued in a calmer tone. "Friends, need I tell you that during the years many men will attempt to rise above the laws that Moses gave you? But never will there be a time without God's authority on earth through man. God's ambassadors will have the right to inflict just punishments on nations for their sinful acts. Because of my penitential life in the desert I have God's graces with me. Let these skins tell you of His credentials within my soul. They are not pleasant to wear, and from the sorrows of such penances I draw my power of conviction. Shall I ask God to send plagues, famine, and pestilence upon you, which you deserve, since you hail Herod as your law-maker instead of God?"

A great cry of, "No! No! Don't send us plagues!" echoed through the crowd as John pointed his finger at one and then at another. "If you have consented in your hearts that Herod is right," he went on, "and if you have had any thought or desire to follow his philosophy, then listen to the roaring flames of Hell that await you. The golden calf of your will has turned into a holocaust of fire to match that of Hell's celebration for you. If such hellish sounds are raging within you, do penance and public mortification, for the price is great and must be paid if you would loose yourself from Hell's door. Hurry, I'll show you the way. Come, follow me into the creek yonder, there to do penance by being washed or baptized with water. To whom are you going to listen? God says, 'Thou shalt not commit adultery,' and Herod says, 'You may.' But I say, 'Go ahead, if you choose the torments of Hell for your eternal life!'"

Then in a more somber tone of voice, "Friends, when I first left my cave home to preach penance I used to say to my listeners, 'Do penance for your sins because the reign of the Messiah is about to begin.' But now I say, 'Do penance because the Messiah is already here. He is so close you may see Him within a few days, for I know He will come this way.'"

A groan of anguish arose, for the throng was afraid of this message. John continued: "Now, just suppose the Living Messiah came here this instant. Could you adulterers face Him? Remember He is God and you could conceal nothing from Him. Do you realize He knows your slightest thought, word, or action? His coming to this generation is comparable to actual death, for you will never know the moment you will be called to die. Could you face Him?"

John lowered his head and gazed with an expression of reverence upon his goatskin clothes and again he asked, "Do you believe me because of my life? You see I wear the clothes of a hermit with great respect rather than with reluctance. These goatskins signify truth, faith, penance, mortification, cold, and hunger, and I tell you I know the God-Man is on earth. I have seen Him and I have talked with Him. I beg of you to hurry with your penance before you die at your own hands through despair, rather than actually face Him within the next few days. Penance will make your souls brighter. I have come into the world to make the paths of your souls straight for the coming of God, who is wonderful and merciful. Here is a surprise for you. The Messiah has been among you already and you did not recognize Him, but when He comes this time you will know Him."

Many in the crowd cheered John as he began his walk to the narrow creek into which he led them. On the way many people asked, "Did you say the God-Man has been here, in this city, in person, and we did not know Him?"

John nodded. "He was here many times in His holy infancy and youth, but it was His will then to remain hidden until now when He is beginning His public life. This may interest you—little Granny Mary who lives on the lake shore is His grandmother."

A sudden hush came over the crowd. Granny Mary? Why, yes, they knew her—they loved her. Their faces paled as they recalled the many times they had seen Jesus with her. Why, some of them, as children, had actually played with Him. They were frightened as they remembered unfair play even in their childhood, and how they shunned Him when He had asked them to pray and not to sin. They questioned one another, "Is it possible that little Boy is the Messiah?" They recalled swimming together in the lake and how, through cheating, some of them had won a race over Jesus. They hung their heads in shame. How would they dare face Him? Others marveled how He had kept this profound secret from them and how even Granny and His other relatives had never said a word. They were amazed and frightened. Several women wept as they remembered talking to Mary, the mother of Jesus, when she visited Granny Mary.

A man with a loud, cynical tone in his voice called out suddenly, "How did you know about Herod and his teachings when you say you have been living as a hermit in a cave? Hermits shield themselves from any knowledge of the world. Aren't you afraid of our king? He could put you in chains for what you have been saying. And he could have you put to death for opposing him in regard to his marriage!"

Calmly John answered, "I'm not afraid of anything but sin, for sin can separate me from God for all eternity. Hurry, my friends, do penance—follow me into this water. While you submerge yourselves, ask God to forgive your sins and promise Him you will try amending your lives."

As the penitents began to return to the banks, a few sneering men hurled scurrilous remarks at them. "Why do you follow a man dressed in goatskins? Why just look at Herod—he is clothed in silks and satins. If he is in sin, it looks as though sin pays, doesn't it? God doesn't seem to mind our poverty or He would strike Herod down this instant."

John paid no attention and went on baptizing the people. Angered, the men threw stones at him, but as each stone came his way John looked heavenward and shouted, "God of our fathers, forgive these men of such ignorance. Allow me to receive each blow as a penance and means of grace for their souls."

Surprised, the men looked at one another and asked, "What kind of a hermit is this? He is so calm and unafraid. It looks as if he would welcome death."

One of them asked, "Hermit, listen to me. Why don't you strike at the root of evil in this town? An adulteress, a dancer of such beauty and grace as you have never seen, lives here. See what she has by means of sin—silks, servants, beauty—a happy, interesting life; why does God allow her to enjoy all that? Is that justice? Man of goatskins, the woman of whom I speak is Mary of Magdala. I dare you to try to entice her into these waters. If you accomplish such a feat we will follow you on hands and knees and believe the Messiah is on earth!"

John answered, "I'll allow no miracle to prove my words. I must diminish that the God-Man will have all power rewarded to Him. Face Him and He will be miracle enough."

CHAPTER 8

Rachel and the Mother of Mary Magdala

NEARLY ALL THE PEOPLE in Magdala received John's baptism. The last person in line was Rachel. In her search for the Holy Family, in order to learn the history of the pearls and their musical expressions of Heaven, she found herself walking along the creek where John was baptizing. She listened to the people in their exuberant hope that the Messiah would indeed be among them soon. She believed the philosophy of the Baptizer, and as she bowed her head before him in a profession of faith, she wondered if he could be that Child who had been born in her stable so many years ago.

Later, as she walked along the creek, she wondered, also, why it would be necessary for the Messiah to hide His identity from such a man as John. In her thirty-three years of searching for the Holy Family, she had asked many a wiseman and high priest whether or not he was the Messiah, but always the answer had been disappointing. To find the God-Man would be to find His mother, and she was convinced that the beautiful woman who had given birth to an infant in her stable was the mother of God. Somehow she began to feel that her search was nearly finished, and she hoped that the wonderful grandmother who had given her the pearls was still alive. Breathlessly, she hurried back to John—she was certain he could answer her questions.

Standing once more before him she asked, "Tell me, man of God, were you by any chance born in a stable in Bethlehem? Do you know anything about a certain strand of pearls from which can be heard Heaven's music?" Evidently she had been too late to hear what John had told the people about Granny Mary.

John's eyes opened wide in sudden astonishment and he asked quietly, "Are you Rachel?"

The expression of joy in Rachel's eyes answered his question. He beckoned her to follow him, and as they neared a hillside he explained, "I am not the Messiah for whom you seem to be searching. However, this much I can tell you: He was born in your stable. I have seen Him. His grandmother told me about the strand of pearls you have. She is still alive and longs to see you and hear your story. Somehow she believes you yet hears Heaven's music coming from your pearls, but she hears nothing at all from the ones she possesses."

Rachel was speechless. At last she had found a way to the Living Messiah. Slowly she began to relate to John the high points of her life, and how she chose—through the miracle of the pearls—to search for the Messiah and His mother. As he listened, John became convinced that Rachel was a chosen soul and asked to see and hold the miraculous pearls.

He knelt on the ground as Rachel handed them to him—all ten pearls were there, alternating with gold nuggets. As he venerated them his expression was one of awe and ceremonial love. He asked, "How did you ever restrain yourself from the temptation to sell these when you suffered hunger and cold?"

Rachel answered, "Within a few days after the Holy Family moved from the stable, I tried to tell my husband of their gift and the heavenly music that came from it, but he scoffed at me and said I was dealing in quackery and witchcraft and to have nothing to do with such nonsense. He ordered me to give him the pearls so that he could sell them and become a wealthy man, which was his aim in life. But since I would not show them to him, nor did I tell him about the gold nuggets, he beat me severely with his whip.

"Finally, he reasoned that I had lied to him about the whole thing and so the matter was forgotten. I vowed then that if I were ever free from him I would search for the Holy Family and return the pearls to the original strand. I knew I was not worthy to have this special closeness to Heaven, and I realized they were something from God and thus should not be sold."

John asked, "Do you still hear the music?"

Rachel nodded. "Whenever I hold them and meditate on the beauty of the Messiah's mother and how her Child was born in the poverty of a stable."

The Baptizer said quietly, "You are greatly blessed by God. Do you realize He has led you to the higher way of prayer, which is called meditation? Just to think about any part of His life, or of the prophets' foretelling His coming, is a great prayer."

Rachel smiled and said, "Hermit John, place the pearls close to your ear and I'll meditate about that beautiful woman and how I led her to the stable at midnight. Perhaps God will allow you to hear the symphonies of Heaven."

John trembled as he wondered if he would once again hear the music of the angels like unto that he had often heard in his house of prayer on the desert island. Carefully he lifted the pearls to his ear.

Yes, he could hear the rhythmical tones of Heaven! For several minutes after the music had ceased, he and Rachel bowed their heads in silent thanksgiving. Then John asked, "Did you leave your husband to search for the Messiah?"

Rachel answered, "A few weeks after I tried to tell him about the pearls, my brother visited us. He was deeply interested in the bracelet and believed that the music came from God. After hearing it he, too, vowed to search for the Holy Family.

"Often at night we walked to the stable and entered the storeroom where the Baby had been born—and while we meditated on that solemn event we always heard the music. We spent many hours this way in prayer, which made me all the more anxious to find Mary and Granny.

"The day my brother left, my husband was drunk and he found the pearls. He took them and was on his way immediately to the city to sell them. My brother caught up with him and in the fight that followed, my husband was killed.

"That night my brother brought me the pearls and fled, a hunted man for the murder of my husband. From time to time during the following years I heard through friends that a folly of obsession overtook him, and he searched constantly for other pearls that would resound with Heaven's music. People laughed and jeered at him, for they thought he had lost his mind. But I understood, and in pity I have prayed for God's kindness to shield him and forgive his sins.

"Just a few days ago I learned he killed a pagan priest in order to take pearls from his altar. I have no other information about him—but one day I hope to find him and console him with the music from these pearls."

John returned the bracelet and assured Rachel he would pray for her brother. Then he debated whether or not to tell her of Granny Mary's nearness. He hesitated, for he did not welcome another night's sleep on those down cushions, and he knew Granny would insist on it if he returned. Yet he did not think it proper to send Rachel alone, for Granny was old and frail, and the shock might prove too great when she learned about the singular gift of music that was still heard upon Joseph's pearls.

He knelt for a moment to pray and then advised Rachel to travel the inland waterways to Jerusalem, where he felt sure she would see Jesus. Rachel was so grateful for this advice that she bent to the earth and kissed the ground upon which he stood. "How can I ever thank you?" she asked.

John lifted her to her feet and answered, "Rachel, I have never asked for anything in life, but now I am going to ask an earthly favor of you—please give me one of your pearls."

Rachel gasped in surprise, but in the gift of silent obedience she untied the bracelet string and loosed one pearl and one gold nugget from the thread. Handing these to the Baptizer she said, "I'm grateful that you asked me to share my gift."

John turned away quickly and went on his way to Capernaum. As he hurried through the stillness of the night he felt into the pocket over his heart. Yes, the pearl was there. What a joy it was to have it in his possession! As he thought back over the events of the day and the meditations of Rachel, Heaven's music came to him slowly and harmoniously. He was exuberant. "God is good," he repeated over and over as he walked toward his hour of death.

John was about to leave Magdala when he realized that he was near a burial ground, for he could hear plainly the crying chant of mourners. He wondered if this could possibly be the burial place of Mary Magdala's father.

In order to find out, he left the road and went toward the group around the tomb. Immediately he recognized Mary's mother, from Granny's description, and he knelt by her side. "The Messiah has said, blessed are they who mourn," he whispered.

Through the darkness he could see the puzzled expression on the face of Mary's mother. Although surprised at the sight of his clothes she asked politely, "Who are you?"

John stood up, but before he could answer, Mary's mother held a lantern close to his face and asked, "Are you a hermit? Are you a prophet of the Messiah who is to come?"

John bowed his head. Bewildered and grateful, Mary's mother fell to her knees, for this was the first time she had been in the presence of a hermit and a prophet of God. Instantly she felt an impelling love and trust for this holy man as she gazed into his eyes, which were gentle and not at all severe, as she would expect to find in such a person. She implored him to pray for her daughter.

John answered kindly, "I know all about your daughter and I am sorry your heart is burdened with such great anguish. Do penance for her and trust that God will listen to a mother's plea. Offer this loneliness that you feel for your husband as an outward sign of penance for her wrong deeds. Penance is an actual gift by which we do something out of the ordinary for loved children, or friends, who have turned from God, or have offended Him. Because of the death of your husband you did not hear my talk on baptism as a means of doing penance. Tomorrow, go to the creek in the city and there immerse your body three times, or just your forehead if you prefer, and while doing this ask God to forgive you and make your soul brighter for His arrival.

"I particularly chose a penance that is really hard to do. Most people find immersion difficult because it requires thought, time, and inconvenience. In the inland territories I advocate immersion of the forehead only, but at the lake and beaches I advise the complete covering of the body in the water. By obeying me because I am a great prophet, one's merit is greater in the eyes of God. You may also immerse yourself as many times as you wish as a penance for Mary, and the same act may be applied for the needs of your husband. This devotion of baptizing for the dead will be followed by many people, but it must be remembered that it is a penance only, and not the baptism the Messiah will give."

Mary's mother bowed her head and said, "I will follow your least command. Tell me, in this hour of my loneliness, will the Messiah be born in this generation as predicted? If I understood you correctly a moment ago, you mentioned that He said, 'Blessed are they who mourn.' Is He now on earth?"

"Yes, He is here," John answered.

Mary's mother followed the Baptizer silently to the roadway. "I have talked to Him," John went on, but asked her not to pass on this information to the mourners, for God's news should not be cast before those afflicted with hysteria, and hired mourners were of that type. Patting her hand, he said, "Little Mother, if you will follow my advice, I am sure something can be done for your Mary. First follow my way of penitential baptism and then journey with your family to South Bethany, near Jerusalem. This great distance will take your Mary away from Herod's court.

"While you are there you will come in direct contact with the Living Messiah, who is preparing, even now, for His crucifixion, which He will allow for the redemption of man.

"Tell no one that I have given you this information about the crucifixion, for in obedience to such silence there is great merit that can be applied later, God willing, for Mary's return to the faith of her father. Take the inland waterways and you will arrive in Bethany sooner than if you travel by land. I shall pray for you. Your children will be safe in Bethany."

Silently they gazed at each other. Tears were now changed to smiles in the eyes of Mary's mother as she found new hope and trust in the words of John. He continued, "Just today, Little Mother, I met a most wonderful woman by the name of Rachel. She is going south on a similar mission. Search for her and say that I have requested you to travel with her. She has a great gift of knowledge and she may interest your Mary. At any rate, I am sure she will be a blessing to you."

Mary's mother hesitated and then asked, "Is there any way I can prove to this Rachel that I have talked to you?"

John untied the knotted thread that held the pearl and the gold nugget together. "Take this nugget," he directed, "and give it to her after you have told her the story and my request. When she sees it she will know you have talked to me."

Enthralled and almost frightened, for she thought she heard beautiful tones of music as John put the pearl close to his heart, Mary's mother could only whisper, "Thank you."

John looked toward the tomb and his eyes blessed the mourners silently. There knelt Lazarus and Martha, his sister. Mary was not there.

Once more on his way to Herod's court, John smiled as he recalled in thoughts of hope that hundreds of people this night were feeling God's gift of peace. He wanted every soul in the world to be made beautiful through his way of baptism. He walked through the night listening to the music from home, the pearl, joyous and happy in the knowledge of God.

CHAPTER 9

The Dungeon

HEROD BECAME BLUSTERY and petulant when the news of John was brought to him by the guards. It angered him to learn that his marriage to his brother's wife was being loudly condemned by the Baptizer. His bellowing voice filled the palace halls and terrorized the servants who waited upon him as he and Herodias sat at a massive table eating.

Herod was a huge man, weighing about two hundred and fifty pounds. The personification of arrogant ugliness, he was clothed in robes of purple and red, and his highly polished leather belt, which was wrapped twice around his body, supported four swords instead of the customary two. The hilts of each were studded with priceless gems. His large, round face flushed a deep purple as a guard re-entered and announced that John had been seized just outside the walls.

Herod shouted his reply. "What? That close? Of all the ignorance and stupidity! He would come here! How dare he? Doesn't he know I could have him put to death? I wonder if he is so stupid as to think he can persuade me to his way of life—and that baptism of his, which is nothing but wizardry?"

Deep tones from tower bells resounded through the halls—it was time for Herod to enter the main dining room where the meat course would be served. As he strode to the other room, with Herodias following, his small, piggish eyes narrowed as he banged his sword on the table and shouted, “Bring that penitential idiot here! I’ll make an example of him!”

As Herod gorged himself on the breast of pheasant, he muttered to Herodias, “I wonder how this wise hermit would like finishing his life in a cell?” He laughed and gulped wine as he toyed indolently with his sword.

The personal guards of Herod summoned the wisemen of the court to appear immediately in the dining hall. Herod deemed it necessary to question them on John’s philosophy and how to deal with a man who had the uncanny prophesying power with which to persuade people against the modern trend of thought on marriage.

He knew he was not dealing with an ordinary man. He frowned as he wondered if it could be possible in this day and age that another prophet had been born. He was of the opinion that all prophets were dead and that the world no longer had a need for them because of the intellectual inroads and progress man had made in the last hundred years. The thought that perhaps here was another one living on earth caused him to scowl. He further argued within himself that in past ages hermits and prophets had their place, but this was the age of the intellect, and people could do very well without them and the Commandments.

Still gorging himself on the pheasant, he questioned a guard as to John’s manner and appearance. “He dresses as one would expect a hermit to dress,” the guard answered, “in skins and robes. Furthermore, the fool and his crowd are always praying aloud for you!”

Herod scowled and then laughed loudly. “So, he does think he can convert me! And he leads the people in public prayers for me, does he? Well, poor man, it is obvious that he is unlettered and not acquainted with the laws of the land.”

But even as Herod laughed, he realized that the Baptizer was both courageous and dangerous because of his influence over the people. A masked sword, as it were.

At that moment the wisemen entered the dining hall. Dressed in plain, brown linen robes, and three in number, they hurried immediately to Herod’s side. But before anything could be said, a guard entered abruptly with the report that there were thousands of people at the palace gates, aroused by John’s courage and eloquence.

One of the wisemen cautioned Herod as he rose to his feet in a rage. “I would use great care dealing with this man. If thousands of his followers are here already—they could revolt against us and the news would carry quickly to their friends in distant cities."

Herod restrained himself with difficulty as he left the dining room for an adjacent hall, where he could talk as he ate after-dinner refreshments. Herodias and the wisemen followed. Seating himself on a lounging couch drawn up to another huge table, Herod looked peevishly at his counselors.

"I summoned you here," he said, "because I want your advice on how to handle this stupid, self-styled hermit who has so aroused the people. Some of them even bow before him as though he were a god, while others say he is a prophet who has talked with the so-called living Messiah. All of them loudly proclaim his words as final law and truth. He is trying to revive the old Commandments, and he particularly fights against my laws, by which I have made it lawful for a man to marry more than once while his former wife lives.

"On several occasions during the past two years, I have received word about his teachings on baptism as penance for past sins, but I gave it little credence. Now, he's here, in this very palace. I believe he thinks that after I listen to his oratorical genius I'll forsake my wife!"

Herod smiled and gazed fondly at Herodias, who pouted daintily as a spoiled child. Her pride and honor had been badly damaged by John's teachings, and she hoped Herod would make an example of him.

The cupidity of her pout captivated Herod and he sighed, "This would be a lovely world if these fanatical idiots didn't creep in by feigning to be hermits and prophets!"

Everyone agreed with him.

Herod smiled at his wife and boasted loudly, "My Herodias, for you I'll put an end to this hermit's teachings. I'll make his punishment so severe and well known to the public that everyone will be afraid to follow in his footsteps. More than that—I shall see that he makes a public apology to you!"

Herodias smiled, rearranged her thin veils about her, and fanned herself with peacock plumes.

One of the wisemen said quietly, "Since this man has convinced thousands of persons that you and Herodias are living sinful lives, we suggest you try the art of diplomacy on him by using gentle persuasion, kindness, and even wealth, with which to turn his fanatical mind more to the love of the world. We also suggest you invite him to a banquet. There in all your regal splendor and in the presence of your entire court, you could offer him a third of your kingdom if he would but announce that he had been mistaken in his visions and in his views concerning marriage. Also, he must admit that he made his mistake because of his narrow way of analyzing things during his life alone in the desert."

While they were discussing plans for the banquet, a crescendo of voices arose from the palace pavilions, coupled with shouts from the guards. Herod strode quickly to one of the massive entrance doors. Throwing it open he gasped with surprise—for there stood his soldiers in a circle around John, their swords drawn. They tried to prevent the Baptizer from entering Herod's living quarters, but he walked straight in as though he did not see or feel the prick of their weapons. In his hand he carried a tall, gnarled, wooden staff, which he held majestically as a king would hold a scepter, but he did not deign to use it as a means of defense. The people cheered and disregarded completely the orders of the guards to disperse.

Herod burst into laughter at the sight of John's clothes. He should be able to dazzle this poor beggar easily. Why bother giving him a banquet? A little money would be sure to convince him of his error. He bowed to the Baptizer and gestured extravagantly for him to approach the banquet table. His feigned politeness was piteous to John, who had the gift of discernment, and thus knew all of Herod's plans. However, he crossed the room and sat down opposite Herodias. Herod closed the door and resumed his seat beside her. The three wisemen took chairs at the end of the table.

The sumptuous array of tray upon tray of refreshments and hot drinks stunned the Baptizer. Never had he seen such a display of ease and luxury and gluttonous eating. He was so overcome with the effects and occasions of sin before him that he hardly noticed Herod as he began his ponderous oration aimed at bringing him around to his way of thinking.

As the eating and the talking progressed, Herod was annoyed at the rabble of voices outside calling for John. Feigning kindness, he asked the Baptizer gently to dismiss the multitude. From a balcony overlooking the palace grounds, John waved farewell to his friends. Then he re-entered the room.

Herod said gleefully, "Ah, John the Great! 'The Great'—that should be your title. No wonder you came here, for you realize your worth to man and country. No doubt you thought I would put you in chains, but I know your value, and now I ask you to put away your hermit way of life and live our way of modern luxury instead. Why, I'll even place you in power over certain of my laws if you will do as I ask."

Herod cleared his throat and continued in a loud manner. "John the Great, how would you like a position in this court? As you know, I have made certain laws in regard to remarriage after divorce, and I could make you administrator of those laws. Why with your philosophy and your ability to speak, you and your followers would have fame and fortune overnight. And more than that. If you will consent to be administrator of laws, I will give you a third of this kingdom.

Herod watched John closely. "However, that honor is yours only on the condition that in the morning, from this very balcony, you issue a law that supposedly came to you through visions tonight, which commands you to abolish the idea that divorce is not lawful. When you do this, I will have you dressed as a prince of the court, and you will become your own lawmaker and live in luxury the rest of your life. I'll give you an hour to consider this offer."

Herod and Herodias resumed eating—they were certain John was so grateful that he was speechless. No one on earth could be such a fool as to refuse that offer.

Seconds passed and John's eyes narrowed in loathing as he gazed at Herod. He was angry—so angry that his desert tan was bleached white. Suddenly he snatched up Herod's sword lying before him, and with the help of its heavy hilt he tipped the contents of the massive table over upon Herod and Herodias.

Startled and screaming with anger and pain, they sprawled on the floor. Boiling water that had been prepared for hot drinks scalded Herod painfully on the legs and wrist. Herodias pretended to faint. Quickly the guards carried her from the hall while Herod, white with rage, ordered John put into chains immediately.

As the Baptizer was roughly hurried from the hall, his clear, powerful voice rang through the room with this prophecy. "Now it is my turn to address you, Herod, as 'The Great.' Soon you will die and worms will consume you within minutes afterward. Because of your sins you are being eaten alive. Already you have suffered much from this rare malady. Why continue to be tormented for eternity with such gnawing pain? Do *penance*! Take upon yourself baptism. Many in this court have already done so—be humble and follow your people. Do penance, for through penance you conquer God's wrath, which shall surely fall upon you!"

Scoffing, angry guards pushed and buffeted John down a narrow, dimly lighted, stone stairway to a cold dungeon directly beneath the banquet hall. The terrible odors of death, sewage, and damp air assailed him. He could well imagine how men suffered in the dank dampness of this prison. He was pushed into a sitting position on the muddy floor, and his arms stretched upward and his wrists locked in iron cuffs attached to dangling chains. The guards kicked and slapped him and then left him to the mercy of his thoughts and prayers. Within a few minutes, thick, slimy mud oozed over his legs.

Slowly his eyes grew accustomed to the dim light coming from a burning torch set in a hall niche at the top of the stairs. Then he realized that the quick, black, darting movements that threw mud splashes over his face were caused by fat, black rats racing across the floor. He winced in shuddering horror—not only for himself but for the other prisoners. The shrill screech of the rodents and the sound of their swishing over the smooth mud added to the horror of this manmade hell, where men screamed in their terror of helplessness as they hung in chains.

The subterranean cell was large—measuring about thirty by forty feet, and it was evident from the dampness that in certain seasons of the year it was filled with seepage waters from Lake Galilee.

The torchlight revealed the remains of a skeleton dangling in chains on the wall across from John. The man had evidently died that way as the rainy season began and his body left to rot away in the muddy waters and serve as food for the dungeon rats. The Baptizer shuddered and bowed his head in deepest sorrow at the thought of the man's sufferings.

After only a short while John's muscles began to convulse from the strain and lack of circulation, and he struggled to rise to a sitting position, hoping to release the strain, but his feet slipping in the slimy mud caused him to fall again, wrenching his arms by this sudden jerk. He groaned.

Courageously he bit his lips and tried suffering in silence. After a time, another prisoner—a very old man—heard his stifled moans, and being loosened from his chains for the night, crawled over to him. Gently, and with great care, he lifted and braced John's body in his weak arms and held him in a lying position until circulation gave warmth and life to his numb arms and hands. All during the night the aged man held or rubbed the Baptizer's body and whispered words of hope and consolation to him. He had known John and his teachings before his imprisonment.

They whispered together about the Messiah, His coming death, and His promise of life everlasting for those who loved Him. When John told the little old man that the Messiah was actually living on earth at that moment, he cried with joy and was glad he had been baptized. He was happy that he had done penance—for now he was not afraid to meet God.

John further whispered, "You are a blessed person—through penance you have been touched by the extravagance of God. No doubt He has placed you in this dungeon to be as a sanctuary lamp to the other prisoners. Look how you have consoled and helped me. God will reward you."

Gray daylight crept slowly over the world. The morning watch arrived and came tromping down the stone stairs. For the hundredth time the little old man lowered John's body to the mud and then he crawled slowly to his own corner.

Presently, the Baptizer and the other prisoners were taken to a dry room above for their food. A tray filled with scraps from the banquet tables was given to each one, together with a cup of hot water. John refused the rich scraps, for his penitential life had turned him against such food. The mere thought of it made him ill. However, he did eat a crust of dry bread and sipped at a saucer of water.

A messenger from Herod arrived to see if John had changed his mind. If not, he would stay there in chains until he did. The Baptizer shook his head emphatically.

Anguished moans for mercy arose from the men as the guards once more lifted their arms to the anchoring irons on the dungeon walls. Only a few were allowed to stand unchained. The others, John included, were pushed down into their sitting positions. While the Baptizer endured his agony, he prayed silently for the kindly old man who crawled from one prisoner to another administering any help he could.

Finally, he came over to John and asked, "John, when you are in such suffering, don't you ever question God's mercy? I cannot help wondering, because you have done so much for the Messiah. Don't you question Him at all when He allows you to suffer?"

John whispered, "I realize I am not worthy of a thought. Then, by meditation, I imagine myself with the Holy Infants who died so brutally without question for the Little Messiah. I want to be worthy to enter into their merits of silent martyrdom and I pray, 'O God, make me so small that I cannot question—let me die without questioning Thee!'"

The old man smiled and answered, "How wonderful, and how wonderful you are, John! Pray that I may share in your holy wisdom and understanding."

Hoping to please the Baptizer, he crawled to the table, and after searching tray after tray he found a ladle of honey. He knew John must be hungry, for he had eaten only that one small crust of bread. John was happy as he sipped the honey, for it had been his main diet and he loved it.

The old prisoner's hands trembled as he held the ladle. Noticing the grayness of death creeping over his holy face, the Baptizer said, "Lay your head on my shoulder. You are very ill and I have something to tell you."

The old man obeyed and John whispered, "God is coming to take you home tonight. In your journey to Him let us meditate upon the happenings of the Messiah's birth. A few days ago I talked to His grandmother and she told me about the wonderful event. When Mary, His mother, knew her hour for His deliverance had come, she could hear Heaven's music from her heart. Others heard it, too. Wasn't that wonderful for the angels, through Mary, to greet the King with music at His birth?"

As John said this, the old man's face became suddenly aglow. He was breathless from death's nearness and also from joy because he could actually hear the faint music the Baptizer had described. He didn't know he was listening to the blessed pearl hidden in the folds of John's garment. With it reverberating softly through his body, the little old man died on the Baptizer's shoulder.

CHAPTER 10

Herod

ABOUT SEVEN MONTHS after John's imprisonment, Herod gave a banquet in honor of Herodias' daughter, Salome, and the noise from it pierced even into the depths of the dungeons. The prisoners listened and frequently made bold comments when they heard the wild, hilarious laughter—the greatest burst of applause and merriment coming when Salome entered the banquet room, as they rightly judged.

From time to time the guards mentioned the events of the evening as they took place. They told of the gluttonous feasting and drinking, and purposely left the dungeon door ajar so that the prisoners could hear the screaming and the boisterous play. Salome was cheered again when Herod announced she would perform the Arabian dance of death, which Mary of Magdala had taught her.

Hundreds of people called for Mary to dance, too, but Herod answered that she had not yet returned from the custom of mourning for her father. Then applause rose once more as Salome entered the room dressed in Mary's Arabian green and gold feathery veils.

In the center of the great hall, which was disguised as the Arabian desert, the guards had placed a huge copper kettle over an imitation fire. Around this setting Salome slowly began her dance of beautiful gestures, keeping time to the thudding tom-tom drums and high, silvery-toned trumpets and stringed instruments.

As the dance neared its climax, five soldiers carried the copper kettle on their sword points in front of Salome as she danced, and slowly removed most of the veils of gold and green that she dropped into the kettle where they resembled billowy, bubbling mists in the glittering sheen of a thousand candle flames.

As this was in progress, Herod and Herodias, sitting in the dim of the candle light, talked about the stubborn-minded John. A soldier entered hurriedly and came straight to Herod. "The friends of John, the Hermit, are assembling in the grounds," he said in a low, urgent tone, "and there seems danger of an uprising. They know you are keeping the Baptizer a prisoner and they demand his immediate release. What shall I tell them?"

Herod, in his usual blustery manner, shouted in annoyance and then sent for the wisemen. While he waited for them he played nervously with his swords. Salome finished her dance and glided, flushed and triumphant, to the table.

The wisemen could not be found, so Herod turned to Herodias for advice. Since toasts for her were in order at this hour of the banquet, she told him they would discuss the matter later.

Clapping, laughter, and shouts accompanied each toast. Then one guest arose and, holding his goblet of wine above his head, said, "Noble men and noble women, it is a despicable crime the way the penitential John, who is now in chains beneath this very floor, has spoken against this gifted woman, Herodias. None of us should allow his crime to pass without public apology and proper punishment. Let your applause tell Herod you are with him in his desire to have his laws obeyed!"

Everyone was in favor, it seemed, of honoring Herodias. In answer to the toast, and to honor Salome, Herod lumbered to his feet and raised his goblet. "I am at a loss," he said, "for words with which to honor this beautiful Salome. Her dancing is an art beyond compare. But to reciprocate for the pleasure she has given us I vow before each one here tonight that I'll give her any favor she desires of me—even if it be half my kingdom!"

This was an advantageous moment for Herodias. Her cruel mind was diabolically busy as she beckoned Salome to follow her behind the heavy drapes, which hung near the table where Herod was bowing and making piteous attempts to conceal his hideous pride.

Back of the drapes, Herodias explained to her daughter the great and serious difficulty in which Herod was placed because of John's narrow views and power over the common people. "It is only just," she whispered, "to help Herod come to a decision concerning this hermit. Why, his people are now at the palace gates causing a riot. Herod should make an example of this man, and now that you may ask for any gift you wish—I beg of you to ask for his head! Beheading is too good for him! You will never realize how he has harmed my character and prestige by his silly preaching. The guests in this room applauded when it was requested that he be punished. You heard it yourself, so I'm sure you will not be alone in your decision. Have his head brought to the banquet room on this silver platter." She pointed to a huge tray in the butler's pantry. "When the common people hear your request there will be an end to the reign of the hermits and the prophets, you may be sure of that."

Salome was startled and aghast at her mother's request. "Mother, are you mad?" she gasped. "Do you not realize this would be murder? Do not ask for this awful thing!"

Angrily, Herodias brought her face close to Salome. "So!" she said in a scurrilous tone, "fanaticism has its fingers in you, too. And I suppose you believe in the stupid Commandments Moses claims to have received from God. Answer me—are you a follower of John?"

Tears streamed down Salome's face. "No," she answered, "I am not a follower of John."

"Well then," her mother demanded, "allow justice to be done by means of this gift, which has been made possible through me. It is the only way for you to honor our laws and become famous. You will climax this party when you make your request."

Regardless of how she pleaded, Salome could not resist her mother. Beaming with success, Herodias returned to her place at the side of Herod. Her fat face was wreathed in smiles of satisfaction as she coyly fanned herself with her peacock feathers. Whispering her plan quickly to her husband, she asked him to call the attention of the guests. Herod drained another goblet of wine and pounded on the table with the hilt of his sword for quiet. Then bowing to Herodias he announced she had something of great interest to say.

Vehemently, Herodias told how brave Salome was, for she now asked Herod to have John beheaded and his head brought into the banquet hall on a silver platter and placed over the copper kettle for all to see. And if they so desired, Salome would again perform the dance of death—this time around the severed head!

Exhausted from too much eating and drinking, Herod fell across the table and slept heavily as Herodias continued to talk and to receive the acclaim of the drunken guests.

CHAPTER 11

Salome

JOHN AND THE PRISONERS LISTENED to the piercing cheers of the people, and knew they had given their approval to Herodias' terrible request. Bowing his head, John prayed for the strength of will and understanding to do all things for God. He hoped he would not question God's holy will any more than would an infant. His mind turned once more to the Holy Innocents and how they questioned not when Herod's soldiers put them to death before the very eyes of their mothers.

He tried thinking of something pleasant. He smiled as he remembered he was a Melchizedek priest and the last on earth. He felt joy surge through his soul as he recalled the singular dignity that was his in the priesthood. Then his mood became pensive as he remembered that this night was ordinarily the time for him to offer the Clean Oblation Sacrifice. Even though the Messiah was on earth it was his duty, following the order and obedience of all Melchizedek priests, to continue to offer the Sacrifice, especially now because he was as a pendulum swinging between the Old Law and the New.

It seemed that he was hoping against hope to have this last hour with God in the divine love of offering the Sacrifice. He tried to meditate on the vision of the great drama of Sacrifice in the New Law and how it would all be made possible through the death of Jesus on the Cross. He thought of the number of times he had anticipated Christ's coming to his house of prayer in the desert, and as he recaptured the reality of stillness and warmth of the desert, tears coursed down his face. Suddenly he was caught up into a Divine Slumber,[10] there to bask and do the desires of his will in God's goodness of transition of space and time.

In spirit, he was bilocated to Mary, the mother of Jesus, and was delighted as he watched her prepare the different articles necessary for his Sacrifice. She did not seem to notice his presence. As she handed her angels the pitcher of wine and loaf of unleavened bread, she bade them take these to John in the dungeon and to cause a deep, unnatural sleep to fall over the other prisoners.

Suddenly, John was awake once more in the prison and the effects of the bilocation left him with a feeling that he wanted to sing aloud his praises to God and to His mother. He could hardly keep from shouting about the great wonders of God when he noticed the other prisoners sleeping and apparently at ease, even though many still hung in their chains. As the angels drew near through the dungeon walls, time—as understood by the world—seemed to stop. Taken into gentle rapture, John could no longer hear the din from the banquet hall above—he was delightfully alone in his thoughts with God.

The angels, in their assumed forms as young men, first released John's hands from the iron bands and bowed to him. Then they bowed again, alongside one another, and in this forward position formed an altar with the straightness of their backs, a position which they held all during this Sacrifice of the Old Law that the Baptizer began to offer for the last time on earth.

As the Sacrifice progressed and John stood transfixed in prayer, a magnificent golden Pillar of God's fire from Heaven descended over him and the angel-altar. As he lifted the unleavened bread high into it, the bread was instantly burned and consumed to the nothingness of gray ashes, which fell as snowflakes into the chalice of wine.

The Old Law of Melchizedek's way of Sacrifice came to a close. Now John could bow in peace at the thought of death, for it was necessary that Christ increase in all freedom and glory. He was glad as he thought of the happiness and privilege that the unborn ages of people would enjoy through the God-Man as their constant companion and

10 Ecstasy.

indweller. Lost in these thoughts, he was overcome in silent prayer of thanksgiving to God and he fell to his knees to worship. Suddenly, he felt appalled to think that God's eternal Light would descend even into a dungeon. Raising his head and opening his eyes into that Light he whispered, "God is wonderful—God is wonderful!"

The angels straightened up as the Baptizer finished his thanksgiving, and once more chained his wrists to the wall-irons. Then all was dark—John had recovered from his ecstatic rest and delight and was happy and ready for death.

In the banquet room Herod sat at the table stunned and shocked at Salome's terrible request, delivered through Herodias. Even in his drunken state he was frightened at the thought of doing such a thing. He hadn't considered putting John to death at this time.

Then fear struck his proud reasoning. He could not renounce his vow! The whole court had heard his promise, and wasn't he considered a man of his word in regard to his laws and promises? Cheers and challenges urging him to carry out the request arose from all sides. Trembling, Herod called the guards and ordered John's beheading.

As the soldiers entered John's cell they looked at one another in surprise, for they were certain they could detect the odor of wine in the air. It was unheard of for prisoners to have wine, even though a banquet was in progress. They called the guards and questioned them severely. The guards swore that no one had entered the dungeon and they, themselves, would not dare give wine to a prisoner, for the penalty of showing favoritism was death. The soldiers searched the room and discovered that the odor came from John's breath.

Buffeting the Baptizer cruelly, they demanded an explanation as to the source of the wine. John would not answer, merely shaking his head. They questioned the other prisoners roughly but they knew nothing—nor could they tell of anyone entering the dungeon. They were too frightened to admit they had been asleep.

The soldiers unfastened the Baptizer's wrists angrily from the wall-chains and pushed him out of the cell onto the descending stone stairway that led to the muddy, subterranean cell below. Once there, they threw him to the floor and spat upon him, taunting and threatening him all the while about not eating food, yet drinking wine. They tried bribing him with the promise of freedom if he would tell them from whom he obtained the wine. Again the Baptizer shook his head and refused to answer.

The soldiers inhaled once more at his breath. The odor of fresh wine was unmistakable. They kicked him and clutched at his throat to choke him when they were brought to attention by the appearance of a commanding officer, who stood on the top step of the stairs with a huge silver platter balanced on his shoulder. He shouted loudly, "What is causing the delay? Are you afraid to behead a man? Hurry, don't keep Herod waiting!"

As the soldiers stood at attention, with their backs to John, the Baptizer carefully and quickly took the pearl from the fold in his garment over his heart and hid it in his mouth. To distract any attention his action might have caused, he asked, "Why did you bring a platter to the dungeon?"

The soldiers jeered, "You are a prophet, you should have the answer. Don't you know that Salome loves your pretty face and wants it on this platter to set before her plate at the banquet? She only wants your head—so we will have to behead you. Stretch out on the ground—you're going to a banquet!"

John shuddered. He was nervous and sick with the thought that men and women could stoop to such debauchery. Yet he was glad his hour of death was near and he recalled the words of encouragement that Mary, the mother of Jesus, had given him for this hour of trial. All he could say was, "Thank You, God, for the words of Mother Mary, and thank You for death."

John closed his eyes rather than look at the soldiers towering above him with their long swords drawn. Suddenly, he could feel the cold weapon points tearing and severing at the knotted cord around his shirt. His body was exposed. Harshly they asked him again, "Tell us where you got the wine or we will tear out your stomach as evidence for Herod to see that prisoners are receiving wine."

This time John answered, "In the honor of truth, no one in this prison gave it to me."

Defeated and scowling, the soldiers cut the Baptizer's abdomen open and removed his stomach. Holding it up they laughed as John writhed and tossed in frightful anguish. His writhing was so great that the soldiers drove thin, wooden pegs through his wrists into the ground in order to hold him still for his beheading. In all his agony, John did not open his mouth to cry out from the pain, for he did not want to expose the pearl in his mouth to the eyes of such awful sinners.

The soldiers laughed as they remarked that this was the first time they had been given orders to behead a hermit. One man straddled John's body and another pulled his head back to expose his neck. The sword was placed across his throat. John whispered, "Jesus, my King!" Then he was suddenly still. He was in a state of shock and thus did not feel the blade as the soldier pushed his weight down upon it.

Quickly, as though dazed and frightened, the soldiers picked up the Baptizer's head and placed it on the platter, arranging his long hair in a neat manner over the edges. Then, in gruesome delight, they carried their trophy from the cell toward the banquet room.

A dead stillness spread through the guests as the soldiers entered the banquet hall and carried the platter to the copper kettle, which had been placed in the center of the floor. As they put the platter on top of it the people tried to laugh, yet one and all were frightened at the grotesque sight before them. Several women fainted, while others ran hysterically from the hall and out into the streets below.

Herod recognized the signs of panic and gave a signal for Salome to begin her dance. Slowly and fearfully she began, but her step was not steady nor was it rhythmical. Her sandals were fashioned of Roman money, and as she whirled the tinkling coins made the only sound in that huge room.

Then a change came over her and she began to dance as though fired with evil daring. Running close to John's head she daintily tipped her foot beneath the platter so that a drop of his blood fell upon her sandal. As it did so she called loudly, "Come, follow me in the ritual dance of the wise Arabians. The Arabian is courageous—he would do away with the Messiah and His followers. Dance and let John's blood fall on your feet! Then vow with me to destroy—as we have destroyed him—all his works and theory and myth that the Messiah lives on earth!"

Hundreds of the guests, many of them drunk, others crazed with evil possession, followed Salome in her dance of death around the Baptizer's head. Each person kicked his, or her, foot toward the falling drops of blood that welled from the platter and took up the vow-chant, with Salome, to kill all John's deeds and theory.

The Baptizer's death mask of horror and pain was terrible to behold. His eyes were open and protruding, while his tongue extended between his partly opened lips, his brow furrowed with deep lines. As the thudding tom-toms increased their tempo, Salome whirled her way to the top of

Herod's table. She stopped dead, an expression of utter horror on her face.

Others followed her gaze and instantly scream after scream rent the air hysterically. John's facial expression was changing slowly to a smile of calm and peace. The furrowed frown disappeared. His eyes closed. His tongue slowly hid itself behind closing lips—and from his mouth dropped the pearl Rachel had given him. There was no other sound now in all that vast room as it rolled and bounced across the floor directly toward Salome!

The dancer's body was rigid with hysterical fear. With all her strength she screamed, "Take his head and throw it to the boars!" Those were the last words she ever uttered, for at their conclusion she slumped to the floor and died in a shuddering agony.

Almost instantly her followers turned against her and tromped upon her body in their mad dance of hatred and death. Herod and Herodias were hurried to another room by the guards. The people turned against them, too.

An hour later the room was silent—the floors and tables strewn with dead bodies. Hundreds of people had died from shock and sudden heart attacks. Salome's body was almost unrecognizable so badly had it been stomped upon. Mourners who had not attended that awful banquet came to claim their dead. They told one another in hushed tones of at least a hundred people wandering through the spacious palace halls as lost sheep, their voices piercing and shrill as they accused one another of having killed a true prophet of God. "Pearls of truth dropped from his mouth even in death!" they moaned. Others said crazily, "God forgive us—forgive us, what have we done?" Then all in unison they howled, "Down with Herod! Down with Herod who has brought this on us! We are a cursed people!"

Finally the halls were cleared and the din of weeping hushed. Herod and Herodias crept through the blackness of the night to the side of the once beautiful Salome. As Herod reached his hand to caress her, he saw little, live worms oozing from out of the unhealed scald-wounds upon his wrist. Screaming with mortal terror he ran from the banquet room cursing John and saying through his sobbing breaths, "John's prophecy is coming true—I am filled with worms!" Then to Herodias, "See what you have caused to come upon us when you made Salome ask for the head of John!"

CHAPTER 12

The Burial

SEVERAL DAYS BEFORE JOHN'S BEHEADING, and the day before the nine-month mourning period for her father was concluded, Mary of Magdala quarreled bitterly with her mother—not approving at all of her decision to establish a new home in Bethany. She was both ostentatious and vindictive as she announced to her family that she would not go south with them, but would return to Herod's court with all possible dispatch.

The morning of the quarrel had other sad moments. Mary was rebellious at any suggestion her mother made that would take her away from her life of pleasure, and she lashed out at her parent with bitter words of ridicule. Her mother was deeply anguished, yet she would not tell any of her three children that John had suggested they go to Bethany, for such had been her promise to him.

The next morning Mary left home alone, her attitude toward her family still one of terrible ridicule. As she hurried through the door with her few belongings, she told her mother vehemently to travel to Bethany without her. No amount of persuasion would change her mind, for she loved every moment of pleasure Herod's court could offer.

On her way to Capernaum she was triumphant. She loved freedom. Aloud she breathed, "At last I am my own boss! I have no one to fear!" Her pride-filled mind was lightsome with the thought that her beauty and dancing would bring the world to her feet.

At the very moment John was beheaded, she was in sight of Herod's palace. At just three o'clock in the morning she entered through the archway that led to the ballroom, and at that moment the soldiers placed the head of the Baptizer on the huge copper kettle. Around this terrible setting Salome was beginning the dance which she, Mary of Magdala, had taught her.

Mary stood aghast and wide-eyed at the dreadful sight. In terror she clutched the heavy draperies in the archway. It was hard for her to believe that Salome would use the beautiful Arabian dance to add thrills to such a murder scene. Horrified, she stood transfixed, as if turned to marble, while people fell prostrate from shock and died of fright as John's face changed its expression and the pearl bounced across the floor. She covered her eyes and became ill at sight of the half-crazed people running and screaming through the banquet room. Then fear that was beyond her control seized her and she ran hysterically from the palace.

She could not shake from her mind the picture of that pearl falling from a dead man's lips. What did it mean? She thought that most certainly it must be an ill omen, or that the person so terribly beheaded was a friend of God. In her fear she vowed she would never perform again—somehow she felt her dance was responsible for what had taken place.

She ran through the dark streets wishing she had a friend to whom she could go—but she had none, unless, of course, one could count her mother. But her mother should now be on her way to Bethany. Tears streamed down Mary's face in her loneliness and desolation. The fact that she was an Arabian made her feel all the more friendless because the people of Capernaum were generally her enemies. She wanted more than anything in all the world to weep on her mother's shoulder and to beg her forgiveness—to tell her she wanted to go with her, after all.

In desperation she hurried toward the harbor, reasoning that perhaps she could find a ship that would soon be leaving for the south. If so, she would board it and hope to catch up with her family. More than once, as she went along, she heard her name openly discussed with such expressions of hate as, "Wasn't Mary Magdala responsible for that dance of death? Let us find her and kill her for it!"

Then she found herself in the midst of another crowd. They, too, were seeking her. Icy terror gripped her heart. Men shouted, "Where is this woman of Magdala who is responsible for the death of a prophet? Her dance led the court into the temptations of debauchery. Her love of dancing for Herod proves she agreed with his sin of breaking the Commandments. Where is she? Let us find her and stone her to death!"

Mary reasoned feverishly that it would be useless to try to explain her innocence to them. She hurried faster and at length reached the waterfront.

As she searched for a ship that would take her south, she noticed people disembarking from a vessel that had just arrived from that direction. In the crowd were Jesus, Mother Mary, Simon, Andrew, and a number of friends.

After having spent several months in Jerusalem and towns near the Jordan, Jesus had visited His mother in Nazareth and His Granny Mary in Magdala. He and His mother had then spent three days of prayer in the desert Bethsaida while their friends, who planned traveling with them, stayed near the shore. It was at this time that Jesus told His mother that this was their last journey together, and that He was taking her with Him to Jerusalem where He would be crucified according to prophecy. The reason for their trip to Capernaum was to visit and say goodbye to their relatives and friends, who were expecting them.

Into this disembarking crowd ran the frightened Arabian, Mary of Magdala. Not knowing who Jesus was and as she accidentally brushed against His arm in her hurry, she cried aloud hysterically as though she had been questioned, "Herod's palace is in a state of chaos! Madness has come upon the people because the hermit John was beheaded there—he was murdered in the banquet room!" Not knowing the complete truth, she assumed that such had been the case. She continued to cry out as the crowd stood still to listen, "I saw his head on the dance floor! Stay away from there lest you turn mad like those cursed people!"

Hearing this dreadful news for the first time, Mother Mary placed her hand gently on her Son's arm to comfort Him as He bowed His head sorrowing. She whispered, "Son, is it true that our beloved John is already dead?"

"He met a most cruel death," Jesus answered, "and yet he offered it in reparation for the sins of the inhabitants of this town. Well did he realize the need for penance. Poor John, how he suffered in life! His only days of earthly joy were spent with you and Granny Mary. How he chuckled at the new mortification of rest on down cushions. He was wonderful."

Simon asked, "Jesus, should we not do something about his body?"

"We shall give it a proper burial," Jesus answered. Then He beckoned them into the darkness of a side street, continuing, "but we must be discreet. I don't want anyone to know yet that I am in Capernaum."

Simon thought the matter over for a moment and suggested, "My men and I are not generally acquainted here for my fleets do not operate this far north. Let us try to claim his body."[11]

"I think it would be best for us to stay together," Jesus answered, "but I suggest that for the next few hours we dress in different attire. That will at least cut down the danger of our being recognized."

The men agreed and Jesus went on, "We will mingle with the mourners who are already at the palace to reclaim their dead. Tell no one who I am and do not address Me by name. It would not be wise, for many of these sorrowing people have heard that I have raised the dead from time to time, and they would insist upon a miracle now rather than allow My will above theirs. I must avoid mass miracles of this nature for the good of all. The few I have raised from the dead were used only as a means to prove My identity—that the Father and I are One."

Turning to His mother, He said, "Mother, stay with our cousins until I return. You will have much to discuss with them. Then plan to stop with Me again in the desert Bethsaida before we go on to Jerusalem for a few days of mourning for John."

Mother Mary answered, "I would like to go with You, but since You have willed otherwise I will do as You ask. But hold him in Your arms for me before You lay him in the sepulcher, won't You?"

The Master bowed His head in assent, and then turning to His men said, "We must hurry now for it will soon be daybreak."

They draped themselves in Arabian scarfs, which they borrowed from friends who had them as souvenirs and thus appeared as any other mourners going to claim their dead.

Jesus led the way to the palace and through the archway into the banquet room. For a moment they stood aghast at the sight of horror before them, and then their attention was attracted by several mourners standing in a circle near one end of the room, their attitudes fearful and strained.

Jesus and His men moved closer and discovered a soldier in their midst telling about the pearl that had fallen from John's lips. It still lay upon the floor exactly where it had stopped rolling.

---

11 Simon's fishing fleet did not operate in this northern area because of a sharp competitor. They always stayed south of Bethsaida. However, they did cross the lake and fish on the opposite shore.

An elderly man asked, "What do you think will become of it?"

The soldier answered, "I imagine the whole palace will be destroyed now—for surely it is a cursed building. As for the pearl—I don't believe anyone would dare touch it—unless it be God, Himself!"

Jesus stepped forward calmly, picked up the pearl from the floor and placed it in His sash. A gasp went up from the people and they fled down the massive stairs, fearing a curse if this Man so much as touched them.

Quietly, Jesus and His men made their way to the cold, subterranean cell beneath the now empty banquet room. A guard demanded, "Who are you and what do you want?"

Jesus answered, "Herod has issued an order that mourners may bury their dead. We are the hermit's friends and have come for the body." Scowling, the guard answered, "Hurry and take it then—no one even wants to touch it. I guess you know he was a cursed man filled with bad signs such as pearls falling from his lips in death as proof of his witchcraft. I order you not to speak to the other prisoners!"

Jesus and His followers stepped into that awful mud dungeon, nearly overcome, as John had been with the terrible odor of sewage and dampness. In forgetfulness of self and their repugnance, they knelt in the mud and filth and offered a prayer over John's outstretched, headless body. They stifled their grief as they beheld the wooden pegs driven through his wrists, and Jesus loosened and removed them tenderly. Taking off His own outside toga, the Master covered John's body and said to Simon, "Carry it to the street and wait in the line of a forming funeral procession. I will meet you there later. Tell no one whose body it is."

Even though Jesus mourned John deeply, He was a study of sculptured calmness as He lifted the Baptizer's body onto the improvised stretcher. Then turning, he walked up the steps ahead of the others and out into the darkness beyond the palace walls.

Once there, He breathed deeply of the fresh morning air. The contrast of dungeon darkness with the beautiful, gray light before dawn caused Him to look upward into the silent ornamentation of Heaven's star-candled lights. He breathed a sigh of admiration as they dimmed before the wide spread of the dawn as it opened slowly, with death-like stillness, over the earth like a huge, oriental fan.

But the beauties of the heavens were not contained in the muddy foulness of the boar pen as the God-Man peered over the tall, wooden fence that enclosed it. The animals had not yet awakened. He studied the enclosure carefully, and finding that which He searched for at last, He leaped over the fence and ran to a shallow hollow inside the main pens. There in the muddy water lay John's head—exactly where it had fallen when thrown from the platter by the guards in obedience to Salome's last order.

The great boars awakened as Jesus, weeping silently, tenderly lifted the head from its muddy grave and hurried away. Every heartbeat of His was a prayer of love for John. Once outside the pens, He knelt beside a stream where He bathed, caressed, and smoothed John's holy features. Washing the slime and mud away, He tore a piece of cloth from His underneath toga and wrapped it about the precious relic. Then tenderly, like a mother with a newborn infant, He carried it to the men who waited for Him outside the palace walls. Those who passed by did not notice when Jesus placed the priceless possession alongside John's body.

The sun was high in the heavens when the long funeral procession began to move toward the city sepulchers and the loud cries and chants of the hired mourners could be heard all over the city. Hundreds of people were awakened by the sound and hurried to see what was taking place, for they knew nothing of the terrible events of the night. Many of those who had been present at the banquet tried to follow the procession, but a number soon dropped from fatigue by the roadside. Others died. Simon and his men busied themselves helping the suffering people as Jesus and three others carried John's body.

After a period of silence and while they rested at one point, Jesus said, "It is My desire to keep John's body intact and free from corruption in order to revive faith in My Church in the last generations. At this moment I am asking My angels to carry it invisibly elsewhere and to bury it in a place set apart, which will someday be an everlasting memorial for prayer in regard to the Baptizer's intercession. Simon, when the procession starts again, keep on helping the sufferers about us. No one, not even you, will know the exact moment when the angels remove John's body from the stretcher. This miracle will be known as coming under the supernatural gifts of bilocation and invisibility.

"Proceed to the sepulchers as we first planned, or scandal will be created and My identity made known after all. My angels will make it impossible for anyone to notice whether you bury a body or just the stretcher with My toga. People will believe you buried a body, and tradition will confirm this belief under assumed understanding until I will make it known in future generations."

BOOK THREE

The Last Mass

CHAPTER 1

Dismas

THREE DAYS AFTER JOHN'S BURIAL, Jesus, Simon, and his crew went with Mother Mary into the Bethsaida desert to mourn for him according to their ancient custom, and to make reparation for the people of Capernaum by fasting, prayer, and denials.

Often after their prayers and meditations, Jesus told them of John's wonderful life and of his sacrifices, but in the evenings the Master hid Himself away into the deeper recesses of the desert to pray alone for the deliverance of other prisoners who might be suffering torments similar to those the Baptizer endured.

During one of His ecstasy flights in prayer, He watched a vision of all the prisoners in time. Eagerly He prayed for them all—but particularly He chose at one hour to pray for a certain prisoner in Jerusalem whose name was Dismas.

God's grace of perseverance fell upon that prisoner and also upon his wife who, at the moment the Master's vision began, was on her way to visit her husband in his dungeon room. Neither one realized the singular privilege that was theirs in such a gift, but they did marvel from that time on at their unusual gladness during visiting hours.

Dismas' wife was a small, frail woman, poorly clad, and she carried in her hands a basket of food for her husband. She hurried through the streets on her errand with an air of dejection because people scorned her.

Arriving at her destination, she obtained permission from the guards to enter the prison, paid a small fee, and descended through the floor by means of a ladder into the dungeon below. As she lowered herself, rung by rung, Dismas greeted her with happiness and presently with caresses when he could reach her. He breathed deeply of her clothing in order to enjoy the warmth and fragrance of the great sunny outdoors that clung to it.

Dismas had been imprisoned because he had permanently injured a man who tried to stop him from stealing a loaf of bread for his hungry children. Now, he was so eager to see his wife that it seemed he asked a thousand questions all at once. The other prisoners, too, were eager to hear the news of the day.

Dismas asked, "Tell us what time it is—did you notice the sundial when you came in? Is today a feast day? Is there a celebration? Are the children well? Have you heard of any wars? Are the children hungry? Where do you get this food you bring us?"

People seldom thought of prisoners and their needs, and the damp dankness of the dungeon gloom kept them away. But Dismas had a faithful wife, and she loved him above all her other obligations. The sacrifice of visiting him was nothing compared to her joy in seeing him.

Caressing his wife, Dismas whispered, "It must be wonderful to feel the heat of the sun! I love to inhale its warmth from your clothing. How good you are to visit me, for I know you came a great distance and you are no doubt treated unkindly for doing so."

His wife only smiled.

Fourteen other men shared the dungeon room with Dismas. Their accommodations were few. An improvised table about twenty feet long and five feet wide served as table, bed, and chairs. The soggy earthen floor was ankle deep in mud. The only window, about a foot square, was some twenty feet from the floor and recessed deeply in the stone wall. The light through it was hardly enough to allow the men to know whether it was night or day.

As the prisoners ate the choice bits of food hungrily, they questioned their welcome visitor about the Man Jesus she had told them of during one of her last visits. They hoped that by this time she might have met Him or heard more of His miracles.

She said, "No, I have not met Him, but the latest news is that He is generally accepted as the real Living Messiah. Surely only God could raise the dead and heal the blind and the lame as I have heard He does. And it is claimed that He travels far and near, both in heat and cold, and stops at nothing to relieve suffering. Why, He has even cured leprosy. Never does He ask for money, but cures the sick only for the love of God, and scoffs at honors. It is claimed He loves the poor. I believe and trust, from what I hear, that He is the Messiah. Just think, if He is God we have great reason to rejoice."

Each time this good woman told her husband and the other prisoners goodbye, it seemed that she had given them courage and new hope for release by teaching them about Jesus. She had the wonderful gift of describing His actions in such a way that the scenes actually seemed to live in their minds. It was ordinarily a difficult thing to convince anyone of a true Messiah in those days, but never had another person performed such miracles as raising the dead and curing leprosy. Surely this Man was worthy of belief.

Daily, as the men waited for Dismas' wife to visit them, they sang their prayers loudly, hoping that perhaps if Jesus were walking by He would hear them. Many people stopped to listen, and usually they called down jeeringly through the little window to the prisoners that they had been fooled and to cease with their cries. This only made the poor men cry the louder, "Jesus of Nazareth, if You are walking by, come down and save us. We believe You are the Messiah!"

A week passed, and when once more Dismas' wife descended the ladder an elderly prisoner asked her scoffingly if she, herself, fully believed that this Jesus was the Messiah—or had her stories only been old women's tales to cheer them?

Dismas' wife answered, "I am convinced He is the Living God. I believe it because of His mercy toward little sick children if for no other reason. How He loves them! Let us hope and pray He visits this city soon and if He does, and I meet Him, I will plead for Him to visit here as well as cure our crippled son." Dismas' child had been a hopeless cripple for years. "If He cures him and he can walk again, I shall bring him here that you may see the happiness of people who have been made whole. Then I am sure you would no longer doubt the truth of this Man."

When it was about time for her to leave, the prisoners pleaded to hear yet another story concerning the Messiah. She smiled and told them of the sudden conversion of two old people, a man and his wife, who were on their hands and knees one day pulling weeds from their garden, which was large and so overrun that the vegetables could hardly be seen. The day was hot and the old man and woman were suffering from the strain of bending and crawling as well as from the heat.

Suddenly, beside them, near the roadway embankment, stood this wonderful Jesus. He watched them as they crawled along to pull the weeds ahead of them in the long furrows of vegetables. He pitied them and called to the old man as he approached, "May I help you, sir? I have the time and it would delight me to ease your burden as well as your wife's, for she reminds Me so much of My own grandmother. She and her husband—who has been dead for many years—worked together in life just as you are doing. Please let me help."

The old man could only stand and stare, for it was indeed a shock to have a stranger speak so kindly, and to salute him as "sir." With a curious eye he studied the Master and wondered all the more because he could see Jesus was not an ordinary fieldworker. He could not answer. With tears of gratitude welling in his old eyes he simply nodded his head.

The Master hurried down the embankment and, falling on His knees, began pulling weeds along with the elderly couple. As they crawled slowly along the old man asked, "Stranger, have you ever heard anything of a man who claims to be a Nazarene and who performs miracles? I have heard He brings the dead back to life. Some even say He is the Messiah."

Jesus did not answer directly. Instead He asked, "Sir, from what you have heard, do you think He could be the Messiah? Are you looking for Him?"

The old man thought this over for a moment and then said shyly, "I'm afraid I would have to see a miracle. If I didn't believe then, I'd fear God's eternal judgment. But that miracle would have to be something completely out of the ordinary, and if *that* ever happened I'd follow the Messiah like a puppy wherever He went. I wouldn't want my eyes to lose track of Him for one moment!"

Jesus said nothing, but He smiled quietly to Himself as He continued pulling weeds.

Presently, the old man groaned as he straightened his back. "It seems the more weeds we pull, the faster and taller they grow. Now that our children have gone into the world I don't know what we are going to do, for the work is getting beyond our strength."

Jesus also straightened up and brushed the dust from His robe and sandals. He said, "It has been a pleasure to help you this last hour, but I must be going now. Thank you, sir. Good afternoon, and God bless you."

The elderly couple watched as Jesus walked back to the roadway, where He turned to wave goodbye. They were completely baffled at His kindness. The old man said, "He is a wonderful person. Bless the father and mother who raised Him. I hope we see Him again."

While they pondered the question of Jesus' identity they knelt once more in the hot, sweltering furrows to resume their work. But now the garden was completely weeded! Nor could they find even one weed that had been pulled during the entire morning!

The old man ran here and there like a delighted child, and then he fell to his knees and shouted at the top of his voice for all his neighbors to come and see the Miracle of the Weeds! "A miracle! A miracle!" he called. "Friends, come see a miracle! That Man walking yonder must be the real Messiah! Only God could have done this to my garden!"

The neighbors came hurrying, all of them in a state of great excitement, and not one could find a single weed in the old man's garden, yet directly over the fence they were shoulder high. Believing, like the elderly couple, that the Man who had helped them was God, they fell to their knees and kissed the ground upon which He had worked. Loud were the shouts of joy from those who were disfigured or lame, for they found themselves suddenly cured!

The old man beckoned his wife. "Come, woman," he said hurriedly, "we promised to follow the Messiah if He proved Himself by miracles. Look what we have before us! The garden is cleared of weeds, some of our friends see for the first time through eyes that were dead, and Jerra can walk and run to his mother. God is wonderful—and to think He was here talking to us, and helping us, for an hour!"

The old man and the old woman hurried down the road after Jesus, and as they went they heard their neighbors rejoicing behind them. Still others came to venerate the ground upon which the Messiah had walked. Many of them exclaimed, "There's not a weed in the whole garden, nor can we even find a wilted one! Where do you suppose He hid the ones that were pulled? Even the ground is unbroken! Do you suppose His angels did the work?"

One man said, "The best thing for us is to do penance as John the

Baptizer preached, for not one of us is worthy to be here in this hallowed field. You must remember John, for he was here several months ago. Come, let us do penance and then our faith will be greater. I for one am convinced this Man of miracles is the Messiah!"

All together they said, "God is with us! God has been in this garden! God is on earth!"

The old man and his wife caught up with Jesus and they fell at His feet, saying, "Why did You not tell us You were the Living God? We would have adored You rather than allow You to work in the garden. We have come to follow You—to obey Your least command."

The Master blessed them as He said, "Come, follow Me. I need your company along the paths of life."

Hand in hand, like little children, not knowing where they were going, or caring, they followed behind Jesus down the dusty road, singing aloud their praises to Him. Neighboring friends at work in their fields were astonished and could not believe their ears or eyes. What was this about a miracle and cures?

The old man shouted in delight and pointed to Jesus. "This Man is the Messiah!" he called. "If you don't believe me just go look at my garden and see for yourselves the Miracle of the Weeds. Come, follow Him!"

A mile or so along the way Jesus and the elderly couple met Matthew and Matthias, who were journeying from a distant city to meet the God-Man. After greetings were over, they walked arm in arm with Him while the old people followed quietly. Far ahead of them in the roadway trudged another old man. He was a cripple, and on his back was tied a bundle of dry willows that he was taking to the city to market.

As they came abreast of him they had to pass in single file, for at this point the path was very narrow. The old fellow was a Gentile, and he acted as though he did not notice them. Jesus stopped and smiled at him. The poor, old cripple smiled in return and then his eyes brimmed with tears of gratitude for seldom, if ever, did anyone smile at him. He thought to himself in amazement, "This Man who smiled at me is a Jew!"

Without a word Jesus untied the bundle of willows from his back and transferred it to His own. When Matthew and Matthias saw this, they protested indignantly, saying that Jesus should not help the old man and He should remember he was a Gentile. Jesus paid no attention. In utter disgust, Matthias said, "Here, let us carry the firewood if

You insist on such charity, but You should not be doing this. What will Your friends along the way think when they see You doing such a menial task? Remember You are the Messiah. Why, they will shout, 'Let the Gentile carry his own wood!' Remember, Master, who You are!"

Jesus just shook His head at their stupidity.

Matthias continued, "Jesus, listen to me. You will lose the followers You already have if they see You so friendly with Gentiles. And beyond that, we don't want people to think we were wrong in our judgment when we chose to follow You as the Messiah. Everyone in Jerusalem looks for the Messiah to be a king and to act above such acts of simple charity. You must act with dignity."

Jesus smiled and said, "I have not told you how My Kingdom is managed. It is not of this world, nor does it follow your laws of life in denying the poor and the suffering."

Matthias reached again for the dry willows and said, "Let me carry them for You."

Jesus answered calmly, "You had the first chance to help this poor old man and you only passed him by. Do you not realize that your personal pride is making you suffer worse than he? Now if you really want to do something for Me, you and Matthew pick up the old gentleman and carry him between you in chair fashion."

The two disciples gasped with surprise and shock, but they could not utter a word. Clasping each other's wrists, they formed the chair and nodded for the old man to back into it. They carried him a great distance, with the Master going ahead, bent beneath His load of willows, while the other old people, who had not been scandalized, brought up the rear, still singing praises and songs of adoration.

Matthew and Matthias were silent—sorry for their rash actions and words. Matthias now could not understand why he had ever been so bold as to suggest ethics to the Master. To make reparation, they tried to console the old man and even tried to prove to him that this Jesus carrying his firewood was the real Messiah.

At this point in the story told by Dismas' wife, one prisoner interrupted and begged her to find this Living God and bring Him there to them. If He was so kind to an old Gentile, surely He would be kind to them, too, and help free them. He wanted to tell Him that he believed in Him and to plead to see again the sunshine, the flowers, and his friends.

At that moment, a new prisoner—an old man who had not been converted—looked up at the small window and in great agitation cried aloud, "There is no God but the God of our fathers, Yahweh. Great God of Abraham, help me not to follow the wiles of this woman!"

He made a terrible din with his loud, constant petition to Yahweh, for he hoped thus to drown out any other words that might be spoken for the Living Messiah. In spite of that, the other prisoners begged Dismas' wife to finish her story. She responded gladly.

"It is said," she went on, "that the little old Gentile complained of his pain as he was carried along and asked to be put down, as he thought it would be easier to walk than to ride. Jesus said, 'This is far enough—place the old gentleman on his feet.'

"As Matthew and Matthias did so, they fell back a step amazed at what they saw. The little, old, bent man was no longer bent nor in pain. He had been cured! He was so thrilled and excited that he ran this way and that and at length, in his delight, he snatched the willows from Jesus' back and threw them to the side of the road.

"'You must be the Messiah for whom Your people have waited all these years,' he said to Jesus. 'How can I help but believe as they do? You have cured me and I know only God could do that! Why, I have never given You the slightest thought—I have ridiculed the very idea of You. I am sorry now. How can You be so good to me when I am such a sinner?' He bent before Jesus in adoration and pleaded, 'Allow me, Master, even though I am a Gentile, to follow You!'

"Jesus led him to the elderly couple, who watched from a few yards away and asked him to join their company and follow Him. Now, three old people—instead of two—took up their chant of praise and thanksgiving."

CHAPTER 2

The Little Children

THREE DAYS LATER, Dismas' wife returned to the prisoners in the dungeon and told them more about the elderly people who, with Matthew and Matthias, followed Jesus.

It was a hot, dusty day. Matthias shielded his eyes with his hand and peered into the distance ahead. He said, "It seems we are nearing a small village. And look! There are hundreds of people assembled near the roadside. Do You think they are waiting for us? I hope they are friends."

Jesus answered, "Do not fear. Many of them are indeed our friends and have come great distances to greet us."

News traveled fast, even in those days. People from the little town ahead, as well as from nearby cities, had heard about this Jesus of Nazareth and His miracles, and that He would be traveling through their district that day. Many of them believed He was the Messiah, and thus it was quite a festive occasion. The women spread their finest linens and tapestries across the dusty road for the distance of a mile for Him to walk upon. Well they knew His holy nearness would be a great blessing and would add considerably to the value of their prized possessions. While they waited, they discussed miracles and how their rituals of worship might be changed through His coming. Among them, of course, were the scoffers who laughed and jeered at the idea of a Living Messiah coming to their village.

In addition, there were hundreds of litters holding crippled children waiting for Jesus to bless them with a miracle. Tired mothers tried to comfort the suffering little ones with kind words. "Have patience and don't cry," they said, "Jesus will soon be here. Perhaps within the hour your pain will end and maybe you will walk again." Others whispered words of hope to little tots who had never seen the light of day nor their mothers' faces. Those of the children who could, kept their eyes on the long stretch of road and called to one another, "Jesus will come soon!"

Excitement grew as the Master and His friends were sighted and drew near. An outburst of pleading voices from mothers greeted Jesus, begging Him to cure their children. They led Him to the linen-covered road and urged Him to walk upon the spotless path they had prepared for Him.

Jesus smiled and blessed them as they strewed blossoms, green leaves, and palms before Him. Matthew and Matthias and the elderly people walked on the outside of this royal path. Moving slowly, Jesus noticed and silently blessed all of the children. He smiled at them kindly, and they gazed back at Him with awed expressions of fear and hope.

After He had walked a distance of about fifty yards and no miracle had taken place, many fathers of the children began to laugh. "Look at the false Messiah!" they jeered. "This is the closest we have come to meeting a god. Behold the impostor! Away with Him!"

Cursing Him, they spat into His path. Jesus did not answer, nor did He seem to hear them as He continued onward. Occasionally, He bent to caress a suffering child and to ask his age and name.

Finally, Matthew was able to stand it no longer. He shouted, "Why did you allow your women to come here? By your very presence you profess some belief, or you would not allow them to spread their linens and tapestries. Only fools would form an assembly to greet an imposter. By your wives' actions you are judged. I tell you this Jesus and God are One. He who hears Him hears the Father. The prophets of old taught us that God would dwell in flesh like ours. This Jesus is the Messiah—be careful what you say and do!"

A loud, booming voice answered, "This is a holiday for us—a day of sport, for we have known for a long time about this impostor's coming here. The moment was too great to miss, and the disappointment of our women and children will teach them to be sensible and not to listen in the future to old women's tales and the fancy of false prophets. It is not yet time for the Messiah's coming!"

Another voice bellowed, "Anyone can see He is an impostor. Look at His fine, clean linen and uncalloused hands. They tell a story that a poor Nazarene is trying to make something out of Himself, but He can't fool us with a silvered tongue. No good, nor proof, can come from Him—He is a Nazarene!"

As the bickering went on, Jesus stooped to caress a tiny two-year-old child who had been blind since birth. With great tenderness He kissed the little unseeing eyes and immediately they opened to the brightness of day. A glorious smile spread over the child's face as he watched the expression of Jesus. Then he ran to answer the familiar sound of his mother's voice. He was seeing her for the first time.

The din and the cries of the suffering children hushed abruptly. A thundering shout arose and then, again, all were silent. To have seen a miracle was to have full knowledge and proof that this Jesus was the Messiah. It was too much of a shock for them—the silence was deadening. None of them knew what to say nor how to act.

The men who had dared to jeer at Jesus were suddenly afraid and ran to hide in the shade and darkness of an olive grove a short distance away. The women stoned them as they ran and rebuked them loudly for being cowards and devils.

When dusk lowered its shades over the valley, all the children, as well as many aged people, had been gifted with perfect health. No longer were they constrained to use crutches and other devices.

A picnic was held in the early evening with Jesus as an honored guest. Many little ones, who were seeing for the first time in life, found the twilight shades delightful as they played with the Master who ran, jumped, and hid Himself in accord with the rules of the games they engaged in.

As the wonderful evening drew to a close, Jesus asked the mothers to go into the villages and see if there were any forgotten children there who needed help. He wanted to heal and bless all in that vicinity before He went on. As they hurried away, He called after them, "Suffer all the little children to come unto Me, for of such joy and trust as the children have, such is the Kingdom of Heaven."

Within the hour about fifty more were brought to Him. As He blessed and healed them, he told the parents not to hurry them away for He loved them near, saying, "Leave them alone and do not hinder them from coming to Me, for such is the Kingdom of Heaven."

The elderly people who had followed Jesus were too awed to speak because of the miracles. But now that things were quieter, the old fellow who had carried the willows went in search of his bundle. Returning with it, he called everyone to stack the litters, straw mats, and other devices used to ease suffering, on top of it. When this was done he set it ablaze and all offered the fire to God as a thanksgiving.

Jesus knelt near the flames with four little children who had that day been cured of blindness. They were struck with wonderment at the golden flames, which reached up into the soft blackness of the night and then disappeared. One child seemed to ask silently, "What is all this blackness around us?" Another little one asked, "Where do the dancing flames go?"

Jesus answered, "Sit down, My little friends, and I will tell you a story about this light which is called 'fire.' Listen to the sound it makes, something like a swishing beat—pounding, pounding, pounding into the air above. Each of you has a fire something like this in your heart. Put your hand over it and see. Do you feel it beat? This fire here before us beats and beats against the blackness of the night, but the beat within you is God's fire and it is known as life."

Each child put his hand over his heart, and each one smiled as he listened to God's little fire within.

Jesus also smiled and continued his story. "That pounding heart within you is saying that it wants you to think good thoughts and perform good deeds, and every time you do, it burns brighter and brighter and tries to make God glad. It longs, also, to be released and to have freedom like this other fire, but as long as you live it will stay within you. Only God can release it, and that will be when you die. If in life you make it burn brighter and brighter, at death you will reach into God's kingdom and have eternal freedom and happiness. Death is beautiful when you are not afraid to go to God. See, this fire before you is not afraid—it leaps higher and higher. Remember this fire and how it tries to reach the stars and you will never fear My Father, nor death. The little fire within your heart longs to enter Heaven, and in its impatience it says with every beat, 'Let me out, let me out! I want to hurry to God!'

"Say this to the beating fire in your hearts, 'Little fire in my heart, when your light matches the color of God's light I am sure God will come down and take you home. I know you are restless—just like a caged bird that desires freedom—but until God comes for you I promise to console you when you feel loneliness for Heaven. This body of mine will take you praying, swimming, boating, playing, and to school. In all our living together let us glorify God.'"

The children were silent and in deep thought. The Master watched them for a while and then said, "Keep that fire within you ablaze and become as little stars for the saints and the angels to see—for when they gaze toward the earth they find you only by the lights in your hearts. You are for all the world like little lanterns swinging over the earth. If the saints couldn't find you each day they would feel that a piece of God's masterpiece was gone. Imagine how you would feel if you looked for the stars in the heavens on a clear night and found none!

"And, little friends, there are people on earth who never think of God and those people are afraid to die. But perhaps your prayers and your deeds as you go through life will save them, and if so they will go into Purgatory, which is a place of suffering and long waiting for the cool, little flame in them to become bright and ablaze so that they may enter Heaven. Keep your fires bright all the time and you will not enter there. When you die I want you to come directly to Me."

One little boy gazing up toward the moon cried out, "I want my crown to look like that—so big that God can always find it!"

A chuckle echoed through the crowd and Jesus laughed. Then He said, "Look at the stars—see how they seem to be twinkling with happiness? Your eyes look like that when you think of God. Through this fire of thanksgiving here on the roadway your eyes twinkle all the more, and the angels and saints way up there know you are happy. They always see the light within your hearts as clearly as you see the stars. How do you think your heart-light appears to them? Is it dim like that star yonder, or bright and gold like this one directly above us?"

The children looked from star to star, and when they discovered one that seemed to twinkle more brightly than the others, they smiled and said joyfully, "We are like that star!"

Jesus drew the four little children who had received eyesight into His embrace and then asked Matthias to lift them to His shoulders, two on each side. From that great height, for the Master was tall, and with their thin legs dangling down His back, they giggled joyously. Matthias placed a wooden pole across their waists so that they would not fall and Jesus, keeping a tight grasp upon the ends of the pole, ran with them back and forth across the roadway and up and down the fields. How the children loved it and how their laughter rang out upon the night air! Turning in the direction of the grove where many men were still hiding, Jesus told the children to call to them as He ran through the trees, "Come, father! We want you to join our fun!"

Smiling sheepishly, the fathers left their hiding places one by one and knelt close to the fire on the road, which was about burned out. The Master put the children down, and picking up a small log He said, "Little friends, I did not tell you about people who die and find they cannot enter into God's kingdom. There is a place so far away from here, and from God's light, that it would frighten you even to think about it. The name of that place is 'Hell.' It is all blackness, as if you looked up at the sky and found no stars there. And the howling of invisible fire would frighten you and the blackness would sting like fire.

"Come closer to this earthly fire, now. As I place this log on the flames, feel how it stings your faces as it begins to burn. That is how the darkness of Hell stings a darkened heart. I don't want you ever to go to that dreadful place, so keep the fires of your hearts bright and clean by thinking good thoughts, saying your prayers, and doing good deeds."

Then addressing the parents, the Master went on kindly, "Unless you become as your little children in simplicity to the laws of God you will not enter into My Kingdom. My way is by faith of simplicity. The way to Heaven is not complicated, for I will make it easy through My coming death. I do not expect you to understand the why to certain mysteries, but they are allowed for your merit. Rise above them and become soldiers of Mine. Make a pleasant game out of life by giving kindness to everyone—it costs you nothing but a smile and a word. This life is not a final resting place—it is a battlefield on which I prove your loyalty to Me."

By this time the blackness of night had blanketed everything, and it was time for the Master and His followers to leave for other destinations. Jesus said to the children, "Some day we will have another picnic. Thank you for this one and for the joy we had in our games."

One by one the children and their parents left for home. As the Master turned to be on His way also, He found a newly erected sign in His path, which read, "Jesus, our God, has trod this path. Forever shall this be hallowed ground."

Once more it was time for Dismas' wife to leave the dungeon. As she hurried away she heard the chant of the prisoners, "Jesus, Jesus, Jesus, we believe You are the Messiah. Save us. Save us, Jesus!"

CHAPTER 3

The Brother of Rachel

AT THE MOMENT JESUS' VISION of the little children ended, Mary of Magdala was making preparations to sail from Capernaum. She regretted ever having left her mother for Herod's court more than words could express. She could do nothing but cry, and as she obtained transportation she hoped her hour of disembarkation would be ahead of her mother's so that they would meet and travel south together.

Flags along the Capernaum beach warned of a pending storm, and she wept again as she realized the consequence of delay. She and a group of people at length persuaded the captain of their ship to set sail regardless of the warnings, and as a consequence they left port early the next morning.

The storm struck them shortly, and hour by hour it was increased. The waves rose higher and higher, but at nightfall they managed to land on the beach of Galilee alongside another ship that was about to set sail for the Dead Sea through the Jordan River. Through the mercy of God, both Mary of Magdala's mother and Rachel were in the group of travelers going south aboard it. Mary saw them walking together on the beach. "Mother, wait for me!" she screamed. "I want to go with you!" Her cry even pierced the churning noise of the lake.

For the first time Rachel met Mary. Regardless of how her mother questioned Mary about her reason for leaving Herod's court, her daughter would not answer. The memory of John's head on the platter was still too vivid in her mind—she would like to forget it. And, she reasoned to herself, it was better not to frighten her mother with an account of that scene of horror.

The mere thought of what had taken place filled her heart with doubt in regard to faith in God. She even began to question free will and the Commandments and became silent, moody, and petulant as the voyage progressed. No one on board knew of the Baptizer's death, and they talked of him as though he were still living, which tortured her still further. Like a caged animal she walked the deck asking herself, "Was he a true prophet? Why did a real pearl roll from his lips after death? What did it mean? Was this the usual phenomena God used to prove His prophets to the people of the world? Of whom could she ask this question?" She wished the whole thing were a dream, but it wasn't—it was true!

When her mother asked what was torturing her, she answered scornfully and with hatred on her lips, "Why did you leave Arabia? Why did you bring us into all this trouble? We could have had peace and contentment at home. We will never adjust ourselves to the culture of the Jews—and look what Judaism has brought upon us—nothing but misfortune, discouragement, and fear. Here we are moving again. We are even friendless unless you say Rachel is a friend. Personally I don't care to associate with her!

"And more than that! I am in grave doubt about the God you profess to worship. I do not believe the Messiah will come as a Man in this generation—nor do I believe that what the prophets say is true revelation. It is possible they were all wrong and you are among the unfortunate people who fell into their snares. Oh, how I wish I were home. I'm going there just as soon as we arrive in Jerusalem!"

Mary's mother was courageous and silent as she listened to the stinging words of her daughter, and clung to the promise John had made her.

Rachel felt sorry for Mary, and hoping to console and interest her she began to tell her the story of the pearls and of the astonishing mystery of music that came from them. She also wanted to tell her that she believed the Messiah was born in her stable and that she knew He was somewhere in the world.

When Mary heard the words "pearls" and "Messiah" she became enraged. Insultingly, she accused Rachel of witchcraft and told her she would hear nothing more about miracles of any kind. But in spite of all her efforts, the mention of pearls brought once more to mind the gruesome scene in Herod's court. The more she thought about that and the mystery Rachel had tried to tell her, the more she wept tears of anger and self-pity. Enraged, she stamped her feet at Rachel and forbade her angrily to speak to her again. She was convinced that anything connected with pearls in any way was an omen of evil. Turning to her mother, she begged her to return to Arabia and to forget all the dangerous quackery that Rachel spoke of. Her mother answered firmly that she believed in the heavenly music that came from the circlet of pearls.

They anchored several miles south of Tiberias, near the mouth of the Jordan, and several Roman soldiers came aboard with a prisoner. He was a huge, surly, antagonistic man who deliberately bumped against the soldiers and spat upon them. He did not mind their orders or commands, and dared them to use their swords upon him before he was judged by Pilate.

When Rachel saw him she gasped and slumped to her knees, clinging desperately to the gown of Mary's mother. As quickly as she could she regained her composure and ran to him, for he was her brother. He recognized her at once and greeted her mockingly, openly chiding her about the pearls and the imaginary music, which he said was the cause of his criminal and wicked life.

Then, glaring at her, he continued, "If it hadn't been for those pearls I would not be here in chains like this. I have spent years, in fact my life, since you last saw me, searching for the other part of the strand from which your bracelet was taken. See what it has brought me! I robbed and murdered in order to obtain pearls. For days I listened and thought about the scene in your stable. But never once did I hear any music—it is all a fake." Then mockingly, he said, "Rachel, you look old. Your search has brought you nothing, either. Go back where you belong and mind the inn."

Mary of Magdala, her arms folded scornfully, heard these remarks and laughed. Now she had a weapon to hold over Rachel, which she would use when the time came to win her mother from the folly of Rachel's beliefs.

As the ship cut through the black lake in the night, Rachel and Mary's mother sat huddled together under a blanket in a far corner of the deck. Silent and alone they meditated upon the scene of the Messiah's birth. Slowly, they became aware of Heaven's music as it came through the little circlet of pearls. Now they felt certain God's blessing was upon them, and they knelt in a prayer of thanksgiving.

The following week, Rachel's brother was thrown into the dungeon at Jerusalem at the very moment the elderly man died who had scoffed at the stories told by Dismas' wife. Now, with Rachel's brother there, they had another scoffer. He delighted in ridiculing the story of the pearls and how his own sister connected the event with the birth of the Messiah, whom, of course, he did not believe would ever come into the world. The next moment he admitted that he had heard chords of strange music coming from the pearls a long time ago, which caused the other prisoners to think him insane, and from then on they paid little attention to his raving and contradictory remarks.

This was the first time, however, that any of the other prisoners had heard the story of the pearls. When Dismas' wife arrived the following day, Rachel's brother demanded, "I guess you must be the one who tells the old woman's tales? Have you by any chance heard about musical pearls in connection with this Jesus whom you talk about and believe to be the Messiah? My, what fools you people are believing in so many impostors. I have met with all kinds of men who claim to be the Christ. Who are you going to believe?"

Dismas' wife said, "No, I have never heard anything about musical pearls, but nothing is impossible with God. Don't you know that through Him Moses made water come from a rock? I don't think musical pearls would be any greater miracle. I would love to hear them."

Dismas asked her to inquire around and see what she could learn about such pearls. She promised that she would.

Meanwhile, Rachel—sad and sorrowful over her brother's behavior and crimes—traveled with Mary's family into Bethany. After she helped them get comfortably settled in their new home, she went on to Jerusalem. She planned to visit her brother, as she wished with all her heart to bring him peace and hope in God.

But this wish was not to be realized, for at the end of each visit to the prison she found herself more perplexed than before entering because she could not answer the confusing questions the prisoners asked her—especially those concerning the ancient prophecies that taught the coming of the Messiah. Vehemently, her brother shouted at her, "Don't come here! I never want to see you again! You are the cause of my life ending this way, for it is said I will be crucified on the feast day. If you find your Jesus, tell Him about me and see what He can do to save me!"

So great was the confusion he made that the guards asked Rachel not to return. Weeping, she walked alone through Jerusalem. Along the same street, but in the opposite direction, walked another woman—the wife of Dismas. She, too, was weeping, for she realized that this might be her last visit with her husband.

CHAPTER 4

The Storm on the Lake

WHILE RACHEL AND THE WIFE OF DISMAS walked the streets of Jerusalem in sorrow and dismay without meeting each other, Jesus, Simon, and his crew left the desert, where they had gone to mourn the death of John and set sail for Capernaum. Mother Mary and her cousins had mourned also for the accustomed number of days and now were watching for Jesus on the lakeshore. Mother Mary, not realizing the pangs of sorrow nor how to mourn because of her purity in not having been touched with Original Sin, kept the mourning days anyway according to the ways of her people. They did not realize her great privilege, or they would have been frightened in her holy presence. Mother Mary followed their ways and thus avoided questioning.

After a short, joyous reunion with His mother and cousins, Jesus and Mary told the others goodbye, and with Simon started for the Dead Sea from where they would travel on to Jerusalem. As their ship left the shore, hundreds of people waved to Jesus and called for Him to come back. They had brought their sick and lame from the inland cities, and they begged Him to cure them. They fell pleadingly to their knees and called loudly, "Come back, Jesus. Come back—we need You!"

Even though Jesus was fatigued and heavy of heart over John's death, as well as grieved over the many souls who could be eternally lost unless they did great penance in reparation for the despicable crime, He told Simon to anchor near the shore.

As the Master disembarked and walked among the people, they prayed loudly for miracles to come to them through His blessings. Old people crowded around Him and gazed steadily into His eyes—and were shocked when they realized that this Jesus, whom they had known for many years, was the Messiah. Why hadn't they been aware of this great mystery before? How and why had it been kept such a secret? Many found this hour one of happy reunion, and smiled and laughed as they recalled how Jesus in His youth had lived with Granny Mary. They had often visited her and even eaten with Him. He had been just another little boy in the world to them then, and to their sorrow they had not paid much attention to Him.

Now, they laughed and cried together as they recalled many beautiful memories of His babyhood days in Nazareth and Galilee. Some remembered holding Him on their knees and telling Him stories about the sea monster they said lived in the lake. They asked about Granny Mary and where she lived now, for they wished to visit her and discuss the events of His life. One elderly man asked, "Jesus, did Granny Mary know all the time that You were the Living Messiah?"

As Jesus answered their questions, they exclaimed at the courage and fortitude with which Granny Mary had lived, knowing all the while that He was her God. Another group of men and women from a little farther down the beach hurried to Him and asked Him to explain the meaning of the Living Bread, or Manna, which they had heard, through prophecy, He would bring from Heaven.

As the Master spoke to them all and continued to answer their questions, He proceeded a great distance along the beach, allowing many healing miracles to come upon a great number who had never walked, nor talked, nor seen the light of day. Everyone drew strength and courage from Him.

It was not long before the night shades fell across the beach and the evening stars appeared. The people had entirely disregarded time and their occupations. Children were heard to ask for food and Jesus, taking compassion on all there, asked how many loaves of bread and how many fish were among them. After they were counted and the number of each found to be less than ten, the Master permitted a miracle of multiplication and all were satisfied. When they saw baskets of food collected for the poor and realized what had taken place through the Master's kindness, they were astonished and fell upon their knees in adoration. Everyone was convinced that this Man was the Messiah, and they sang praises to Him as He waded through the surf to Simon's ship.

As Simon lifted anchor, Mother Mary asked her wonderful Son to look again at the shore. Through the darkness He could see great crowds coming from the south, waving lanterns and pleading with Him to return. Once more He left the ship and walked among His friends. He cured many of them and talked to all about eternal life and the Living Bread He had come to give to the world. He promised that many in that throng would receive that gift before they died. For two days He remained with the oncoming crowds, and again He permitted the multiplication of the loaves and the fishes.

At last He was able to sail, but the voyage was destined to be eventful, for a few hours later they were overtaken by a severe storm. At Jesus' command, Simon—after ordering his men to remain with the vessel and to keep it anchored in the deeper water—took Mother Mary and the Master to the beach in a small boat. Once more on land they peered through the darkness, hoping to find a place of shelter for Mother Mary for the duration of the storm.

As the fierce gale bore down on the beach Simon, although within two feet of the Master, called at the top of his strong voice, "In all my years of experience as a fisherman, I have never seen such a storm!"

The raging wind was now of a hurricane nature. The sky was inky black, without stars. Thick, black, hanging clouds could be seen through lightning flashes as if they were falling and sprawling in unbelievable phantasmal designs across the lake and shore. Suddenly, they were pushed and whipped high into the air, and thin spray like frozen fringe cut across the faces of the Master and Simon. Mother Mary was shielded in the strong embrace of her Son's arm. Simon's ship was forced farther and farther from shore. The anchor didn't seem to hold.

Deep, thunderous roars rolled through the heaven's canyons with resounding and terrifying crashes, as though a petulant god in the sky's synagogue would give his oratorical words of hate and revenge to the world through the sound of noise. In this terrible storm, which was bad enough for anyone to think the world was coming to an end,

Jesus calmly assured Simon—who for the moment was completely lost—that the shoreline was just ahead of them. Then He bade Simon not to follow them further, but to return to his ship and help encourage his crew, for He felt sure He and His mother would find shelter.

Instead of going directly to the ship, Simon paced the shore. Afraid that Jesus and Mother Mary would not find shelter, he called aloud, hoping to hear in response that they were safe.

Receiving no answer to his frantic call, he hurried to the lakeside. Once there he shuddered at the water's terrible unrest. Certainly it was a holocaust of rising mountains and deep valleys, all filled with heinous shadows and rumbling moans. Even the beach seemed to sway as if from an earthquake, as challenging, red thunderbolts of fire plunged into the depths of the lake. Through the cloud-mist made bright by the heaven's quick flashes, Simon could see his ship buffeting the waves as if it were a straw on the water and his crew clinging frantically to the rails, for oars and sails could not be used.

Then suddenly, tidal-like waves crumpled the shoreline where Simon stood and made new inroads to the desert. Great cylindrical holes and gullies were opened as the black, coiling waters rushed inland only to be swallowed by Mother Earth. Simon hurried to the top of a hill, from where he could see into the darkness of the desert, hoping to glimpse even an outline of Jesus and Mother Mary when lightning flashes permitted, which would assure him of their safety, and to watch his tossing ship in the lake. He shouted again at the top of his voice, "Jesus! Jesus! Jesus!" The wind, in its contemptible destructive violence, smothered his call and he wearily retraced his steps to the water's edge.

Dejected and alone on the far edge of the beach, Simon recalled the simple laws of obedience the Master had taught him during the forty-day retreat in the desert. He remembered with a smile how Jesus had told him that doing even the most insignificant task under obedience to lawful authority was the will of God, and very meritorious in obtaining an answer to prayer. Quickly he remembered then that he had commanded his men to stay with the ship. Their obedience put him to shame, for the fury of the storm was enough to cause any man to swim for his life. He was suddenly shocked as he realized they were obeying him better than he was fulfilling the will of Jesus. The

Master had asked him to return to the crew, and yet he lingered on the shore hoping to help Jesus. Was this not lacking trust? All this time his men had stayed with their tossing ship—he could even hear occasionally their frantic calls for further commands as to whether or not they should abandon ship or to continue trying to save it from being dashed against the shore.

He waded into the water, hoping to swim to the ship, and prayed aloud asking God's forgiveness for his carelessness and neglect. As he made his way some great distance from shore, his ship was tossed toward him on the crest of a huge wave. His men helped him on board quickly and then, as if driven by an opposite wind, the small craft was carried swiftly far out into the blackness of the lake.

Simon took his place at the helm and tried with all his strength and skill as navigator to bring the ship under control, but his task seemed hopeless. The storm grew steadily worse.

In the meantime, Jesus had found lodging for Mother Mary in a farmer's house. Leaving her in his care, He hurried back to the lake to help Simon. Through the terrible darkness He could occasionally see the outline of the tossing ship and hear the frantic men shouting, "Jesus, save us!"

The frightened crew thought their ship would surely capsize when it was thrown shoreward toward ugly, projecting rocks over which they tried to throw their anchoring ropes. In a moment's time they were washed out again into the churning water. Simon tried to calm his men by reminding them to practice silence as Jesus had taught them on their retreat. Through the prayer of silence he believed Jesus would hear and help them, for he knew the Master could calm the storm because he had watched Him silence other storms, both on sea and on land.

As the men prayed silently, they were caught up into the great phenomena of rapture according to their different degrees of grace. Into the delights of that ecstatic sleep they felt God's protecting love flood through their souls. Suddenly, all was calm—both human hearts and the lake. The sounds of the buffeting waves and the howling wind were now the delightful reverberations of Heaven's music piercing their souls. As their united senses listened, they were lulled higher and higher into the state of fearlessness where all is love.

Just as their ecstatic rapture swept over them, their ship had been lifted high on a mountainous wave, where for a moment it balanced back and forth as if it were on the edge of a precipice. If it had plunged into the deep valley below, it would have meant instantaneous death for all the crew, but the peace of God came over the lake and the huge wave lowered slowly without the sound and turbulence to rise again.

In ecstasy's delights, the crew could see in vision's mystery that the lake now resembled a huge, glistening mirror. In that picturesque vision, they watched the radiance of another mystifying light appear on the surface of the mirror, as if it were a moving, white light. Some of them, not having been gifted to stay in the deeper ecstasy delights, began to feel the pangs of a worldly fear creep over them. In that cloud-like haze, coming out of ecstasy, they actually asked one another what that approaching light might be.

They were fearful and sensed that it was something powerful and real, and yet they were at a loss as to whether or not it was an omen of good or evil. One man thought they were seeing a ghost. In this semi-state of ecstasy, they were far more frightened as the light continued to approach than when they were helpless in the howling storm. They became rigid and immovable.

Presently, it looked as though the ghost-light would pass by the ship. Two of the men cried aloud in their fear that this mystery of light meant the end of the world. They became hysterical.

Then from out of the cloud-light all of the men—regardless of their depth of ecstasy—heard Jesus say, "Have courage, it is I. I am here to help you. Have you forgotten Me so soon? I am the Light of the world. Why do you fear Me when you see Me as Light instead of Man? The Father and I are One. He who sees Me sees the Father. Fear not."

The men were both startled and speechless. They watched as the dazzling, great light slowly diminished to the proportions of a man as it lingered about twenty feet from the ship. One man asked, "Can it be possible this Light is Jesus?"

The man to whom this question had been directed could not answer, but Simon—rising to his feet and leaning over the rail—spoke to the Light saying, "Jesus, if it be You, tell me to come to You over the water, for I believe nothing is impossible with You. I believe I heard Your voice. Speak again, Jesus."

The Master became visible to them. He seemed to have walked out of the cloud and smiling, He beckoned Simon, saying, "Come on, Simon. Come."

In the extravagance of God's grace, Simon climbed over the side of his ship and stood on the surface of the water. Noticing the smoothness of the lake upon which he stood, Simon smiled, and glancing at Jesus saw in vision's knowledge the deeper truths in the mystery of the water on the earth. The lake was no longer a body of liquid water, but was made up of individual drops of small and transparent bubbles that did not break as they rolled above or beneath one another. It was a sea of pearls! He was seeing the original beauty of the waters as they were in their dress of perfection before the fall of Adam. Now he understood that when man fell and the earth mourned, the seas wept and became liquid running water, and the individual drops merged into one another's individuality as if seeking consolation.

Each fragile pearl held in its lights the knowledge and the beauty of all the stars, sun, moon, and all the silver dawns and golden sunsets as they rolled and tumbled in rhythmical melody of tones capturing by the moment new light and beauty as time became lost in its own vastness.

Simon, watching this inconceivable mystery of color and beauty, marveled in the knowledge that came to him from earth's own story of its original perfection in which it was created. Ah, what a masterpiece! He took a step forward on this beautiful density of water, and then he heard the original hum of the sea, which became understandable language to the semi-sense of his body, "God, we praise Thee for creation. All glory to God!"

The uniqueness of such unspeakable knowledge was a shock to his soul because the sleep of ecstasy was less in its gifts, or he would have died from any further duration of such knowledge, and this caused him to feel a tinge of natural fear because of his unworthiness to be the recipient of such a gift. Because of this slight fear, he heard faintly the noise of the real, angry world, and he could see dimly the blackness of the sky's storm-tossed clouds above him. As he watched the sky as if he had never seen it before, he heard the sorrowful tones of the lake, in its reality, splashing its wrath against his feet crying, "C-r-u-c-i-f-y! C-r-u-c-i-f-y!"

Fear clutched at Simon's heart. He was coming quickly out of his state of ecstasy and its gifts of levitation that he had been enjoying by walking on the water. As he took another step in the direction of Jesus, he felt himself sinking into the swirling black water. As Simon reached toward Him, the Master caught hold of him and lifted him to his feet, saying, "Simon, why did you lose faith? I dislike fear. Remember with Me you can do all things. You must have greater faith, Simon."

Arm in arm they walked back to the boat. The crew immediately arose from their depths of ecstasy slumber and fell in worship at the Master's feet as He stepped into the ship. They all remembered—and without doubt—that they had seen Jesus and Simon walk side by side on the water of the lake. They exclaimed in their adoration, "Jesus, You are the Living Messiah. Oh, God-on-this-ship-with-us, forgive our former unbelief. Jesus, You are the Living Messiah!"

The Master asked them to pray with Him that the lake would stay in this state of calmness for the rest of the day. After a short period of rest and relaxation, the Master asked Simon to drop anchor near the shore. As He and the crew walked on the beach He bade them rest and wait, for He was not in any hurry, and He would take the time before sailing on to visit alone with His mother.

CHAPTER 5

The Last Hour

AFTER JESUS AND HIS MOTHER THANKED the keeper of the little house in the desert for her lodging and food, they walked back to the beach. On the way they found a warm, delightful cove with a dry sandbar upon which they could rest while they further discussed their problems, for the Master had told His mother He wanted this hour with her alone. Resting in the late afternoon sun they talked about coming events, such as the Living Bread that He would give at the Last Supper, and the crucifixion.

Jesus said, "O most illustrious mother, there are many important future events that I desire now to discuss with you. I trust you will take them into consideration for the future needs of My friends who will be born in the coming generations.

"There will be many great ages of faith as well as ages of great coldness to Me as I repose on the altars of time. In the generations of little faith you may participate as an active mother of the people by your personal appearance in apparitions, through which you may warn them of their neglect of Me in the tabernacle. However, before you take this active part I must have your consent. That is as necessary now as when you gave your will that allowed Me to be born into the world. To many people you will truly be the Gate of Heaven, for you will point the way, through apparitions, to the altar where I will live in silence and be imprisoned until the end of time. Rather than allow some people the risk of being lost without some warning that they should make haste and return to My love, it will be necessary for you to appear through the mystery of visions and reproach them for their little faith. The fear of the supernatural will always stir the human heart, whereas tradition and the written word may find its truths on the shelves of myths. There is no further need now for another John to introduce Me for I am here, and any new hope for the sinful, forgetful people will be through you. When I die the rest of time will be lifted to an intellectual knowledge of the supernatural, and both young and old will find it within their power to acquire the contemplative life. The world has no further need of prophets, for I have said that now each one must be his brother's keeper, or leader, which is to help one another attain the Kingship of being one with Me."

While Jesus talked, He allowed His mother the immediate gift of vision through which she could see all her future appearances in the world. One after another they unfolded before her eyes, as if time were but a fleeting moment. Then like a huge scroll coming to an end, Mother Mary gasped for breath as she watched the greatest apparition of all. Its magnitude and beauty were beyond human understanding and wisdom. The whole world seemed to be swallowed in the light of a golden vapor, which in no way bore any resemblance to the glow of the earthly sun. It resembled in its mystery of light a huge monstrance tipped over the earth in such a degree that the Host could be seen by everyone in the world. The center of the imaginary monstrance appeared to be above the nations of China and India. Thin vapors, like bead-like fire, rained upon the earth from the center of the golden light.

Millions of people saw that apparition, yet none were harmed nor frightened. Many bowed to the earth as they heard chords of heavenly music. Instantly, as if inspired, they prayed these words at once, "Mother of God, the possessor of God's ethereal sunshine, pray for us."

While Mother Mary watched the glorious light and the vision, Jesus said, "This apparition represents the Golden Age of Faith. This age will come into existence when the majority of My friends, instead of the minority, will have risen through the ascetical life to the contemplative. It will be in this glorious age that I will reign in royal victory through My indwelling in human hearts. Through real friends I will continue

My life of the Resurrection and bless the world with peace, which will last several hundreds of years. However, My special friends through the ages leading to this Golden Age will fully understand My words, 'If I be lifted up *in you* I will draw all things to Me.' I am the Prince of Peace, and therefore will give peace to the world in proportion to those who allow Me to continue the life of the Resurrection through them.

"The indwelling will begin to be practiced at the Last Supper, but few people, through the ages, will fully understand its depth and meaning until the era of the Golden Age is reached. I have asked My friends to follow Me all the way, and that does not mean that they will stop at the Crucifixion, for I will live on earth forty days after My Resurrection. I want My followers to live this part of My life also by allowing Me to dwell within them—which means that their bodies will be My other borrowed humanity.

"They can follow My death and yet live, for those words mean death to their senses in desiring even the thought of sin. By My burial they will come to understand they must be hidden from the world and must feel the sorrow of desolation, loneliness, and the slow attainment of disinterestedness in worldly pleasures. Then My Resurrection through them will be their living in the world according to the laws of vocations, knowing all the time that it is I who bless with My presence in and through them.

"The yellow race at the time of the Golden Age will offer Me love and victory over evil above all other ages and peoples of time. Many of My successors will be of that wonderful race, and they will put to flight many heresies that will spring up through misunderstandings and human unkindness in My Church. Following the Golden Age, ungoverned intellectual pride will slowly undermine peace, and faith will quickly crumble, bringing with it the end of time."

Mother Mary bowed before Jesus and kissed His feet, whispering her willing consent to appear in future apparitions according to His will for the good of the human race.

Jesus kissed her, and then as a surprise showed her the pearl that had fallen from John's lips. Together they smiled and listened to the beautiful music that seemed to come from its hidden depths. It was the same expressive music that she had heard when her Son was about to be born. Again it told her she would give new life, this time to souls in the ages to come through the gifts of her apparitions. She was joyous as she heard how the simple gem had played such a part in the drama of redemption by bringing many people back to God's Commandments instead of listening to the heresies of Herod.

Giving the pearl to her, Jesus said, "Perhaps in after years you will find a way to use this pearl in its mystical phenomena to some advantage. Do with it as you wish and also use your power to give My friends the help they need."

Mother Mary held the pearl tenderly, close to her heart, and said, "Jesus, give me a suggestion."

The Master answered, "Perhaps the original strand could be copied and used as prayer gems following the manner in which David prayed on his many-colored prayer stones as he sang the psalms. Or, you might give the story of the pearls to My friends and teach them to meditate on the stable, My birth, the swaddling clothes, or the general events of the day. And here is a suggestion that may give you joy: you could allow the musical tones that accompanied My birth to return to people through their prayer-stone replicas. All of this would be a means of teaching appreciation for holy and blessed objects, which will someday be know as sacramentals."

Mother Mary said, "Thank You, my Son, for the suggestions. I will find a way to bring all of Your ideas into use for Your honor and glory."

Jesus took His mother into His embrace and said quietly, "O illustrious mother, it is My desire, and one of My last earthly gifts to you, to tell and show you through vision the last Holy Sacrifice at the end of time and just how you will play a marvelous part in that solemn moment. You will then know the reason for your eternal title, Everlasting Tabernacle.

"The wonderful Golden Age of people living perfection will be made possible through the knowledge of the fires of My Heart. In many centuries from now, I will give—through private revelation—the greater meanings to the mysteries of My Heart which, of course, is My Father within Me. It is the only possible way for My Father's presence to be seen by the human eye and yet allow that person to live, for the prophets have said, 'No one shall see God and live.' But I have promised a few chosen souls on earth, and many to be born, a foretaste of Heaven while they live on earth, and any foretaste of Heaven is to actually see the Beatific Vision. To be favored with just a one-minute glance graces the soul with wonderful gifts of knowledge, understanding, wisdom, and love, which ordinarily could not exist in the human mind.

"The Father and I are One, and naturally it is My desire to scatter His fire (love) over the earth through the knowledge of My human heart. Little by little I will give this wonderful knowledge to a few favored friends, and even though it takes centuries they will work together as one in mind and purpose, giving to the world the beautiful steps that will lead to the world's last devotion, the Mystical Humanity.

"The Golden Age will have its evil hindrances too, however, for as long as time is time there will be two shepherds. Only at the last minute of time will there be One Shepherd—I will triumph! I am the Good Shepherd and the devil is the other. He will walk in great strides along with good people, and he will try in all manner of ways to overcome truth and faith by the wrong use of science and through educational laws that compel people to listen to worldly philosophers. But many times I will confound their intellectual powers when they try striking a deadly blow against the faithful by manifesting the simple gifts of God, such as fragrances and tonalities, which could be said to be Heaven's music. This great grace will make the faithful strong in defense of faith and My laws, for they will know that supernatural gifts cannot be tampered with in scientific analysis because faith knows no boundaries, and through faith people love the mysterious.

"Mother," Jesus continued, "the Golden Age, too, will die as every age of faith has risen and fallen, and this will continue until the end of time. As I have said, ungoverned intellectual pride will be its downfall and faith will quickly die. My indwelling in human hearts will become a legend, and a myth, to the people living in the last century. Those people who could have given Me a castle of light and rest through their heritage gifts through the faith of their fathers and did not, will cause Me to become a lonely pilgrim and a degraded outcast. I will be a lonely God then, as I am now, apparently alone. I am in the world and the people do not know Me because of their intellectual pride, which rationalizes the prophecies to mean that I should come in power, pomp, and wealth, and with all the honors of an earthly king. Little do they realize that My Kingdom is not of this world. The dangers of rationalizing without faith and the government of will in regard to the Commandments mars the mind in the same way as sunlight (not the true light) dims the depths of a beautiful night in its cloak of golden star-lamps scattered over the sky.

"As whole nations fall in the time of the Golden Age, the satanic powers of Hell will actually possess people and through them cause diabolical miracles to appear as God-given. Wars and terrible Church persecutions will take place all over the world. Both Church and people will suffer degradation until My followers, in small numbers resembling wandering gypsy bands, will mourn daily as they hear the news that another priest has become a martyr. Day by day My priests will become fewer in number until at the very last hour of time there will be only one living priest to represent the entire ideals and power of My Church.

Jesus and Mother Mary smiled through their tears at each other, and then rested for a moment in quiet musing about that last terrible day and hour that will come upon the world. Then Mother Mary asked, "Jesus, tell me about the very last hour of time."

The Master said, "Mother, evil will have so ruled the people up to that hour that the majority in whole nations will feel its effect over the world, and individually they will be uneasy and fearful. Their soul's intuition of pending fear will give them no rest, even though others will shout boldly and vivaciously of victory over the Church. A few will go so far as to wish for madness when they realize they have invited evil government by not voting against men who had no convictions about the existence of God. In their helplessness and fear, courage will fail them and they will not look for a priest, nor make their mind-intentions of hope known to their friends.

"During this time the atheistic leader will have only one aim in life, and that will be to completely defame and try to bring to nothing the promise that I shall give to My elect as we eat our last supper together. That promise will be, 'The gates of hell shall not prevail!'

"During the last hour, the atheistic soldiers will delight in their search for the one last priest. Through the latest scientific inventions, the complete world of people will know minute details in regard to this search. When his death is announced, a worldwide celebration, long planned, will supposedly begin with such hilarity and joy that history, even if it had the time, could not boast its equal.

"The majority of people in every nation will not be content to wait for the final word of victory, and they will march through the streets chanting that the powers of man have prevailed over My word. They will scream at the top of their voices that they have proved there is no God and therefore no Heaven, or Hell to worry them—they will believe themselves free to do as they please. Banners upon which are written the Ten Commandments will be burned in public demonstrations of that freedom. While this takes place a few soldiers will find the last priest—at the hour when he is beginning the last Sacrifice in his hiding place in a dark cave in the presence of a few faithful worshipers."

The Master stopped speaking, for sorrow had overcome Him. He sat quietly beside His mother. She whispered, "Blessed are the worshipers in any age of time who are not afraid to die for You."

CHAPTER 6

The Last Mass

WHILE THAT MOST EXTRAORDINARY TALK between Jesus and His mother regarding the last priest on earth took place, Mother Mary was enwrapped in an ecstasy where all the wisdom of God is ever-present. Her spiritual gaze beheld the actual scenes and events as they would be lived in the last hour of the world.

The general attitude and actions of the people displayed a great unrest. Happiness was gone from the face of the earth, and many groups who had the power of voice agreed that man in his greed and hate had destroyed the essential gifts that had brought happiness to their ancestors before these gifts were banished by godless leaders.

Now they would do anything to bring Christmas—with its story of Bethlehem—Easter, and other feasts back into their everyday living. They were convinced that only thus could peace of soul and joy be revived, even though they knew these feasts only as mythical subjects of historical interest. As they studied plans to restore them, they did not know that godlessness had destroyed time—that this was the last hour. They failed to realize that in the power of the priesthood rested the actual timing of the world. The priests, to whom the mystery of the Transubstantiation was entrusted, could bring Christ to the world at any hour, and from the altars He invisibly influenced the world, Heaven, people, time, death, and peace.

As Mother Mary watched that wonderful and most awesome apparition of the last hour, she knew intuitively that all the people in the world—except the few soldiers who were on their way to the cave where they hoped to kill the last priest—were caught up into the gifts of bilocation. Their actual sense of reasoning did not allow them time to understand this ecstatic condition. All government, business, the trials of home, nations, the sick, and the dying were ended for all time.

Suddenly they were invisibly present, and without crowding, in the small cave-church. In the semi-darkness they could see the priest who was vested and beginning the first prayers of the Sacrifice. They were awestruck by the supernatural effects of bilocation as semi-reasoning slowly returned—yet they could not act of themselves. Hundreds were frightened and filled with despair and called on the rocks of the cave to fall upon them and kill them. All seemed to have one mind—and somehow they recalled the story of Bethlehem—the cave in which they now found themselves being conductive to this thought and meditation. They were compelled to think about Jesus and of Christmas, and fear left them as long as they kept these thoughts in mind.

As the few soldiers entered the mouth of the cave they did not realize their vast invisible audience of silent bilocators about them. They voiced loud, vindictive expressions of victory for they had found the last priest's hiding place, and along with him his handful of faithful worshipers. They, too, were to be martyred.

A low ledge of rock protruded from the wall of the cave in front of the priest, and this formed a natural altar upon which reposed two lighted candles, an altar stone, a missal, and the chalice. Even though the priest, vested in green, heard their shouts of victory, he continued with the Sacrifice. The altar bells, rung by an old man serving as altar boy, tinkled low as the priest knelt in adoration before His God in the sacramental veils. As he raised the Sacred Host for public adoration, the soldiers fired. Slowly he slumped to the dirt floor, tenderly holding in his quivering hands the last Sacred Host on earth.

In that second of time the complete earth was hushed. A death-like calm of ecstasy swept over the few worshipers. Now they, too, were like the bilocated people watching a supernatural wonder. The Little White Host was no longer a Little White Host in appearance—it was aglow with God's Light, which resembled the noonday sun at rest in the cave.

In that deep hush of death and through the supernatural Light of the Host, the people could see Jesus, the High Priest, in His humanity, standing in the entrance to the cave, richly vested in the robes of a bishop. He, too, wore green. Slowly and deliberately He walked through the crowd toward the altar. Bowing to the holy body of the martyred priest He said aloud, "I have come to finish the Last Mass."

As the Golden Light dimmed in the Sacred Host, which still reposed in the dead priest's hand, the people gasped from both fear and delight, for there—kneeling beside him—was Mother Mary clothed in a green, satin-like gown that glistened with hundreds of diamonds and pearls. Gently she pillowed the priest's head in the curve of her arm, and with her other hand she gently unclasped his stiffening fingers from the last Sacred Host.

With great reverence, Mother Mary handed Jesus the Living Bread. Smiling, Jesus reached for the Gift from Heaven, and when it was in His Sacred Hands He turned to the altar. In the quietness of the cave every person could hear the last breaking of the Little White Host. In that intensified moment of wonderment and fear, each one watched a vision appear above the head of the Master—the actual scene of the real crucifixion that had taken place when He died on the Cross!

Jesus raised His eyes to the vision and pleaded with His Father to forgive the sins committed against His priests. As He prayed, the prayers of the people rose mystically with His, and were like the groaning sound of the sea as they all pleaded forgiveness and to be saved.

Turning to Mother Mary, Jesus gave a portion of the Host to her and miraculously it seemed to enter into her heart. At the same moment He said to the people, "I have said Heaven and earth will pass away, but My Word will not pass away. I am the *Word* John wrote about, and I am Life Everlasting!"

Then, pointing to His mother, He continued, "Behold thy mother. She is the Everlasting Tabernacle in which, and through which, I will live forever under the Accidents of Bread. The saints may see Me, the Living Bread, for all eternity through her heart when they recall how they were nurtured on earth by the living miracle, the Blessed Sacrament. My *Word* will not pass away with time when the world ends within the next few minutes!"

Mother Mary smiled tenderly on the frightened crowd, for they were afraid and amazed as they watched the glowing fire of God within her heart, which seemed to be as transparent crystal with many facets revealing all the fires of Heaven. They cried aloud again for mercy and forgiveness. Kindly, Mother Mary spoke to them. "I am your mother, too," she said. "I have not come to frighten you—be at peace." Then, looking at the fires rising from the Sacred Host within her heart she continued, "Look to His heart aflame within me. I am His mother and His tabernacle. Be at peace, and ask Him to forgive you. He is merciful."

Instantly, and as quickly as a bird takes flight, she ascended into the heavens. Clouds seemed to fold around her and the stars—symbols of Christ's saints—appeared as white doves flying around the world and centering about her as a halo of light in the eastern sky. As this light disappeared, all the stars dimmed and were to be seen no more. The heavens became a meaningless ugly depth of unfurling blackness throughout all space. This was intensified, by the moment, by loud, blasting sounds that brought roaring chaos to the world. The people watched the phenomena, which was now outside the governing laws of order.

In great fear they realized they no longer had the intercession of the saints to help them. Stunned, they looked to Jesus, Who said kindly, "You have no further need of My saints. I am with you. Their mission in life was to bring you to Me. Now they have gone with My mother into the heavenly spheres of My Father's Kingdom. You spurned their gifts and help because of your pride and indifference. You wanted to rule."

Turning to the altar He prayed aloud for them. They were afraid, and many groaned in spiritual and physical agony, which certain degrees of bilocation allow. Now they believed in Jesus as God on earth, His Church, His priests, His mother, the saints, and the existence of Hell.

Desperately trying anything for salvation, they sought to revive the dead priest by blowing breath into his lungs and by lifting and lowering his arms. Now they bitterly understood, and believed, the meaning of Confession and absolution according to the laws given to the Church by Jesus. They were as drowning people grasping at a straw. Others clung to the cold body of the priest, hoping and believing that when time was no longer time, being close to a martyr's body would be the means of grace that could earn their eternal salvation.

Slowly turning to the people, Jesus said as He lifted the chalice, "This is My Blood which was shed for you." He was finishing the Mass.

Tears glistened on His face as He lifted the chalice to His lips. While He drank of the Sacred Blood, as He had done at the Last Supper, the whole world was silent. This was a solemn goodbye to a wonderful memory and profound truth—this was the last chalice of His Sacred Blood on earth! Lowering it before He had completely consumed its contents, He said, "I am the Beginning and the End. Alpha and Omega. It is I who said the gates of Hell shall not prevail over My Kingdom on earth, the holy Church.

"My priests tried to tell you that one Sacrifice of the Mass was more powerful than all the combined powers of Hell, but you would not believe the invisible world, which is far more real than life. Neither would you believe the promise that I would not leave My priests and their flocks, orphans. Now that you have taken the life of My last living son, I have come to finish the last Mass for him as well as to bring the last moment of earthly time to an end. *This is the end of the world. You are witnessing the end of time!*"

The people cried fearfully for mercy and forgiveness as the Master stood holding the chalice, facing them. Extending His arm, He slowly tipped the cup toward the priest's body. Drop by drop His Blood poured over it as He said, "In the name of My Blood in this chalice, and for all the merit My Blood has brought to the world through the ages of time, I command the devils to be put to flight wherever they may be hidden in the world or in people."

Quickly, every evil power left the earth like wild animals falling over a precipice. This was the world's greatest exorcism. Now fearful sinners were free from any further temptations and evil promptings.

Face-to-face with Truth, the people wept and there was gnashing of teeth in remorse for their sins. They were so ashamed they wished they could hide even from Jesus—but where could they go? Their eyes fell once more on the dead priest—oh, if he would only live once more! They watched every second for a sign of life, and even shook his body again and again in an attempt to make him breathe. To whom could they turn for help? Science, national power, and greed were gone from their thoughts and grasp. The earth had even lost its laws of order, and any principle of action they could hope to use was lost. Yes, this was the end of time.

They heard the voice of Jesus as if it were the sound of a thousand seas, "Now there is only *one* fold and *one* Shepherd. For ages of time, My true followers have prayed and made sacrifices in order to gain this hour for Me—it is My hour of triumph. *One* fold and *one* Shepherd. Lucifer is no longer the other shepherd. The love and the sacrifices of My loyal followers have merited for you, My friends, complete forgiveness, for they believed this hour would come. It is their triumph for souls. Well they understood that this terrible last hour would be a severe purgation for those who lived in this generation. This hour has been your Purgatory; you have suffered in this hour what most penitents suffer for hundreds of years according to time in the city of Purgatory.

"You are saved from Hell because My friends believed all My words—and especially did they believe and understand that they were their brother's keeper. By practicing the love of denial and sacrifice for the good of others they became saviors of men. They understood through faith these words, 'If I be lifted up [in human tabernacles] I will draw all things to Me.' They allowed Me, through them, to continue My life of the Resurrection. I am the Resurrection—I was the new life I gave them to live before they were taken to sleep in death. Within a few minutes you will be with Me in My Eternal Kingdom. This earth, the sky above, and Purgatory will pass away forever within this hour."

A prayer of thanksgiving escaped from all the people as the Master finished speaking. Kneeling beside the dead priest's body, Jesus raised the stiffened arm, and with it He made the Sign of the Cross over the millions of people while He, Himself, said the words of Absolution, "*Ego vos absolve a peccatis vestris.*"

The people were stunned and silent. Returning to the altar, Jesus reached His right hand forward toward a burning candle and extinguished the flame. Now there was only one earthly light left in all the world—the one, low, burning candle on the altar. He was about to extinguish that also when He turned again to the people and said, "I have taught that you would be changed from this life to the other in a twinkling of an eye. When I extinguish this flame—that quickly will you be with Me in Heaven. But first let us pay homage to the world and watch its last moments in time."

A brilliant cloud of silver shone in the eastern sky, and with it came the sound of angels singing praises to God. Through the gift of this heavenly light the people could see the earth in all its depths and beauty. It was as though an artist's brush had spread its dew quickly across the canvas of time—covering, as it brushed in gentle strokes, the death of each animal and insect. Ferns, trees, shrubs, and flowers became frosted in death's white brilliance. The people thrilled as they heard through the great distances of the earth the last call of the mourning dove. In vision's gift of sight they watched the last dog raise his head and bark farewell. It was delightful to watch a purring kitten twist gently on his back in the dust and then pause and stretch again into his pleasing eternal sleep.

All of them smiled when they felt the last touch of the pines as they bent in the caressing breeze to say goodbye. Sparkling brooks and the splashing of fish in the rivers where they had frolicked threw a mist of tears across all human hearts—that was a sad goodbye. One by one the lights of the fireflies dimmed and died into calm blackness. Every person understood he, too, was saying goodbye to the elements that had served him as home.

Breathlessly they turned to the Master and seemed to whisper, "Take us, Lord." Jesus turned to the altar and said in prayer to millions of racing hearts, "Lo, the Mass is over. Come with Me."

He reached for the last flickering candle. Light and time were gone forever.

The cool evening breeze pushing through the cove seemed to awaken Jesus and Mother Mary from their ecstatic gifts regarding future events to the startling reality of the hour in which they lived. Smiling at each other, they rose and began to walk in silence toward Simon's ship on the lake.

BOOK FOUR

Mary of Magdala

CHAPTER 1

Jesus Comes to Bethany

SIGHS AND SUBDUED WEEPING came from the corner of a sunless room. That almost silent sorrow could only tell of a longing and a hope from the heart of a mother who offered each sigh and tear to God as pleading trust and penance for the reconversion of her daughter—the Mary of Magdala. Mary's mother was a little woman, frail in stature, wrinkled, and bent. Hourly she whispered her requests as she smoothed across her knee a handkerchief dampened with penitential tears. Even though she mourned and felt disgraced because of Mary's life, she firmly believed, and hoped, in the penance of pardon that John had taught her when she had met him in Magdala. Through willing penance she believed she would see the Living Messiah, and that He would show her Mary the paths of faith. Her hours of loneliness were heroic as day after day she prayed these words, "Oh, God, I praise Thee. O my God, though our hope in Thy coming to this earth, and even to this city, forgive my daughter, Mary."

Bethany had become a place of destination and hope for her because of John's prophecy, but Mary was no stranger here and she continued her boisterous and sinful life without interruption. Her careless way, her beauty, and her style of dress had all the effects of a dazzling, fiery torch upon the men. Their women reproached her only to back away frightened by her scurrilous attacks upon their ugliness, their lack of culture, and their poverty.

She also took delight in provoking Rachel by tauntingly accusing her of witchcraft because Rachel held to her conviction that heavenly music came from such things as pearls when she prayed. This brought about vicious quarrels. Without establishing peace, Rachel told Mary's mother goodbye and left for Jerusalem to search for her brother, whom she found several days later in a dungeon.

Mary, in a mood of fear that frequently came over her when she thought about Herod, now confided to her mother the terrible events of his palace, where she had actually seen John's severed head and had watched a pearl roll from his lips. Mary's mother listened kindly, and in an understanding view of her daughter's fright, wondered if her present life were not an escape from sorrow rather than a deliberate maliciousness of rejoicing in sin.

Mary was the symbol of evil and daring in Bethany. She became the town's example of glorifying evil among the young girls, and they looked up to her as their model in dress, actions, and a new freedom in life. Her name, and the fact that she was a former princess of Arabia converted to the Jewish faith, were topics of conversation for the passersby and the gossipers, as well.

Martha, Mary's younger sister, was a reserved, quiet girl who followed closely in the footsteps of her mother by sharing the sorrow of her sister's disgrace and in doing penance to God for her. She and her brother, Lazarus, in their daily visits to the synagogue where they often prayed for Mary, stopped often, either coming or going, to listen to a Man named Jesus. They loved to hear His answers as He replied to the questions of the people who gathered about Him. How eloquent was His voice and how kind He was. They marveled at His wisdom and His wonderful sense of humor, for He tried to make people smile. On several occasions they had even searched for Him when they heard He was in town.

One evening Martha shyly approached and asked Him to give her advice concerning her sister and her sorrowing mother. To her astonishment He addressed her by name as if He had always known her! He said, "Martha, I am glad you came to Me. Remember this. Before any petition rises to God for the needs of another person, it is necessary for you to have order and peace in your own soul. Be a doer of the word in deed as well as in thought. Practice peace, calmness, and patience at all times before you venture to help a relative or a friend. The laws of peace and calm in My Father's Kingdom, which is within you, are only accomplished by self-discipline, for the will of God, through motives and actions to overcome self-will, which is governed by the five senses. Find the love of God, above self, in all things."

"Martha, when you have become master in the government of your own soul, you will rest in My Father's embrace of love. All things you desire will be accomplished through that sublime way of the knowingness of love because you have asked for others rather than for yourself. Let Me assure you that God will not be outdone in generosity. You will share in the gifts of wisdom and love according to My Father's generosity when you are embraced in His love. That is the way to become saviors of men; you are your brother's keeper. Learn first this way of love and then ask for your sister's return to God and also for your mother's return of peace."

Martha realized as she listened that her soul had been unveiled and that she was face to face with Divine *truth*. She recognized faults that she had failed to see in herself before, and now in God's plan she wanted above everything in life to practice His way of perfection. It was wonderful to know He had a plan for everything in life! As she gazed into the eyes of Jesus she felt a deep, satisfying love come over her, and she felt certain this Man was the Messiah and not just a prophet.

She returned quietly to Lazarus, and on their way home she discussed with him the will of God in regard to the discipline and government of one's own soul. They resolved to help each other in their climb to perfection, and their hearts were filled with new hope for Mary. Later, they ardently professed their belief that Jesus was the real Living Messiah when they stood in their mother's presence.

Astonished and speechless, their mother wondered silently to herself, "Can this be the fulfillment of the hermit John's prophecy? Can this Man Jesus be the True Messiah?" Even though her heart was filled with expressions of hope, she kept the knowledge of John hidden within it. With great composure she expressed her desire to meet Jesus, and asked Lazarus to extend her invitation to Him, the next time He was in Bethany, to come for a meal and a visit before He returned to Jerusalem.

That evening, as they sat talking together, she reminded her two children that they should meditate very seriously about the great privilege that was theirs if this Jesus should be the real Messiah. She said, "Just think of the honor that will be ours! Why should we be so privileged as to have Him visit our home? If He accepts our invitation, we must try to realize that it is He whom the prophets longed and hoped for. But we must pray that we will not be deceived."

They trembled as they knelt to pray and to thank God for the age in which they lived, and they hoped that grace would lead them all to truth. The real significance of asking their Creator to visit their home in person, certainly a privilege beyond the intellect of man, made them afraid that they might not know how to act in His presence. Martha asked, "How shall we greet Him? What gesture should we make when He first enters through the patio gates? Should we fall on our knees and worship Him and if we do what will we say?"

And so the questions continued. "If we are convinced He is the Living Messiah, then what should we say in regard to confessing our belief? Would He be shocked to learn that we may have doubted His authenticity? We must remember that if He is God He knows even our most secret thoughts. Will it be proper to profess our beliefs?"

Lazarus said at length, "If He is the Messiah He will already know our belief. In fact, He should know what we are saying this very moment. Isn't it a sign of pride to try to figure out ways and means as to manners and words to be used when He arrives? Wouldn't it be better just to act naturally? If He is God He knows us as we are."

This logic was unanswerable. His mother led them in prayer to ask God to guide them to the knowledge of truth as to whether or not this Man, Jesus, was the real Messiah.

CHAPTER 2

The Eyes of a Little Boy

A WEEK LATER JESUS WAS A GUEST at the home of Martha and Lazarus and had dinner with them. The house was built in the form of a half circle about the large, central patio where grew a tall palm tree. The mother's room was at one end of the half-circle and Mary's at the far other end. Martha's quarters were next to the serving room and Lazarus had his room next to his mother. The kitchen was in the very center of the house and opened directly onto the patio, where meals were usually served. A huge gate of wood and iron closed off this patio from the street, which was within a few yards of it. Mary had refused to stay and meet the honored Guest. Because of her attitude, the evening was far more pleasant.

The mother became convinced, with her children, that Jesus was the Living Messiah. For the first time in her life she experienced peace, joy, and the knowledge of freedom. She listened eagerly to the Master's philosophy of hope and trust, which He taught them as He ate. For the first time in months she smiled and laughed with her family instead of sitting in silent mourning for her husband, or in sorrow for Mary's disgraceful life.

In the months that followed, Jesus came often to their home. He loved this holy family and often laughed, played, sang, or even wept with them all according to their moods.

On one occasion Martha asked Mary to eat with them and meet the wonderful God-Man. Mary raised her eyebrows and answered disdainfully, "Oh my fanatical family! The Lord deliver me from your wild opinions!" Then in a high-pitched voice she continued, "Martha, I have all the men I want at my command, and above all I wouldn't choose a common street preacher. Preachers are weaklings and filled with fear they just don't know life. Never mention Him to me again!"

With her slave she hurried out of the house, before Jesus arrived, to the home of a friend, a woman who both admired and lived Mary's way of life. Here, less than a half mile from her own home, she often made herself ready with fine robes, jewels, and scented body oils to meet an Arabian prince, a meeting as much against her mother's will as everything else she did. This prince had come in search of her, and finding her at last in Bethany wanted to marry her, take her back to her homeland, and reinstate her in the beliefs and traditions of her people. For months he had showered her with gifts—silks, jewels, Arabian horses, and slaves, most of which she kept at her friend's house. However, because she demanded it, one slave woman was permitted to stay in her room in her mother's home, but she never busied herself around the house or the patio.

In serving dinner to Jesus, Martha was always helped by a friend whose name was also Mary. This girl, both beautiful and good, was the same age as Martha and she loved sitting at the Master's feet just to listen to His voice, for in each word He spoke she found delight and awe-inspiring new worlds of thought. Often she was caught up into ecstatic slumber and appeared to be sleeping, or just resting at His feet, which often provoked Martha as she hurried preparations for dinner.

One day, after Jesus had visited the little family in Bethany, this Mary spoke to Mary of Magdala in these words, "You think you have met the greatest men in the world, but you should meet this Jesus. He is the most handsome man on earth—tall, dark, strong, and every inch a true man. He is not a weakling as you called Him just because He talks about the love of God. Let me tell you one thing: He is a Man your lustful eyes can't capture, for He will have nothing to do with loudness, or anything that takes away from refinement and modesty. Even though you are beautiful you are covered with trinkets that tell of nothing but vainness and lust!"

Raising her thin brows Mary sneered, "Oh, I could win Him if I wanted to; I've never failed yet. Tell me, does He ever quote poetry and speak of mythical pearls and of music that seems to come from them?"

Tossing her head as though she knew all the wisdom of the world, Mary of Magdala started for her room, feeling that she had cleverly placed a stumbling block in the path of the other Mary.

At first the other Mary was stunned, but before the boastful Mary could enter her room she said, "His words and His smile are not for everyone. To have heard His wonderful philosophy only once is to hold it in great respect. No, He does not speak frivolously about music or pearls. He has great respect for value and the beautiful things of the world. He has never mentioned jewelry and trinkets, which dazzle your eyes, but He does have the great power of knowing your most secret thoughts. People are His pearls and their thoughts His music. His great gift of knowing the human mind proves to me, without a doubt, that He is the Messiah. I think you had better meet Him; you may lose your soul if you refuse."

Mary of Magdala curled her lip in an expression of scorn and was about to answer when the calm Mary continued firmly, "Even you would fail in any gesture of dance, movement, or jest to make Him smile. His culture would put your Arabian prince to shame. His voice, when He speaks of Heaven, would cause you to tremble. The sound of His step would thrill you and make you want to follow Him. His eyes are dark and piercing and you cannot stand His gaze. He is like a physician finding the trouble within your soul. Either good or bad, He removes the cause by telling His friends to love Him and to follow the Commandments of Moses. He cures the blind and the lame. Mary, please meet Him. He would help you and I know you would return to the faith of your father."

Mary of Magdala stormed about the patio and swore she would have nothing to do with Martha's friends. Stamping her feet, she glared at the other Mary and screamed, "All Martha's friends are ultra-pious and reserved in prayer and poetry! That's not living!"

Poetry and prayer and speaking softly were impossible things to her, something that only angels understood, and certainly Mary of Magdala was not considered an angel by any of her friends. She told the other Mary sternly to mind her own way of life and to leave her alone. After all, someone had to enjoy the world and she had chosen her way. She loved riches and the comforts they brought her. Brushing the other Mary aside, she hurried to her room.

Within a few minutes, accompanied by her dark-skinned Arabian slave, she left the house in the direction of her friend's. As she hurried along the pavements in the road, an elderly woman shook her finger at her scornfully, saying, "Ah, beautiful creature of evil! You are the Mary of Magdala. So, you are the woman to be feared? Evil one, don't you realize that someday you, too, will be old and filled with memories? The thoughts of broken hearts will pierce your soul as if they were seething tongues of fires. You will find no rest, nor peace, unless you turn to God and the life of the Commandments. Then in agony death will come and you will see God. What account will you give then of your actions? Beauty of face and body will not be considered in the will of God. I pity you. Just today I was told you have reached your height of earthly achievement and that soon you will be married to a prince. An Arabian prince at your command! His wealth and the world at your feet, but what is that in the sight of God when He calls you in death? Remember, you cannot take any part of the earth with you, no not even the effects of earthly love.

"I cannot understand why you are so different from your sister, Martha. Why don't you follow her and sit at the feet of the greatest Man on earth? He is the Living Messiah, and you have Him in your home often while I am content just to see Him pass through your gates, but I understand He knows of my love for Him. I should realize that your sinful soul could not face Him, you would cringe at His gaze! Your prince may have wealth and jewels but the Living Messiah holds the key to your deaths. He will judge, therefore, who is the greater. This Jesus is the Messiah whom your own father worshiped. Follow your father in courage and be reconverted. He taught you the prophecies; have you forgotten them? He was not a fool!"

Mary was indignant that an old woman should so taunt her. Hurrying on, she thought to herself that, of course, she knew the prophecies, and anyone would know that her father was not a fool. She was angry and her intellect wounded.

The farther she went the more angry she became. "Since everyone is so sure this Man would not follow me," she thought, "perhaps it would be fun to capture Him. He's the impossible Man who is posing as the Messiah, is He? Why should I be scoffed at when He is the greater sinner? To capture Him would be a new game! And above all I would prove to Martha and that taunting old woman and the rest of this town that I can get any man I want. And if He is handsome well, why not try? It would be fun for everyone and I would unmask an impostor. Maybe if I did a public good like that people would think a little better of me."

After she arrived at her friend's house, she began quickly to make inquiries into the workings and the teachings of this Wonder Man. She asked her giggling friends, "Do you know if He has traveled with women other than His mother? Is it true He is the most handsome Man in all Jerusalem? Does He know the magic touch of silks, the lure of perfumes, and the power of a woman's smile?"

As she listened to their answers her interest grew. This whole thing would be quite a lark! She would dress as she had never dressed before in her best silks and jewels, and she knew she would capture this impossible Man. Then she would parade Him through the streets proving to everyone that false messiahs were still lurking among them.

Suddenly fear struck her. Quietly she said, "You know, I would never carry out this plan if I thought for one moment that He really is the Living Messiah. Somehow I don't think the God-Man would be swayed by smiles and luxury. But on the other hand, I am sure there never will be such a man! When I was younger I believed what my father taught me but during this last year I am not so sure there is any truth in the old prophecies. Perhaps the men who had visions of them were only dreaming which, of course, is what everyone thinks nowadays. Before I danced for Herod I believed everything my father told me, but when the Messiah did not come according to calendar time as we thought He would when we came from Arabia, I came to believe His reign is just another simple story made up in the mind of man."

Mary thought again of the old lady in the street, and she wondered why she had not silenced her, for generally speaking, people were afraid of her. And why did the old lady's piercing eyes frighten her? They didn't show anger nor malice. In fact, there was a certain kindness hidden in their stern depths. Where had she seen eyes like them before? With a start, she remembered a childhood incident in Arabia.

A small Boy had once looked at her with that same kind of understanding. It had haunted her and she had often found herself instinctively looking for eyes like them in other little boys and later, in men.

During the years in which she grew into womanhood, she had even searched for that Boy but had never found Him. If He were still alive He would be about thirty years of age. She wondered if she would recognize Him after all these years.

She smiled as she recalled more minutely that scene of her childhood. She had been about five years of age. With other children she was playing a game of crack-the-whip when a wonderful Jewish Child and His father arrived to buy an Arabian pony. The little Boy joined in the game and took her hand, which placed her at the end of the line. As the leader ran and brought the human whip into a quick swirl, she fell and skidded for some distance on the ground before the Jewish Boy ran to her side and helped her to brush the sand and dust from her skinned knees, elbows, and nose. He said gently, "Don't cry, I will help you. I'm sorry you fell."

Looking at her badly bruised and bleeding knee He went on, "Do you know that some day the God-Man will fall in the dust and His knees will bleed just like yours? I wonder who will brush the sand out of His scratches? Then He will be crucified on a cross and His feet and hands will bleed, too."

Mary remembered how she had shuddered. She recalled just how the Boy's eyes had searched into hers at that unforgettable moment. She said, "Who will crucify Him? How could anyone crucify God?"

The little Boy answered, "The Jews, His own people."

Mary said, "They wouldn't crucify Him if I were there. I wouldn't let them. To be crucified is terrible; I have heard stories about it."

The Boy dried her knee with the hem of His cloak. "The God-Man's knee will look just like yours," He said, "swollen and bruised when He hangs on the cross. I trust someone will be kind and wipe the sand and blood away."

Mary, with tears of pity in her eyes, answered, "If I am there I will do that for Him."

"You will be there," the little Boy said, and then hurried to His father, who was calling Him to come look at a pony.

All during the years of her younger life, Mary had asked her parents about the Jewish God Who would be crucified. She could not forget the vivid scene, which seemed to have appeared as a vision before her as the little Boy told her about the crucifixion. When her father traveled north, after that, he questioned the scribes and wisemen in regard to a God-Man Who would one day be crucified. His questioning mind and his philosophy, which taught him to defend honest conviction, led to his conversion at last to the Jewish faith. To escape disgrace and defeat from his own people, he fled from Arabia with his wife and three children and established their home in Galilee.

CHAPTER 3

The Preparation

MARY'S FRIENDS WERE AMUSED at her expressions as she thought about the Master. They could tell she was frightened, yet at the same time, shrewd and cunning, as she planned to capture the Miracle Man. They brought in others who might help unmask Him. How they laughed about His life of denials and poverty, details of which they learned from the general conversation of the people in the streets, who for the most part professed their firm belief that at last they had found the true Messiah. How they scoffed at the idea that anyone from Nazareth, and apparently knowing nothing but poverty, would dare claim that title. They believed the God-Man would have power over all people and have uncountable wealth at His command. He would also be the most cultured and diplomatic of persons, and would sit with the elect of the land, where He would teach the learned in the robes of a king. And this Man whom the people wanted because of a few miracles dared to preach in the streets as if He were selling Himself! Mary and her friends could not believe that God would stoop to such lowliness, and they raised their eyebrows at the thought of His life without women either to love or to marry.

Brazenly one woman said, "Poor Man, perhaps He has never heard the rustle of silk!"

Other women shook their heads slowly and pretended to weep as if they were paid mourners crying over His poverty and denials. All were convinced that it would be easy for Mary to lure Him into their way of life. Anyway, even if she should lose it would be worth a try. If she succeeded, she would be doing the country a favor.

The words, "Impostor, Messiah, Jesus," and other silent promptings within her heart, caused Mary some concern, for her knowledge of the prophets and the truth of their statements haunted her as she recalled how her father had schooled her in the new faith. Then her thoughts took an opposite turn, and she reasoned that surely this generation just could not be the age in which the Messiah would appear in person to the world. But what would she do if He did prove to be the real Messiah? As much as she disliked admitting the truth about Martha, she had to say that her judgment was not often wrong. These frightening thoughts about truth and their results caused great beads of perspiration to appear on her forehead.

She was both frightened and worried. How she wished she could back out of the whole scheme she had invented, but she would not allow her friends to laugh at her and chide her for being a coward. They noticed her concern and said, "Come, Mary, carry out your plans. It will be fun to watch the people as you lure this Man away from them!"

The following week Jesus came to Bethany. The Arabian prince also arrived, lavish in all his regal splendor, and he brought a great parade of servants, hoping surely to take Mary back to Arabia this time. With him came jewels, silks, slaves, dancers, and many Arabian horses.

Mary accepted both his proposal and his gifts and then told him about Jesus and of her plan to trap Him. She bragged of success. The prince entered into her plan wholeheartedly, and even suggested an elaborate parade, for he found pleasure in the thought of his coming bride placing herself thus before the public eye. She was indeed beautiful! Why, he would arrange an event that would startle the mind of man!

First would come trumpeters, followed by a hundred dancing slaves with castanets who would sing the Arabian wedding march. Then a long procession of marching slaves carrying love offerings of gold, rings, gems, incense, and tall vials of precious perfumes to be placed at the feet of Jesus. Last of all would come Mary, riding upon a white Arabian horse draped in gold brocades and crowned with emerald pom-poms. And alongside her horse would walk another saddled in full dress for Jesus. The prince was certain no man would turn his back on this fabulous display of wealth, or on the equally fabulous beauty of such a woman.

He laughed heartily, for he believed Jesus would not have a chance to keep His identity as God. Inwardly he sought revenge, for he was constantly reminded of Mary's father being a traitor to his faith and country, and he planned that if the Master did come away with them, he would have his slaves escort Him out of the city into the desert and there murder Him.

Word spread through the town of Mary's intentions, and when it was learned that Jesus was to be a guest at her mother's house upon a certain evening, excitement spread. Mary boasted tauntingly to Martha that she would show her feminine powers and win this Miracle Man. There was nothing she would like better than to prove that her sister and Lazarus had been duped.

Martha was afraid Mary would carry out her deliberate plan, and was tortured by the thought of Jesus being ridiculed and by the embarrassment it would bring upon her family. Suddenly she realized, with shame, how little she practiced and believed that the Kingdom of God was within her, and that God knew all things at all times. Reason taught her that embarrassment was the direct effect of deception and shallow learning when it was allowed in the thought to restrict God. How few people had learned that God was really everywhere and knew all things, even if He was only visibly present in the flesh of the Messiah.

Meanwhile, Mary's slaves and friends went to great lengths to prepare her for the meeting. Great foaming tubs of perfumed oils were poured into huge copper baths, in which she reposed for hours while her slaves patted incensed ointments into her delicate olive-colored flesh. After the bath, other hours were given to the styling of her hair, which was moistened with oil of roses brought from far distant Persian markets by the prince for his bride. Her curls and braids were held in place by gold pins formed into rings, and each was studded with an emerald and a pearl. Across her brow rested a crown of gold set with a band of dazzling emeralds. Hanging around her neck were long strands of white and black pearls. Her strapless gown was made of gold brocade and the long, sleek, shimmering skirt hung in long, narrow panels, which revealed her naked legs as she walked back and forth in dainty practice through her halls and rooms. She wanted to make sure her step was perfect in its rhythm and grace.

From her bare ankles to her knees coiled gold bracelets in the form of snakes with wide, glittering emerald eyes. Her sandals were made of gold and silver coins, and from the narrow ankle-straps dangled gold nuggets and tiny bells that tinkled as she pranced her dainty way. Restlessly she walked back and forth through her friend's patio gardens. She could hear the horses in the street stamping with impatience as they were led to their places in the procession.

Finally, the sound of trumpets announced that the parade was about to begin. The hundred slaves in front of Mary's horse, with their rhythmical castanets clicking and glittering in the sunlight, hummed the chant of the Arabian wedding march as Mary mounted her horse. She was on her way.

As Martha began to serve dinner, she was startled by the sound of the blaring trumpets as they came nearer and nearer. Jesus rested on a lounge near the table, which served as a chair during dinner according to the custom of the day. Hurrying to Him, and falling on her knees, Martha pleaded, "Jesus, hurry away, for I believe Mary is coming. She is carrying out her threat to try to win You to her way of life. With her will come all the townspeople, and they will watch what takes place and cause You great embarrassment. She has told me her plan. Hurry, Master, there is no time to lose. Leave here at once!"

Jesus answered quietly, "I am not going."

Martha continued her pleading, for she felt the Master did not understand His danger. "Surely," she said, "You do not realize the power my sister has over men. I have seen her sway the best of them. Please hurry away."

Jesus gazed into Martha's eyes, searching for a trace of trust instead of fear, and then said, "Martha, why are you so fearful? Do you not believe that I am the Son of God, and that I can do all things? Do you not know that it is I who created Mary, as well as you and that I have power over her? Do you not believe that I know her least action and desire? I know there is as much goodness and courage in her as you know of her evil and sin. Do you not realize that it is for Mary and for friends who follow in her way of life that I have come to be crucified that they may find the courage to correspond with grace and fight for salvation? I cannot interfere with free will, other than give them that gift which will help them find themselves. Just keep praying and she may recognize My gifts. Often My greatest possessions lie in people like Mary. That is why the devil has so blinded them in the wrong use of wealth and earthly power. Especially does he try to magnify the power of beauty in attractive women, which is often their downfall both in life and in death."

Martha was ashamed of her little faith. Now she realized she had not learned the very first principle of trust in God above everything else. She felt she had offended Jesus by asking Him to hurry away because she had not trusted in His wisdom and had further displeased Him in her efforts to boss Him.

Jesus reached forth His hand and patted her head as she knelt in shame and adoration before Him. He said, "Martha, always kneel beside Me as if you were a little child who trusts her parent without question. When Mary arrives, just sit here silently as if she were not present. Keep your mind occupied with Me."

The marching slaves with their noisy trumpets and castanets neared the patio gates. The white Arabian horses drew to a halt. Before Mary could dismount, hundreds of people pushed their way into the patio, and pressing close to the walls of the circling dining room, eagerly waited in huddled groups to see what would happen. Jesus said quietly to Mary's frightened mother, who sat directly across the table from Him, "My peace be with you. Look not up, nor about you, but proceed to eat as if we were alone. When Mary speaks to Me it is not for you to hear. Keep your head bowed in silent prayer. Help Me win her with your prayer of silence and obedience."

CHAPTER 4

The Meeting

MARY TREMBLED WITH EXCITEMENT as a slave helped her dismount from her horse. With great care and grace, she stepped upon a wide strip of gold brocade that had been unrolled upon the ground and stretched from the street through the patio gates of her home and up to the very table where Jesus reclined. A little afraid, yet coyly, she walked toward the Master, clicking her heels to draw His attention, and at the same time unwinding, with her right hand beautifully poised, a sheer scarf from her neck and shoulders. It fell, like a cloudy stream of gold, onto the brocade strip.

Jesus did not lift His eyes to welcome her nor did He give the slightest indication that her pomp and gestures attracted Him. He sipped His goblet of wine slowly and was silent.

As Mary drew closer, and when many other veils had been discarded prettily, and still Jesus did not notice her, her face flushed in embarrassment. She had not planned on this cold greeting, especially from her own family for they, too, took no notice of her. She was being ignored! This had never happened before. How dare they act so stupidly and in such an ill-mannered way as not to introduce her to Jesus? She regarded their bowed heads with disgust.

Finally, she could hold her poise of self-assurance no longer. With her hands on her hips, and tossing her head backward, she said rudely and loudly to Jesus, "It is the usual custom of my family to introduce me to their friends. In view of their stupidity I will tell You who I am. I am Mary of Magdala, the great Arabian dancer. Martha has told me about You and how You claim to be the Messiah!"

Everyone watched Jesus intently. Slowly He rose to His feet and faced Mary with a slight bow of recognition. With one glance of His understanding eyes He looked piercingly at her. Then He closed them tightly as though He had seen a dreadful horror.

His quick, shuddering expression frightened Mary and she remembered how horror-stricken she had been when she saw the severed head of John. That one glance from the Master had completely disarmed her. His eyes seemed to be the eyes of that little Boy who had helped her brush the sand from her own skinned knees so long ago in Arabia!

She shivered and fell back a step. "Can this be true? Can this be true?" she asked herself over and over. Backing still farther away, she whispered to herself, "Can this Man be God? Is He the Messiah? What have I done? Could I have been mistaken when I caught that quick glance of His eyes and thought I had seen them before? I must see them again, I must!"

She stood like a marble statue and Jesus broke the stillness by whispering to her, "Mary, My once lovely little friend, don't you know Me? Don't you believe My words that you will be with God when He dies on the cross? I have waited all these years for you, and now that I am here you are not ready to follow Me. I am He Who is to be crucified!

"Mary," he continued, "if you could only see what that other shepherd has done to your once beautiful soul. He has marred it completely. You are not the lovely creature that I would have you. Once you were adorned in beautiful bridal gowns of simple faith, not in these gowns of filth. My little playmate, Mary, I had to close My eyes on you because I could not bear to see your soul so clothed in hypocrisy. Why, just a few hours ago you trembled when you thought of Me and you hoped silently that you would not live to see My reign on earth. But here I am, downcast and sorrowful, standing before you."

Shock and dismay seized Mary as she continued to back away, but she froze as she realized this Jesus was speaking of her most recent secret fears and thoughts. Now she understood how, so long ago, He had known her childhood name without being told, and how He could speak her language so fluently. Why shouldn't He? He was the Child Messiah who knew everything. Why, she had been singularly blessed then even to see Him, and now look what she was doing!

She was afraid and astonished at the magnificent tone of His voice, which told of love and confidence in the very way in which He pronounced her name. She wanted to hear it again from His lips. Then she felt a terrible fear creep over her. "Just suppose at death," she thought, "I don't hear Him call my name? Suppose my judgment will be as silent as this moment for silence is between us now, and it is agony. Surely this is a symbol of judgment!"

The God-Man stood before her with His eyes closed, refusing to look upon her earthly beauty. The thought of her life made Mary cringe, and perspiration covered her body. Was her body not weeping as it faced Silent Truth?

Breathless and defeated, she glanced in a dazed manner at those about her, and then in a wild gesture of sudden pride she ran to Jesus. Frantically she whispered to Him, "Pretend! Pretend, Jesus, if nothing else pretend that You see and hear me. Save me from the laughter and scorn of the people. Another day I will come to You. I will leave Bethany and follow You. I believe You are the Messiah now, and I am sorry for my sins. What shall I do? Please save me from scorn. Pretend You see me. I am far more afraid of the people's wrath than Yours!"

Mystically the first choir of cowering devils known as "Pride" could be seen departing from her soul. Motionless and silent as stone, Jesus continued to stand before her as she looked wide-eyed at Him. After a few minutes, which seemed like years to her, He said, continuing to keep His eyes closed, "My little child, I pity your helplessness, but why do you care about the world and what people may say? Look at yourself and see what the world has paid you: gifts of silk and useless tinsel. You were at one time most beautiful before you became dazzled like a moth before a light. Your terrible sin of pride caused you to ask Me to be fickle, too. You have many slaves in this life, but it is a good thing you cannot see the servants of the devil who wait invisibly upon your least little whim. I keep them hidden from your eyes or you would despair. When you ask Me to pretend and act in your favor, you ask Me to compliment hypocrisy. Mary, I love you so much that far rather would I die on the cross than sin for you. It is as though you asked Me to die so that you may sin. No one with a spark of love and loyalty to his fellow men would dare make such a request. It goes against reason."

Mary's face paled. Could there be a truer love? Jesus' words, "I love you so much that far rather would I die on the cross than sin for you," reverberated through her soul. For a moment she thought she could answer, but stubborn devils who stayed within her reminded her memory of beauty, riches, esteem, and worldly love.

She stepped back, her eyes welling with tears, as she looked at Jesus. Her earlier training by her father taught her that the Messiah would come into the world to save sinners who had shunned the Ten Commandments. Certainly she was a sinner then, of the worst kind. Also, the truth that the God-Man would die for her shocked her!

Hiding her eyes with her jeweled fingers, she tried to compose herself as she thought how much she did not want to meet her Creator like this. She wanted to be pure and she wanted Jesus to be proud of her. She found envy in her heart for the purity of her sister. She suddenly felt she had lost everything, even eternal life. This was like sudden death coming upon a person who then had to stand face-to-face with the Messiah. It was too late to go to the high priest for a sin-offering in sacrifice for the deeds of her life. How she wished for some avenue of escape, even to be an infant again in her mother's arms! Sadly she wished she had never been born as she glanced toward her mother, who was in great anguish.

The spectators began to laugh and jeer as they saw pity appear upon her face. They called to her loudly, saying, "At last you have met a Man who dares to close His eyes on your beauty and to tell you of your ugliness and filth, which you have earned through sin!"

Others said, "Ask Him if He knows what you have done to our sons and husbands and about the sorrow you have brought into the homes of innocent children!"

In great anguish, Mary, torn between pride and humility, whispered to Jesus, "At least look at me and show my friends that You do acknowledge beauty and clothes. How can You despise magnificence when it was You who created the sun and the stars and all things beautiful? Please look at my adornments. Please do this for me and then I will throw them all away and follow You to the cross, for without a doubt I am the sinner whom You wished to save!"

Her acknowledgment that she would follow Him to the cross caused other choirs of evil angels to leave her soul. As they went she felt the terrible nakedness of her soul and she hated the nothingness of her life, as well as her meaningless friends who, a moment ago, had meant so much to her. She was ashamed she had asked Jesus to acknowledge clothes as a means of bribery. Now, in this moment of freedom from evil, she realized she would have to follow Him in perfect disinterestedness.

With His head bowed in sorrow and His eyes still closed to the shame of His creature before Him, the Master spoke kindly, "Little friend, would you have Me look on sin when I have seen your soul clothed so beautifully with trust and love for Me?"

Before Mary could answer, loud cheers arose from the onlookers, telling of her defeat. Again she was torn between pride and humility. Stepping close to Jesus, she raised her fists as though to strike Him, and cried frantically, "Jesus, open Your eyes to me, open them! I must see them again as further proof that You are the same person whom I met in Arabia when I was a little girl. I can tell only by Your eyes!"

Jesus did not move, nor did His eyes open. Exhausted and almost fainting, Mary sank down at His feet. She cried in bitter anguish, "Jesus, I must see Your eyes. Oh eyes of Jesus, eyes of the Boy Messiah, look down on me with mercy. Jesus, I am dying! What shall I do? Look, I am at Your feet. You are the Messiah in whom I know I will find hope!"

Tears glistened on the Master's face, yet He kept His eyes tightly closed. Kindly He said, "Mary, would you still have Me look on sin? I only wish to save you from greater shock and humiliation by not gazing at you. Try to understand that you would cringe at My look. Do penance, and then you will see Me as you desire."

His kind words pierced her soul. Devils fled from her, and for the first time she experienced freedom and new courage. She felt she could ask Jesus to allow her death instead of His. Now she understood that His tender words and merciful gaze were only for the pure in heart, and she suddenly wanted nothing because she had everything—she was at His feet. She had more than she deserved. Hadn't she heard Him speak kindly to her? He was the Living God on earth. Hope revived in her heart and love was made strong.

The Arabian prince, standing in the entrance to the patio, was deathly silent. The spectators were amused as well as amazed and wondered what Mary would do next. They asked one another, "Is her gesture of sorrow a part of her acting to win Jesus? Is she sincere? She is a clever girl, you know."

Weeping bitterly, Mary kissed the Master's feet, and then, going to the onlookers, she asked forgiveness from sorrowing mothers and loved ones whose hearts she had broken because of her sinful ways. Many women, in great grief and bitterness of soul toward her, merely shook their heads. They could not forgive. They laughed and made scornful remarks as Mary even kissed their feet and pleaded again and again for their forgiveness. She stormed their hearts sorrowfully, but to no avail. At last she took the heavily jeweled rings from her fingers and forced them into their hands, but they would not accept them. Instead, they threw them at the feet of the Master, saying, "If you think He is the Messiah, give everything to Him so that He may appease the wrath of God!"

Mary then knelt at the feet of other mothers, and these had the charity of heart to forgive her, and many of them also offered her a smile and a word of consolation. Seeing this, a number of others loudly proclaimed their immediate conversion to the Man Jesus and His teachings because they knew that no one but God, Himself, could have changed Mary from pride to such humility.

As though she could not bear His absence any longer, Mary hurried back to Jesus and again she begged Him to open His eyes. Calmly, He answered, "Mary, I desire to see you when you are clothed in the radiance of love through sacrifice and penance. Many of your ill-gotten jewels are here at my feet. Bring all your wages of sin to Me."

Mary quickly removed all other gems and trinkets from her body, and from her hair she took pearls and emerald pins and threw them all to the ground, where she tried to crush them beneath her heel as she breathed words of hate for sin. Her beautiful, auburn hair fell as a heavy cloak around her uncovered shoulders. As she knelt again before the Master, she reached to the table for a pitcher of water. Splashing this water over the dust-covered patio stones, she rubbed her hands into the thin dust-mud it made and smeared it over her hands and face as an outward sign of humility. Looking up at Jesus, she pleaded to be accepted now as a victim to His love.

Jesus did not answer.

Then she remembered that she still wore the famous serpent bracelets around her ankles. Tearing them off she hurled them to the floor. Going to the patio gate, she gave her slaves their freedom and ordered them to ride her Arabian horses into the desert and there turn them loose.

Her prince, in his white satins, gilt emblems, and heavily adorned headdress, confronted her. She was frightened and speechless as she looked into his slowly narrowing eyes. Cursing, he struck her viciously and scornfully across the face with his folded whip, making a deep laceration that marred her beauty for the rest of her life. In great pain she forced and commanded him, as well as the rest of the people, to leave the patio. In silence she locked the gate after them.

Trembling, she thought that this was like turning the pages of the book of life. Hurrying to her room she collected all of her silks, drapes, rich clothing—all her symbols of sin, and brought them back into the patio. Quickly she built a mountainous pyre and lighted it before Jesus. Kneeling, she watched the fire melt away the effects of her sins. Through the flames she looked at the closed eyes of Jesus. They did not open. Silently, her mother, Martha, and Lazarus left the table and went into their own rooms. She and Jesus were alone.

Jesus walked close to Mary's side and whispered into her heart, "Come, My Mary, come into My Heart, as you are now hidden in the prayer of quiet. Only through prayer will the Light of My Father in Me be shown to you while you live on earth. My joy is to have you capture My love, and understand My will, while you live on earth. I have come into the world hoping to enkindle many friends with the knowledge and wisdom of love. I have come to cast My fire[12] out upon the world."

While the Master spoke these words into her heart, Mary kept her eyes closed, transfixed in perfect joy in the Master. It was enough to feel the interior embrace of knowing He loved her.

Opening her eyes, she reached to touch the hem of His garment, but He drew back, saying, "Don't destroy the first fruits of the interior knowledge by touching Me. For a few days do not even search for My eyes; just keep the interior blessing of My love within you, for I dwell within your heart and walk and talk with you by the hour. I shall never leave you. You have already touched and delighted in the flames of My love."

12 The Beatific Vision.

While He spoke of the higher way of love, Mary spiritually saw His eyes in vision knowledge, as they had looked that day in Arabia when He was a child. That vision was all her spiritual eyes could stand.

Quietly, Jesus left the patio. Mary continued to kneel in prayer, trying to recapture the melody of His voice and the expression of His eyes.

As she listened to His receding footsteps, she thought to herself, "If the earthly sound of His step gives this marvelous delight to my soul, what must His Kingdom be where He is ever-present? It is no wonder that human senses, without transfiguration in the sense of knowledge, cannot enter there."

Mary loved the ecstatic gifts more than she loved Jesus' human nearness, for they were tastes of Heaven, beyond the mind of man, even though taught by the Master. The infusions were rays from His Kingdom.

Many ecstatic hours were hers as the night thinned into day. The embers of her sacrificial fire were cold and gray as the dawn crept over the patio wall. Mary's mother came and knelt beside her daughter, and happiness filled her heart. Then she helped Mary to bed and bathed her hands and poor, scarred face.

A few moments later Mary arose, troubled by a dream. She thought she had seen Jesus standing near her dressing table. There, on one shelf, reposed an alabaster box and many vials of priceless ointments and perfumes. She knew the dream was for a great purpose; the Master had shown her that she had not yet given all of her ill-gotten gifts to Him. Some she had overlooked.

With her mother's help she gathered all the vials together in the box and hurried into the streets in search of Jesus. While she hunted she was tempted to sell them and give the money to the poor. As she pondered the question, she noticed the little old lady who had scolded her a week before, smiling up at her. The old lady had seen the great sacrificial fire the preceding night through a grill in the patio gate, and thus understood Mary's problem. Also, she could see the alabaster box beneath her arm. Mary sobbed, and falling into the old lady's embrace, asked for advice.

The old lady said, "Mary, the real poor people would not want money from ill-gotten gifts. Far rather would they starve in the poverty God gave them. Hurry to Jesus, you will find Him, and give the box and ointments to Him. Bathe His feet with the perfumes and I am sure you will see His eyes, again."

BOOK FIVE

The Cross

CHAPTER 1

The First Holy Sacrifice

THE BANQUET ROOM where Jesus with His apostles and disciples had assembled for the Paschal dinner was a thirty-foot-square room on the second floor of a large building. A second-floor porch, ten feet deep, which was supported by tall, graceful pillars, surrounded it and was reached by a wide, gently ascending outside stairway that started at the front, angled across the side, and reached its destination at the back. At least one hundred and twenty-five disciples stood on this porch, from where they could view Jesus and His actions through floor-length, draped windows, even though they could not hear His words because of the noise in the street below, the size of the room, and the low tones in which the diners spoke.

Jesus and the twelve apostles were the only ones reclining at the table-benches. In a smaller room at one end of the banquet room, Mary, the mother of Jesus, and four other women busied themselves with the usual work of serving the dinner.

The huge U-shaped table, which was in the center of the room, was covered with spotless linen. The walking space inside the U was for the women to use as they served the meal, since the reclining benches took up much of the outside space. It was the custom of the day for guests at a feast to recline on lounge-benches at table level, and find ease with both elbows on the table. In this manner, men spent much time in the discussion of current events, and the reading of judicial and ecclesiastical laws.

Peter was at our Lord's right hand, and John, later known as the Beloved, was on His left at the head of the table. The other ten apostles occupied places on either side of the long U-shaped wings. Judas was next to John on the left wing side. He it was who had given directions as to where each apostle was to recline. Also, he called the women's attention when each course was to be served. Anxious in his watchful care, he checked from time to time to see if the food would last. The apostles had voted that he handle the purse with which the Paschal lamb and other foods were purchased.

Jesus was the guest of honor. A lamb, cooked whole, was before Him on a platter. He served it according to the Old Law's traditional custom, which consisted in breaking the meat loose from the backbone, with His fingers, and tearing thin shreds as far as the meat would hold in one piece. This was then rolled in a wild lettuce leaf and served. In this manner no one but the guest of honor ever touched the meat.

Jesus was kept busy serving other helpings to each apostle as fast as he consumed his lamb and lettuce. Judas grew nervous when he noticed the wild leaf lettuce had diminished before the lamb had been completely consumed, for they were to be eaten together. He hurried to the markets in the streets below and purchased more lettuce, also a sweet bread loaf, which was to be eaten later as a delicacy, for each piece would be dipped into a syrup mixture. This was known as the "Course of the dipping bread."

While the apostles ate they conversed about the old mystery of faith, which commanded them to sprinkle their doorposts with the blood of the lamb. This was an emblem and a sign for the Destroying Angel to pass over and not molest them. They talked also about the mystery of the unbroken bones of the lamb, which prophecy and tradition in the Old Law had taught them. They marveled at how generations of people had reverenced the ancient prophecy that the Messiah would be slaughtered as a lamb because of His love for man, and that not a bone in His Body would be broken. The guest of honor lived that symbolical tradition at every Paschal dinner by being most careful not to disturb, nor break, a bone in the lamb as he tore the meat away.

The apostles wondered, now that the Living Messiah was actually with them, whether or not this symbolic feast would continue. If not, who would give orders to the world that it was at an end? They did not realize, of course, that the Love Feast, the Mass, in another manner of sacrifice and holy banqueting, would continue every day until the end of time. Instead of the cooked lamb, people who would believe in the teachings of Jesus would have the privilege of consuming bread changed into His Flesh, and in that Little White Host (bread in appearance) they would see and have the undiminished extravagance of the Creator, the slaughtered, crucified Lamb of God always with them.

Mother Mary was dressed in a gray-colored gown, and over her head hung a long, thin, lighter-colored veil. She paused for a moment at the head of the table before Jesus, bowed slightly, and reached for the platter of unbroken bones. The other women cleared the rest of the table for the next serving, which would be the dipping of bread.

However, before this took place, Simon Peter noticed that Jesus reclined quietly on His couch and that He prayed silently. The big fisherman motioned for the others to be quiet. No one spoke as the women finished clearing the table.

After a few moments, the apostles began to whisper among themselves. "This would be a most opportune time," they said, "for Jesus to give us the Bread of Eternal Life that He has promised." The brothers, John and James, asked, "Do you think we should remind Him? It is seldom that we are all together like this, but do you think there will be another hour tonight for that great occasion?"

Andrew and Bartholomew grew pale as they discussed whether or not they would dare look upon the Living Bread from Heaven. Bartholomew said, "It is inconceivable to think that we may actually see something from there. I'm frightened even with the thought. I wonder what it will look like."

Andrew answered, "Let us pray, for I feel so ignorant on such sublime questions. God help us! Now that the hour is here I feel an utter loss of courage."

Jesus arose and removed His couch from the side of the table. He asked Peter to bid His mother bring His chalice from the kitchen along with a loaf of unleavened bread and a pitcher of wine. The big fisherman was joyous and his smile rapturous as he whispered to the apostle next to him, "This is the hour. God, make us worthy." Then he hurried to Mother Mary. Judas eyed his departure with envy. He wondered why Jesus had not asked him to get the chalice.

Jesus knelt facing the table after His mother brought the bread and wine to Him. With great care He placed the chalice and the small loaf of bread in front of Him. Raising His arms high above His head He formed the symbol of the Trinity by touching His fingertips together and slightly bending His elbows. Then He lowered His arms slowly, encircling the bread, and bowed His head to pray.

Electrifying silence filled the room. Mother Mary and the four women knelt close to the table. Fear touched these four women as they saw a beautiful descending light, or cloud-like mist, which seemed to envelop Jesus and the apostles. The ecstatic silence pained their ears. They were somewhat afraid of this new mystery before them, yet they felt secure in the presence of Jesus. Tears of gratitude and thanksgiving streamed down their faces as they reached out to touch Mother Mary, for she appeared quite unafraid. They did not know that she was quite accustomed to the phenomena of ecstasy and its light.

Near Jesus, and from out of the dense light, walked an angel in the appearance of a young man. He spoke to the apostles, and it was evident that no one else heard his message, unless, of course, Mother Mary did. He said, "Seek first the Kingdom of God and His justice and then all things will be given to the world."

Even though they did not realize it, Peter and the apostles were in states of rapture and ecstasy, and in that beautiful grace Peter spoke aloud. "O my fleeting soul," he said softly, "wherever you may be, either adrift in the world, or weakened through sin, awaken and make haste in your return to my heart. None of me must miss one word of the angel's tidings to the world. Hurry, O soul, for I would not have you miss the vision of the Master's love. Help me, O soul, to proclaim to everyone that this Jesus is the Christ. O soul of mine, do you realize that you are present in the Light of the Omnipresent God in Jesus? Hurry, soul, into your cell, my heart, and there love God above self and the wooings of time and its pleasures. Stay in my heart in obedience. See, the higher way is discipline and I will keep you a prisoner. Dare not venture forth for an evil thought, nor listen to idle gossip. Ah, soul of mine, you are God's prisoner! He wants you refined, tried, loved, and calmed by His way of perfection."

Peter sensed, for the first time, his true conversion in the Light of the wisdom that had just been given him. He stood dazed with the wonder and the meaning of his words. He looked again into the golden, cloud-like light, and then he realized that all the apostles had heard his pleading prayer and all had answered, "Amen." He could still feel the heavenly warmth within him that had motivated his colloquy of love, and he longed to continue basking in its enveloping embrace. It was wonderful! It was wonderful praying in this union with God!

For a few minutes he remained in that holy transfixion of ecstasy. In a moment of time the eyes of his soul saw Jesus in the full dress of a king acknowledging the angel's words. Instantly, as in God's way of vision in ecstasy, the transition of time was gone and the Divine King was once again Jesus as Peter knew Him, clothed in His brown, linen robes.

With Peter, several of the apostles then witnessed another rapturous delight, through which they saw the Messiah's clasped hands encircling the bread on the table. His hands appeared as though they were pierced and bleeding with a fusion of reddish light, which filled the room.

Suddenly the rapturous depths were over. All the apostles watched Jesus' countenance turn gray as in death, and as tears glistened on His face He said, "Become enlightened with wisdom, which can only be gained through prayer. You must have wisdom, through discipline, to understand My words, 'This is My Flesh, which you must eat in order to have life everlasting.' I came into the world with the hope that I may give you a foretaste of Heaven while you yet live in the flesh. When you eat and drink of this mystery that I will give, you will be putting on new, eternal life before death, and it will be I indwelling in you. It is I who will enkindle your clay nothingness into the Light of transfiguration. Then you will no longer be just potter's clay of little worth. You will be My children clothed in Light. My Father in Me, hidden from your sight, is Light. If you did not see My Body, as a temperer, shielding you from His glory, you would burn to a cinder. Therefore, I am the Light of the world, and I have come to give you My Father that you may grow in grace, become perfect, and resemble the light and glory of your first parents before their fall."

As the Master spoke these words, several of the apostles were caught up into another rapturous ecstasy, and there they understood the deeper meaning of His words. Their soul's eyes could see the loaf of bread on the table and how it was transfigured before them. It shone as though it were ablaze with a golden light. The knowledge of such a miracle dazed them and they bowed to the floor in adoration.

Slowly the vision faded and they relaxed in the beautiful silence of wisdom. They could find no words with which to express themselves. Jesus broke a small portion from the loaf, and cupping it in His hands, turned to Peter and said, "Simon Peter, take this, My Flesh, and eat."

Trembling and afraid, Peter raised his own cupped hands and received the Living Bread. He was dazed with the thought that here for the first time since creation, mere man was holding the Manna from Heaven. He was in such wonderment and fear that he seemed paralyzed and found great difficulty in lifting the Sacred Bread to his mouth.

He heard Jesus say tenderly, "Come now, Peter. My peace be with you. Eat, for I want you to share in life eternal. When you receive Me into your body that will graft us together as one. In the mystery of that great incorporated miracle you will become One with the Father as He and I are One."

Peter's eyes were fixed steadily on the face of his Master, and while he reposed in that gaze of peace, he consumed a part of the Sacred Bread. At that moment, because he was the head of God's great Church, it was quite necessary that he taste of all knowledge through the intuitive gifts of rapture, which taught him the holy truths of the God-Man's Nativity and the fulfillment of all ancient prophecies in regard to the mystery of the Virgin Birth. Through this mysterious gift, which breathes upon the soul in silence of thought, he understood why he and the other apostles had been graced with supernatural favors.

Well he understood the mystery of the Love Feast, and that it had lifted them out of actual time, for Jesus had not yet died, even though the breaking of the Bread depicted His death. It was an anticipated miracle so that they might understand that all is ever-present in the mind of God. With Him there is no time, nor is anything impossible.

While the ecstasy effects lasted over Peter's body, Jesus returned to the head of the table and broke off another piece of the Living Bread from the main loaf and gave it to John the Beloved. Then He gave a fragment to each of the other apostles, and they were gifted with different degrees of knowledge according to their needs and their degrees of grace, in proportion to their belief in the mystery before them.

Judas was the last to receive from the Hands of the Master. He awaited his turn wistfully and wondered just what had so appalled the other apostles. He was not favored with supernatural gifts because he had not repented of his sins and disciplined himself as had the others. He watched Jesus closely as He broke the Bread, but could see nothing out of the ordinary. He failed to understand why the other men had fallen to their knees in holy demonstrations of affection and adoration.

He rested his elbows on the table, and with his chin in his hands watched the proceedings arrogantly and disdainfully. All the events that were clothed in such mystery appeared a waste of time to him, and any kind of waiting was distasteful.

At last it was his turn. Kneeling, he feigned an act of humble adoration and obeyed Jesus immediately when he was told to eat. Without vision's restraint, or rapture, he placed the Bread into his mouth. Quickly he puckered his lips into a pout, disappointed that he did not feel any bodily reaction. Nor did he want to pray like the others in their surprising raptures.

He wondered whether or not he might be able to see anything on, or about, the Living Bread if he should look at it in a better light. He was determined to search for that which had so captivated the other apostles. With his eyes partly closed, he looked to see if anyone was watching him. Furtively, he quickly removed a portion of the Bread of Heaven from his mouth and placed it in his pocket. The other particle he swallowed.

As Jesus reclined once more on His bench, Judas mused about prayer and the beautiful Mary of Magdala, who had so captivated his thoughts ever since he had watched her bathe the Master's feet with her precious ointments. He wondered what she would do, or say, if she were present at a scene such as this. He remembered with hurt pride that she had not even noticed him when he had chided her about wastefulness. Why hadn't she sold her perfumes, if she no longer wanted them, and given the alms to the poor? He resolved that the next time he saw her he would speak to her again about it. Perhaps he would even be able to gain her friendship. His mind, filled with desire to win Mary, or any other beautiful woman for that matter, caused him to pay little attention to the Sublime Gift of God that he had just received.

After a moment of silent prayer and rest, Jesus broke other particles from the Sacred Loaf, and with great reverence carried them to His mother and to the other women as they knelt near the table. As these holy women received, they presented a scene of complete quiet and happiness.

Returning to His place, Jesus brushed the remaining crumbs from the table and consumed them, Himself. Touching Peter on the shoulder to awaken him, for he had fallen into deeper ecstasy, Jesus said, "Peter, awaken and eat the rest of the Sacred Particle that I have given you."

Slowly Peter's black, piercing eyes opened wide upon the visible Jesus standing before him, and he exclaimed, "Lord, I am not worthy, I am not worthy. Here, give this priceless gift to someone else."

"Courage, Peter," Jesus answered. "I have chosen you to eat at this Love Feast with Me. Try again."

"At Your command, Master, I can do anything," Peter said, and consumed the Host.

John, too, lamented his sins, saying, "Lord, I am not worthy."

"Take Me into your heart, John," Jesus told him. "There is no other way if you follow Me. We must become incorporated in Oneness. Fear not any condemnation, for I will only give you love."

John quietly obeyed.

Turning to the great Matthew, Jesus whispered kindly, "Wake up, Matthew. Take Me into your heart. I want to be your prisoner."

Thomas, the next apostle in turn, had risen to his feet and as Jesus approached, said lamenting, "Lord, tell me what to do. I know the baseness of my soul and I tremble from fear. I am not worthy to eat the Bread of Life. Allow me to give it to someone else—perhaps to an innocent child."

Jesus touched the trembling Thomas and guided his tremulous hand with the Sacred Host to his lips. Thomas obeyed and then put his head on the Master's shoulder and wept tears of joy and thanksgiving.

Within a few minutes Jesus had consoled and comforted the other apostles in their different moods of sadness, fear, and joy. All the while Judas watched and listened and wondered at their deep emotions. Why in the world should these men weep?

CHAPTER 2

Consecration of the Wine

THE UPPER ROOM WAS STILL. For a few minutes Jesus and the apostles lounged on the benches, allowing their thoughts to dwell on praise and thanksgiving. From time to time the men glanced eagerly at the beautiful chalice, in front of the Master, which was decorated with an array of jewels set in high relief carvings of gold. Some of the jewels had been given to Mother Mary and Joseph by the Magi, and it was Mother Mary who had had a craftsman set them into the chalice wall as a remembrance.

Rising, and without saying a word, Jesus smiled at the apostles, and taking the chalice into His hand He poured wine into it. Then extending His arm in a gesture of welcome to them, He said, "This is My Blood."

Jesus sipped of the Sacred Sacrament and continued, "All of you drink of this, for this is My Blood of the new covenant, which is being shed for many unto the forgiveness of sins. But I say to you, I will not drink henceforth of this fruit of the vine until that day when I shall drink it anew with you in the Kingdom of My Father."

He handed the chalice to Peter.

Peter was about to drink when he was caught up into ecstasy, and there before the eyes of his soul he beheld Jesus in all His majesty as King. He knew, through the gifts of intuitive knowledge, that most of the other apostles were seeing the same vision.

The vision disappeared, and Peter heard the kind, coaxing voice of Jesus saying, "Drink, Peter, we have no time to lose."

Peter answered fearfully, "Help me, Master. Now that I have seen Thy majesty in all the Light of Thy glory a second time within the hour, I am far more afraid of my unworthiness. Help me!"

Jesus answered, "It is My love for you that compels Me to ask for your obedience."

After Peter had sipped, Jesus took the chalice and, walking around the table, poured the Sacred Blood, in equal portions, into wooden saucers, which were before each man. Then He gave the chalice to His mother, who drank and passed it to the other women. The Master drank the last few drops, Himself.

As if they were one, eleven frightened apostles looked at Jesus; they were afraid to lift their saucers. But not so with Judas. He was very troubled and showed signs of great nervousness. His mind was filled with questions, which brought a look of pity from the Master's eyes as He glanced toward him.

Smiling at the apostles, Jesus said, "Drink now of My Blood, which I have given you."

Like frightened little children, some of the apostles obeyed quickly and then came and knelt in a circle around Jesus. Those who could not drink held the saucers in their trembling hands and looked pleadingly at the Messiah. Bending over one apostle, the Master took his saucer and placed it gently to his lips, saying, "Do not be afraid. I will help you."

Andrew was as pale as death, and leaning toward Peter, he whispered, "God help us! Are we dreaming? Is this true?" Tears streamed down his face as he, too, slowly obeyed the Master's command.

Jesus touched at Andrew's tears with the hem of His cloak and answered the question he had directed at Simon. "Andrew," He said, "you are not dreaming. The drama and events most dear to the ancients are now fulfilled in this, the Living Bread of Heaven, which you have eaten. Praise the ancients because of their holy longing to have this privilege that you have had. Andrew, you and I are One with the Father. I have multiplied you as I did the loaves and fishes." He looked at all the apostles. "I have made you My priests, other Christs."

Thaddeus, holding his saucer toward the Master, pleaded, "Forgive me my sins. Allow me to take the saucer filled with Thy Blood to my home.

There in silence before Thy eternal Self I will make reparation according to the laws of John's life of penance. Allow me to make myself worthy of this sublime Sacrament. As I am, I am not ready, I am not worthy."

Without answering, Jesus helped him drink.

James, sitting on the floor in complete abjection to thoughts of self, held his saucer in front of him, and gazing in adoration upon the Sacred Blood recalled aloud his sins, one by one. He wept bitterly, saying as his tears fell into the saucer, "Lord, I know You have made a mistake in choosing me to be another Christ."

The Master answered kindly, "James, come, discipline your will to Mine. I chose well, but I cannot, and will not, go against your free will. Come, I plead for obedience."

More like a frightened child than a willfully disobedient one, James replied, "Master, I am Your most unworthy servant. How can I be another Christ? Lord, my body would contaminate Yours in our union together. I am so afraid. I am not worthy to allow Thy presence to pass into this ugly and sinful body of mine."

Jesus helped him press the saucer to his lips and said, "You love Me, James? Then cease with your fears when I have commanded you to believe that I have chosen well."

The Master moved on and stood before Judas, who knelt with the others. Jesus was about to speak when Judas quickly drank the heavenly Gift without question, or without showing, or feeling, the least sorrow for sin. He then arose and left the room hurriedly. The other apostles were so busy asking questions and praising Jesus that they hardly noticed his departure.

Mother Mary noticed it, however, and she knelt quickly in prayer, asking that he have the courage to return.

Jesus began to speak, and the apostles heard that it was necessary for them to learn of His Nativity and kingship through the singular and particular gifts of actual and intellectual vision, for they had not yet been gifted with the silent teachings of invisible Light of the Holy Spirit. The visions and the knowledge they had received that evening would fortify them with hope and courage in their divine calling until the Paraclete came upon them.

Then, speaking quietly, Jesus told them His crucifixion would take place the next day.

The miracle of the holy anticipated Mass, or Love Feast, was over. But before they left the banquet room they remembered they had not yet observed the last symbolic action that foretold the Resurrection of the Messiah. Its tradition recalled beautifully the ancient prophet's words of Christ, "My delights are to be with the children of men." A bowl of thick syrup had already been placed in front of Jesus on the table, and now each one dipped a piece of sweetened bread into it as the Master passed it along. As this bread was eaten, Jesus raised a chalice of wine and offered a toast of thanksgiving to the Eternal Father, another ancient tradition. He then sipped the wine, and handed the chalice to the others who, in turn, poured a small portion into the wooden saucers yet before them. After they drank to the toast, Jesus consumed what was left in the chalice.

During the eating of the bread and the sipping of the wine, they talked of the forty days in the desert and of the beautiful temple John had built. Jesus told about little hidden details in regard to the Baptizer's holy life, death, and mystical burial. Lastly, He asked Peter to give a talk on the details of John's island tabernacle.

Judas hurried along the street toward a house some two blocks away, where a group of his friends were holding a party. He could hardly wait to tell them about the Paschal dinner. He knew it would furnish them with an interesting bit of gossip and fun.

The night was flooded with the golden haze of a beautiful full moon. Judas stopped for a moment and admired the majesty of the night, for he loved beauty. He remembered the piece of Bread in his pocket and that he wanted to examine it more carefully alone and in a good light. Taking it from his cloak he turned it slowly in his hand and observed it closely. It still looked just like an ordinary piece of bread to him. Shaking his head in wonderment, he recalled how the other apostles had knelt in states of awe and fear.

Returning the Bread to his pocket, Judas thought sneeringly of the Master. "Surely," he said to himself, "this Jesus must be an impostor. Mary of Magdala once believed He was not the true Messiah. Perhaps it was His kindly manner that had won her over after all." His mind shifted. "What was it He said about the Melchizedek priests? Why, that we are to follow their order in the ritual of sacrifice. Well then, if this Bread in my pocket is nothing but bread it will convince the world, when it becomes known, that Melchizedek's sacrifice was also a feigned act of worship."

He neared his destination, his thoughts still skipping from one subject to another. He was now prepared to swear that Jesus was an acknowledger of the ancient rite, which in those days had become nothing but a myth. He could even magnify Mary Magdala's act of belief and perhaps make her come over to him! It would be just punishment for her, for hadn't she ignored him completely when she bathed the feet of Jesus?

Judas smiled at his clever analysis of the situation and hurried into the house where the party was in progress. He would use this Bread to good advantage!

Instantly he was surrounded by women who asked him, "Where have you been, Judas—haven't you missed us? Why didn't you hurry? What about this Jesus Who keeps you away from us? Who is He? The night is nearly gone and the party is well spent."

Judas boasted, "I have been to another kind of party, a boring religious banquet. You wouldn't believe its piety possible in this cultured age of free thinking. I would much rather be here, believe me. But I am under obligation as a civic duty to be there. I'll hurry it to an end and then we can have the rest of the night together. Many of you are Gentiles and you don't come under the law, which I no longer believe. You can prolong the party as long as you wish."

Gulping wine from a huge goblet, Judas began to talk and dramatize, with willful jesting, the beautiful happenings of the Last Supper. With boisterous contempt he feigned a weeping act in order to prove his sadness of heart in being taken in by an impostor. Then in his analytical way, he told them that anyone would naturally expect the Manna, which the true Messiah was to bring from Heaven, to be different in appearance from common bread. Human reason would prove that. His friends applauded his conclusions loudly.

In order to prove his words, Judas took the Real Living Bread from his pocket and allowed each person in the room, twenty-five, to handle and laugh at the Precious Gift. He told them that Jesus had said it was His Body, and they all agreed that it looked only like ordinary bread. In complete accord, they decided that in order for them to believe in the Living Manna, it must first take upon itself a phenomenal expression of Heaven, such as a golden light, or warmth.

The screams of laughter were long and loud as Judas burlesqued the beautiful gestures of Jesus kneeling at the table and the actions of the other few chosen men who "pretended" to be carried away in ecstasy. Judas pointed out that even Peter, the thinker, of all people, had feigned adoration and appeared to have seen a heavenly ghost!

Lastly, he told them this was the great hour that past generations and religious fanatics had looked forward to seeing. He made a mock face of sorrow and pointed out the disappointment Jesus had brought. Holding the Sacred Bread high above his head, he pretended to weep. Then he dropped it into his pocket once more and promised, "I have to go back now, but I'll return here as soon as the dinner is over. I'll tell you everything that happens."

One man said as he left, "Hurry back, Judas. This is the best party we've ever had!"

Peter was just ending his talk about John and his beautiful island synagogue, when Judas re-entered the upper room and slid into his place at the table. He began to dip the sweetened bread with Jesus and the apostles as though he had not been absent at all.

One of the apostles asked, "How are we going to conduct ourselves at the hour of the crucifixion?"

Jesus dipped His last crust into the syrup and answered, "My friends, I do not speak of all of you, but . . . (here His voice sounded broken as though He were in great sorrow) . . . that the Scriptures may be fulfilled, he who eats bread with Me has already sinned against Me, and one of you at this table will betray Me."

The apostles dropped their crusts of bread, and in a stunned manner looked at one another with silent, questioning expressions. As though not believing what he had heard, one apostle pointed to his heart and asked, "Lord, is it I? Tell me if I have sinned, or that I will sin against Thee, and I'll confess and beg to be humbled by Your hand."

Andrew, half standing from shock, gasped, "Lord, is it I? God save us from that terrible sin!"

Judas, in a petulant mood, and with an expression of indifference, feigned to be particularly devoted to the Master, and drawing near to Him whispered, "Is it I, Rabbi?" He used the word "Rabbi" mockingly. The apostles had always addressed Jesus by the titles of "Lord,"

"Master," or "Jesus," but, in his sin of pride, Judas would be different and thus deviate from the usual custom.

Jesus leaned toward him and answered quietly, "Thou hast said it. Do what you are going to do quickly."

The other apostles heard only the low whispering and simply assumed that the Master had asked Judas to purchase more syrup because some of them had only partially eaten their crusts, and it was the custom that both bread and syrup be consumed together by the end of the meal.

Throwing his cloak tightly around him, Judas again left the room. He was suddenly afraid with the knowledge that Jesus already knew of his sins, but then he began to question whether or not he had heard correctly. He shuddered with the thought that he had told his friends about the Living Bread. Perhaps he should not have done that.

Shrugging his shoulders, he thought, "How could Jesus know that I betrayed the events of the Paschal dinner and His words? I know He didn't leave the banquet room. Is it possible He can read minds? There are some people in the world who claim to be able to accomplish that feat. Did He know I have the Blessed Bread in my pocket? Surely, if He had known, He would have asked for it."

He stilled his troubled conscience quickly by remembering how his friends had cheered him. He also found consolation in the thought that it would be necessary for the Living Bread to bear some resemblance to life in order for him to believe in it.

Judas was a weak character who wanted attention and sympathy. He was also easily angered. Now his pride was crushed because Jesus had not taken him into His embrace and flattered him, as Judas thought He had done with the others. His smoldering, crushed pride turned to revenge. By the time he reached the house where the party was being held, he flamed with anger.

When the drunken party-guests caught sight of him, they begged him again to re-enact the Paschal dinner. Their laughter was loud and coarse. Judas answered sneeringly, "This Jesus, who claims to be your God, surely put on an act tonight. He had every one of the men He calls His apostles on their knees. His acting was nothing but the height of superstition and sentimentality! I merely watched in order to reject openly His belief that He is God. I'll never forget how He said,

'This is My Body!' Imagine! There He was, actually posing as the God-Man, and at one and the same time holding God in the Living Bread. Of course, we thinking people know this is not possible, and I'm sure the ancients would not believe Him, either. Why, He would have all of you austere, and long-faced, from the way His chosen men were behaving tonight. And the way Peter acts would make you laugh, for he knows better. We have esteemed his intelligence and decisions for a long time. What kind of power does this man Jesus have over him?"

While Judas talked, one of the women in the party was told, in a low tone by her husband, that they could get a reward from Caiphas if they disclosed where Jesus and His men were. This news was whispered to the other guests, and it was not long before they all agreed they should share in the money. The husband hurried from the house and ran toward the palace of Caiphas while the others kept the party in progress, not telling Judas what was transpiring.

CHAPTER 3

Peter's Hands

AS JUDAS ENTERTAINED THE PEOPLE at the party by telling them of the Love Feast, the Master and His apostles lingered in the upper room. The apostles noticed that the expression upon the Master's face was sorrowful and they knelt beside the table, folded their hands, and in silence prayed together as they looked at Him.

Peter's eyes fell upon the Master's exquisite hands. This was the first time he had noticed their extra fineness, and yet how strong and firm they were, and how beautifully clean and well kept. He thought, "O Lord, now that I am another You, I must make my hands resemble Yours. Look, O spirit of mine, how clean His hands are kept and look at mine, sea-worn, rough, and grimy. Hands, you must become like His.

"Just think, O spirit of me, these hands will hold the Sacred Body of God crucified, and clasp the chalice filled with His own Sacred Blood. And in moments when God possesses me, He will speak through these lips of mine these words, 'This is My Body,' and 'This is My Blood.'"

In deeper thought, Peter continued as he watched the Master's hands clasped in prayer, "O spirit of me, to think the power and gift of transubstantiation is ours on earth and that it begins through us, today. The thought alone leaves me breathless and afraid. What a mission, O God, You have given me. Match it with courage and trust, and make my hands like Yours. Spirit of me, I am about to die in the knowledge of my weak nothingness at such a miracle and holy truth!

"Ah, rough, calloused hands, He has placed a great gift upon thee. Help me, spirit of me in thy free will, to make this body worthy of His sublime care and possession."

For a moment Peter was shocked upon looking at his brown hands on the spotless linen. He felt an enveloping shame creep over him as he recognized his own stupidity for having neglected the neatness, cleanliness, and order of his body, especially when he was in the very presence of God. To think he had been near the Master all these weeks and had failed to copy His manner and culture in life! Slowly he hid his hands beneath the hanging fold of the table linen.

For a moment his soul was graced with divine wisdom in a colloquy, which re-echoed into words from his heart. Quietly his soul breathed aloud, "How far, O body of mine, and especially these brown, ugly hands, art thou from the Master's likeness. How far, O sinfulness of the world, hast thou taken me from God? To think that I am in the presence of God makes me shudder at my unkemptness. I should have thought of this embarrassment before this stark moment of reality, for we must believe that we are always in the presence of God. Can we ever leave Him? Can we ever say that He does not know where we are, and what we are thinking?

"Ah, holy chalices of time, I am the first in this era to call upon thy contents, His Sacred Blood, to understand my frailty and cleanse me into His likeness. Look, angel, caretaker of the chalice who will meet the Master in the garden, see my ugly, unkempt hands. Pour His blood in drops across my gnarled, calloused fingers that they may glisten with His jewels, for I must have some part of His hand-likeness.

"Ah, Humanity of God, take these hands of mine and cleanse their ugliness made repulsive through sin in the fountain of angelic purity. And cleanse my human nature, now tarnished with sin, to show forth Thy invisible living Humanity in this my substance of potter's clay. Ah, unspeakable God, govern me, humble me, and cleanse me, step by step, in Thy way of love. Make me less of self and more of Thee while I live on earth. Make these hands like Thine."

Peter's interior self felt the affections of God's grace fall upon his soul as if it were a cloak, and in that gesture that was quietness itself, he became aware of his soul's interior peace. Slowly he lifted his hands from beneath the table linen.

His hands clasped, as a person does in prayer, he slid them slowly close to the Master's hands and prayed silently, "O hands, calloused, ugly, and brown, you are the cause of great embarrassment to me as I hold you close to the God-Man's magnificent hands. However, your ugliness and former earthly strength will no longer cause me such feelings of distress of conscience and self-conceit. For, O hands, He has chosen you as instruments of redemption and peace.

"O ugliest of my possessions, you are now His to do with as He wills. You are the hands of God! Just think, He has exalted you and He will lift you daily into the Kingdom of His invisible love. O hands, hold steadfast to your ecstasy of love in your flights with Him when He comes within me to say, 'This is My Body, and This is My Blood.'

"O hands, even though He has not said so in so many words, you are graced with golden gauntlets, the symbol of true love. How could you ever return after this hour to the impulses of any earthly desire? May your calluses remind you of the gauntlets that only you and I realize are symbolic truths. May the hardness of tired skin become beautiful for Him, and cease from ever giving me, these earthly moods of mine, the desire to do anything for myself. May you be solely the Master's hands.

"Thank You, God, for what You have given me. Thank You for choosing these ugly hands for Your instruments to bring You from Heaven's throne. Thank You, God, for allowing these hands to know the mystery of unlocking Heaven and linking its Light to earth."

At this instant the Master and Peter exchanged understanding glances. They loved being loved.

Jesus arose, and addressing the apostles, said, "It is time for us to depart from this room. The night ahead is filled with both sadness and adventure. You may merit for yourselves and for My Church as you wish, through the wisdom and the knowledge I have taught you. Remember that I would have you fearless above everything else at this hour, for time is changing its course in the mind of God. It is His will that the face of the earth be renewed through you.

"There is nothing to fear even if you are put to death for My sake, for the shroud of My Father will encircle you with the sweetness of calm silence. I am the Shepherd and I will lead you through the valley of tears. I will not leave you orphans. Death will come to you in many ways. It is better that you do not know the hour, nor the instruments of torture that will be brought to bear upon you as I know of My hour and crucifixion. I spare you that in the mercy of My love, but remember that death in any form is just a passing of sorrow into happiness. Be courageous, come now, pick up your crosses, your bodies and their care, and come follow Me throughout your lives.

CHAPTER 4

The Exchange of Hearts

QUIETLY JESUS AND HIS MOTHER, arm in arm, led the procession of apostles down the stone stairway outside the upper room to the main street of Jerusalem below. They grouped together at the bottom of the steps for a moment in the semi-darkness of that midnight hour and the apostles embraced Jesus for the last time, expressing their farewell with anguished sobs. Well they understood that this would be the last embrace of love they would give to the Master in His Humanity on earth. They fell to their knees and wept in uncontrollable anguish as Jesus tried to console them with kind parting words of hope.

One by one the weeping apostles left His embrace, and departed for their homes, or hiding places. There they were to wait for dawn and word from James, who had been voted the one to relay messages and who would also tell them where they would meet for the hours of the crucifixion.

Jesus beckoned for Peter, James, and John to stay with Him. A few minutes later, the three men, arm in arm, walked silently ahead of Jesus and His mother through the city's dark streets until they reached a narrow, descending path that led down the hillside to the gardens of Gethsemane. Before they began the descent, they paused and exclaimed aloud at the beauty and the mystery of the night as the garden beneath them shimmered in the soft, frost-like sheen of neither dawn nor dark night.

As their eyes shifted from one fairy-like wonder of green-black shade outlined in gold to other depths of utter blackness, Jesus and Mother Mary caught up with them and they, too, breathed in the beauty and majesty of God's art in His silent immensities, which lay beneath them.

After a few moments of silence, Mother Mary said, "The valley reminds me of God's hand holding an invisible paintbrush. For our joy, He is at work showing us the flight of time by the quick-changing hues and colors that come, from minute to minute, over the moving shrubs and trees as they bow in the quiet breeze."

Jesus turned to Peter and said, "Bid My mother goodnight and descend by this path to the garden below. Take James and John with you and wait for Me at the main gate of Gethsemane. I desire to have these last few minutes alone with mother—this is the last hour in which she will see Me in the perfection in which she raised Me."

With Heaven's bright star-candles their only light, the Master and Mother Mary watched the three men make their way slowly to the valley of darkness. Then, taking His mother close to His heart Jesus said, "Mother, do you realize this is our last hour together on earth as we have always known each other?"

Looking up into her Son's eyes, Mary noticed they were welling with tears, which fell one by one across His adorable face. She dried them tenderly with her linen headscarf, her expression one of wonderment. She could feel neither sorrow nor pain because she had never felt the sting of her senses through the curse of Original Sin. Sinless, she did not come under the banner of knowing loss and sorrow, which the sin of Adam allowed the whole human race.

Looking into Jesus' eyes she said, "My Son, because You have clothed my spirit and soul in such a spotless gown from all eternity, I know not the feelings of grief, nor loss, as do other mothers. I know when I look at You that there is no loss, and that every happening in the world is meant for eternal gain through You. Many times I have watched mothers and fathers mourn because of death and suffering, and their expressions of loss were most sad. Often they wished they could die instead of the loved one. Yet I did not understand. I only watched and wondered about your twofold plan concerning them and myself, who am so singularly blessed. Now in this hour that could be of such great sorrow, I wish I could share in their sorrow and know enough loss and anguish to say, 'Son, would that I could die for You.'"

Holding her close to His heart, the Master could only say, "Mother." Then, in a low whisper He continued, "I have never refused you a request and I shall not refuse you this one. In order that you may understand loss and suffering, I will give you My Human Heart, which is known as My Second Nature, and in exchange, I will take your heart to Myself in spirit. This exchange[13] will be known to My other friends through the ages as the mystical exchange of hearts, or mystical marriage, complete union. This can only be given to soul and spirit through the beautiful sleep of ecstasy and its mystery, which is death to the soul before actual death to the body. But because you have always been sinless you will never die in body as My other friends must taste death. Other friends who receive this exchange of hearts will know that life, in its sense of reality through this miracle of being confirmed in grace, is nothing more than suspension, and the body will act as a puppet in the mind of God. Life will be an act to win souls as I have done in My Second Nature. However, all that they do will not seem perfect in the mind of man anymore than I was considered perfect when I picked up the whip and drove the money-changers from the temple.

"The life of suspension will be the greatest of martyrdoms, and I will choose friends to live it from every state of life and in all ages of time. From now until the end of time, a few of My friends will enjoy this particular gift that they may become sharers in the redemption. Through it they will know in themselves the torments of man's infliction of wounds upon the Son of God in His Humanity. It will be known in them as the indwelling knowledge."

Suddenly, in that holy embrace of Jesus, Mary appeared as a great flame of fire reposing in the furnace of His heart. Mystically the exchange of hearts took place and from that moment Mother Mary could understand and feel the keenness of pain as only her Son understood the awfulness of sin. Had He not taken the effects of sin upon Himself? And from that wondrous exchange she knew the deeper mystery of His indwelling within her. Thus would He never die to the world,

---

13 Publisher's Statement: With the exchange of hearts, Jesus granted Mary a new understanding of earthly suffering. United with Jesus in this mystical way, she would endure the most intense sorrow quietly watching the suffering of her Son.

but would continue to share through her and His friends in the great mystery of the exchange of hearts.

In that most sublime moment, Mother Mary's request to die for Jesus had mystically been granted. There in a vision before her soul's eye, as if it were a picture transfixed over the valley of Gethsemane, she watched the crucifixion as it would take place in reality the next day. With a smile she recalled the prophecy of Simeon, who had told her that her heart would be pierced with a sword. Now before her, in anticipated vision, she watched the soldier, with his spear, pierce her heart in Jesus.

For the first time in her life she felt pain. She understood its terrible meaning and depths deeply as only Jesus could understand. What a shock was this suddenness of pain to one who had never before felt its pang, or want, or misery. She trembled with fear within the embrace of her Son.

Jesus asked, "Mother, are you trembling because you fear that now you know suffering you will not be able to stand the actual events of the crucifixion?" Mother Mary nodded. "Now I know it is indeed a sorrow to part with You," she answered. "How real a mother's tears are when in anguish she prays, 'God, let me die that this child may live.'"

"The hour we have often talked about has come," Jesus continued softly, "and I know that even though you feel pain you will be courageous. Offer no restraint tomorrow against the angry crowds. I am asking you to do this in obedience, for I am the High Priest. Now that you have the natural instincts of a mother's heart, you will no doubt want to plead for My life with My other friends. When those thoughts arise, remember obedience, and you will find new strength and courage. Now, while I go to pray, it is My desire that you rest and sleep because I will need your smile and words of courage tomorrow."

Mary could not answer. She just gazed in silence out across the valley of Gethsemane. Then Jesus tilted her chin upward with His gracious hand and said, "Little Mother, I know your thoughts back of those searching eyes. Your eyes are beautiful, and they have always been as guiding stars leading Me through My life of sorrow. Would it please you to realize again that I know your least little thought? You are not alone in this world, for I will never leave you."

"My Son," Mary replied, "it is always music when I hear You speak, and now greater than ever for I feel consolation through Your voice because of the sorrow and pain that I understand and feel. I have often wondered all these years just what Your last words to me would be—and now, I fear even that thought, which before I smiled upon."

Jesus said, "Mother, the effects of sin are horrible in their pain of fear. Fear is the greatest of pain, and that is why I have used the expression 'Fear not' more often than any other when I spoke to My little ones. And now to you I say, 'Fear not,' for I know you realize you are looking upon Me for the last time in My perfection of health and cleanliness, which you have both given and taught Me in life. Because of your wonderful care I stand before you without a scratch, or blemish, or bruise. You have guarded Me well; let that console you. I am grateful for your tender and devoted care. Little mother, tomorrow when you see Me bleeding, scarred, and bruised, promise you will try to remember Me in this state of perfection as we stand here in this our last hour together on earth."

A faint smile spread across Mother Mary's face as she answered, "I will remember Your desire and hope for me in this new understanding of earthly suffering. I will try to be close to You when You carry the cross. I will smile through my tears and offer You words of comfort rather than say one word that might restrain the angry crowds.

"Son, because I am not yet fully acquainted with this new life of suffering and pain, and because tomorrow is so near, please draw a curtain between my angels and me lest I forget obedience to You, my God, and ask them to help You."

In anguish, Mother Mary cried tears of sorrow as she leaned against His heart. She was afraid with the thought that the cross was so near. Then tenderly she gazed upon His face. Slowly she raised her hand and caressed His smooth, unbroken cheek. Tomorrow, His face would be torn and terribly bruised. She shuddered as she thought that within a few hours she would no longer see Him smile—a bitter loss! Caressingly she stroked His well-kept hair. Tomorrow, it would be encrusted with His dried blood. His eyes, now sparkling with health and love, would tomorrow be glassed in death. She fell before Him shuddering, and lovingly caressed and kissed His feet. Looking up their eyes met, and she asked, "Now are you going to pray with Peter, James, and John?"

"Yes," He answered, as He lifted her to her feet. "For whom would you have Me pray?"

Mother Mary said simply, "Pray for my son by adoption, Judas."

Jesus kissed her beautiful, uplifted face, and this gesture of tender love was His goodbye. His tears splashed on her cheeks and His body shook with His heavy sobs. He could not say goodbye. He turned quickly and ran down the narrow path toward Gethsemane.

Mother Mary's sorrow was most intense. She fell to her knees crying, and kissed her Son's footprints. She saw Him join the others, and the four holy men walked in the roadway. It was their last walk together, and Mother Mary shuddered at the thought of their parting.

Then a smile flickered in the depths of her eyes, for they began to sing as they walked arm in arm, their feet kicking up the feathery dust of that hallowed ground. Their song touched her heart, for it was a lullaby, the same lullaby she had composed and sung for Jesus in His infancy.

She smiled through a veil of tears, for she realized this song was His farewell to her. He could say it no other way. She had wondered how He would say it, and now these were the words. She joined in the song quietly as she knelt on the brink of that quiet valley.

The dark-blue shades and shadows of trees in the garden hid the holy men from her gaze a few minutes later, just as she finished singing her responses to the lullaby. Still kneeling, she gathered the sacred dust of her Son's footprints into the folds of her gown, and while she prayed, she scattered it completely over her body from head to foot. Arising, she stood mantled in a most sacred garment of sacramental dust, a dust that glistened as if each speck were a diamond. Her gown was a sacramental—His feet had touched this dust, and in this way it was blessed.

Stretching out her arms toward the garden she prayed aloud, "O sacred dust that mantles me, God, thy Creator, has blessed each particle of you with a particular grace, which in turn will bless all those upon whom you fall, upon earth or sea, when I give you to the commands of the wind.

"O sacred dust, O sacramental most blessed of all earth's dust, you are my cloak. My Son, my God, has walked upon your crest. My hope is that all the people of time will know that anything He has touched, or will touch, through the Bread of Heaven, will become great sacramentals for man and earth. O dust, I know your worth!

"And now, through the repose and power of my Son's heart within me, I bless this my mantle of dust, and command the angels to scatter it to the breeze over Gethsemane in order that the Master of all may bless it again with His nearness while He prays tonight. Then, O angels, take all the particles and scatter them across the land and sea of this great earth so that they may nourish the golden wheat fields, for out of dust so blessed the world will flourish with bread, from which will come the Living Manna through the priests of time."

Mother Mary took one last glance at peaceful Gethsemane. Then in a whispered prayer she said, "Good night, my Son. Thank You for the glorious mystery, the exchange of hearts, and in thanksgiving I promise to do all in my power to enable others also to receive this great Gift, which will make them more of You than of self. O heart of Jesus alive and beating within me, allow the sweet murmur of grace, which is Your indwelling, to fill all hearts with love of Thee."

She turned away from the dark valley and retraced her steps along the path to the city. Presently, she arrived at the home of John for the obedience of rest.

CHAPTER 5

Peter's Enthronement

NEAR THE GATE to the garden of Gethsemane lay an old log upon which Jesus, Peter, James, and John rested for a time before going on. Jesus said, "Peter, remove My sandals."

Peter was startled. His expression was one of grave question as he turned to his friends, but they did not offer him any help or word. Kneeling at Jesus' feet, the big fisherman looked up at Him and said, "Jesus, I am not worthy to remove Your sandals. Only this minute I was remembering Your prediction that before dawn I would deny You. How then can I be worthy enough to perform this action? Lord, I am not worthy even to touch your sandals because I believe Your words. You are Truth—You are God. Lord and Master, save me from denying You before the cock crows at dawn. I cannot bear the thought. Please Jesus, give James or John the singular privilege of carrying out Your request."

Jesus moved His foot forward kindly and gently, and without another word Peter quickly removed His sandal. At this moment of tremendous crisis of obedience, James and John walked on quietly toward the gate, for they believed Jesus wanted to speak alone to Peter. The expression on Peter's face reminded them of the way he had looked caught up into the sleep of ecstasy when first he took the Living Bread into his hands.

Peter held the Master's sandal to his heart and bent forward in a mental prayer of gratitude and humility. Jesus said, "Peter, I have said that you will deny Me three times before the cock crows at dawn. Come, sit beside Me, while I tell you why I am allowing you, a victim to My will, to suffer the agony of such humiliation, which will cause you to be chided, scolded, and ridiculed in the presence of friends until the end of time. There will be few people in time who will understand the true providence of God and His strategy in His war for souls and how I will use you and your successors, to the ends of endurance, as justifiers for Justice. This is both possible and reasonable when you understand that with Me there is no time and all is as present. I must take you into that realm of understanding and embarrass you for the need of great merit, through mortification, to you, yourself.

"Also, few people on earth will understand the deeper truths of My will because they will fail to believe that as long as time exists human life will consist of warfare, on an actual battlefield, between the phenomena of good and evil on earth. Every soul must be a soldier who is either for Me or against Me. That is why there is life and a battlefield.

"Because of all this, Peter, I have chosen you to be captain of My great army on earth. The effects of your mortifications, resulting in merit and grace, will be felt among your successors until the end of time.

"It will be the duty of such successors, or captains, to plan defensive maneuvers, not only for the day, but for the centuries to come. I have chosen you to suffer this great humiliation of denying Me because I have great need of the merit you will thus earn for the successors of My Church, which must be built on the foundation of humility. Peter, because you are hidden for a moment in the depths and truths of My will, I want you to know that mother and I have also exchanged hearts in this same fountain of union of wills together. Now that you and I have passed through that channel of greater love and perpetual understanding, you, too, will act for Me while you live on earth.

"In this the night of your soul, or agony, known as partial suspension of will hidden in the delights of My love, I am allowing you to understand for this hour only the plan of the great work I have prepared for you to accomplish. You see, I trust you will accept this humiliation, just as a soldier accepts a command to go alone into the night in order to save people whom he will never know, nor see, in life. A true soldier does not question why he is chosen, he simply obeys, even if it costs him his life, for hasn't a soldier given his will to conform to that of a superior for the greater good?

"Peter, your memory, according to earthly ways of thinking and reasoning, will cease to recall our present words and plans after this hour of great ecstasy. The state of ecstasy has a way of deadening the human senses for a time according to quick reasoning, just as schooling teaches the mind. Our language consists of no words, but only the striking of My will upon soul and spirit, and one's actions and words are often motivated by habit according to the place and time and how he is questioned.

"After the denial tomorrow, you will recall this hour slowly as if it were a dream when your mind is refreshed in the finite way of life, but you must keep your thoughts and My plans to yourself. Before you deny Me, and at a time when you will least expect it, I will withdraw special graces of loyalty from you. In your own human weakness, because you will try to save yourself from My enemies, you will deny Me in a moment of soul-weakness, which is governed by fear in its pursuit of security.

"Later, in the finite expression of awakening to reality, your spirit will feel the greatest inner pain of remorse, because you have now, at this hour, tasted of ethereal knowledge through ecstasy. I will allow the whip of remorse to strike your spirit as though it were a scourge as a means of meriting humility for you and your successors. I also want another kind of merit, which comes from silence. Keep silent on these matters when you are accused, rather than try to excuse yourself or explain our plan for your successors. I will allow all these plans to be made when I will.

"Peter, you will gain great merit in your silence and tears, and a furrowed brow will be your earthly crown. Spiritual nights will take hold of you and you will at times think all is delusion, and the knowledge of My interior voice error. It is necessary for you to be clothed in the cloak of humility, for in humility, on humility, and through humility there is safety in the world for you and your successors. This ecstatic gift of intuitive knowledge is great and unique, and will not be enjoyed by many of your successors. There will be great captains in the last ages to come, and you will help them because of your penances and mortifications and willingness to follow My plan in the worldwide war for souls."

Jesus smiled and continued. "Since you have removed My sandal, Peter, it pleases Me to tell you that your gesture of holding it in your hands is your actual enthronement such as exterior manifestations are allowed in our poverty. Most of your successors will be enthroned in the ceremonial splendors of their day. They will wear elaborate robes and gowns and colors for all occasions, but these poor, worn sandals, Peter, are all I have to offer you on this, your day, to assume your kingship on earth."

Peter's spirit was still wrapped in the delights of ecstasy. Kneeling before Jesus, he found himself watching the illustrious light and knowledge of Heaven's gifts through which he was permitted to see, as well as understand, this sublime moment of his enthronement. Untold numbers of Heaven's angels watched and honored him with unequaled grandeur of celebration and pomp, and assembled at the Master's feet to await his coronation. Through the shimmering light from their crowns of celestial light and power he viewed, as with prophetic interest, all the coming ages and the splendor of his successors' enthronements. He saw each one with his vices and his virtues—nothing was hidden from the celestial vision given him, for all is present in the mind of God. And seeing certain pontiffs upon whom he frowned, he looked at Jesus and said smiling, "I will gladly follow Your plan. Give me all the humiliations You wish."

Turning again to the vision's light of knowledge, he smiled as he watched the angels attend each of his successors, and was enthralled as he heard most of them sing praises to his name for his sorrows and willingness to suffer all manner of ridicule until the end of time for having denied Jesus in, and through, the plan of providence.

Peter awakened from his divine slumber of ecstasy and exclaimed aloud in awed wonderment, "Jesus, permit my name and my faults, especially my fault of denying You, to be discussed throughout the ages to come. I understand it is all for the greater good. Humble me, Lord, at every moment of time. And while I live, allow me the privilege of becoming a victim of tears and silence in order to prove my love for You, and my charity for Your friends. Jesus, my will is Yours for all time do with me as You will. O, if I could only will never to die in order to suffer this humiliation every minute of time. Well I understand, in the wisdom You have taught me, that there is really no time according to the understanding of ethereal knowledge. Therefore, to spend a life of time in order to win souls, even through the gift of tears and humiliation, I know would, and could be, the greatest joy on earth.

As Peter's colloquy of holy desire ended, and he was once more free in the exterior world of thought, he removed the Master's other sandal without being bid to do so. Jesus arose barefoot and motioned Peter to be seated in His place. Then the Master knelt before him and removed his sandals quickly, replacing them with His own. As Jesus tied the laces, tears coursed down Peter's face, for he realized humbly the wonderful significance and profound meaning of being dressed in the clothes of the Master. He was the first Vicar of Jesus Christ on earth.

Still kneeling, Jesus clasped His hands in prayer and bowing His head in Peter's lap, said quietly, "Most Holy Father on earth, I humble Myself as your subject. I beg your permission to enter the garden with James and John to pray. And I beg you, Holy Father, to accompany us. We desire your holy friendship."

Peter was awestruck at such self-abjection, reverence to authority, and humility Jesus was showering upon him. He could not answer. He could only gasp for breath. This was indeed a shock of greater depth than his wearing the Master's sandals. He didn't realize that from that instant Jesus was his prisoner. He, Peter, was the prison-keeper and the keeper of the keys!

Then, remembering the Master's reason for his enthronement, obeying and honoring the privilege given him, he raised his hand in blessing over Jesus, and setting an example for all future priests and successors, exercised his authority, which gave his spirit and body a foretaste of martyrdom, by granting God—this Jesus on earth—permission to pray in the garden. He reasoned to himself that Jesus was giving him a lesson on how men should follow Him by first asking permission from one in authority before attempting any work on earth according to one's own will and pleasure. Indeed the Master humbles Himself to His servants! In that moment of asking Peter's permission, Jesus as True Man had willingly, and for a moment, forgotten His divinity, better that He might shoulder the burden of True Man, by humbly asking permission from one in authority. Christ is the way! As True Man He was preparing Himself for the Agony by this humble submission of asking permission.

Peter answered, "Jesus, Son of God, You have my permission to enter into the garden with James and John. I will go with You."

Jesus kissed Peter's hand, turned, and going to where James and John waited, walked with them through the gates of Gethsemane.

Peter, carrying his own sandals in his hand, followed the little procession in stunned wonderment. He tried to walk in each footprint made by the bare feet of the Master as He led them through the narrow paths to the interior garden.

CHAPTER 6

The Beginning of the Agony: The Holy Grave

JESUS LED THE WAY into the accustomed interior grove of Gethsemane, where they had often prayed together. Now Peter was his usual impetuous self and free from the cloudy effects of ecstasy, which a moment before had taken him from the world and its stifled knowledge. Rather than carry his own sandals he tied them to his wide leather belt. Joyousness was his since he was wearing the Master's sandals. He realized he was privileged. First he walked ahead of Jesus, James and John, who were deeply engaged in low conversation concerning the hour of prayer ahead of them, and then he dropped back to talk to some of the hundred and twenty-five disciples who followed. Somehow these disciples had learned that Jesus was going to pray at this hour and had waited patiently for Him. Seeing Him they did not cheer or make any noise, for they were accustomed to the prayer hour of quiet. They were content to stop some distance from the inner grove, which was their custom whenever they followed Jesus there to pray. Many of them smiled and chuckled at Peter's over-anxiousness to hurry.

The three holy men of God with Jesus appreciated and understood the graces of enlightenment and wisdom that had been given them through their speaking to, and being near, the Master. James and John became silent and then began to feel a weariness, or heaviness, creep over them. They wondered whether or not they would have further delights with God, and questioned one another about the strange phenomena of weight, and especially about the prayer of quiet they had felt and loved during the Paschal dinner. They said nothing to Jesus, however, and did not realize that the tremendous gift of weight, or heaviness, which often comes over a body during ecstasy, is God's symbolical way of showing that the gravity of Heaven's knowledge is manifested upon the body as supernatural weight and rigidity.

By this time Peter was far ahead of them. They could not keep up with his impetuous stride. God was slowly allowing them to fall into the prayer of quiet, even ahead of Peter, for they were not yet strong enough in faith, or courage, to watch the Master in His prayer, which He had told them would later be known as "The Agony."

Peter arrived at the designated place in the grove, and stood waiting for the others with his hands on his sword hilts as they hung at either side from his belt. He had purchased the two swords when Jesus told him to go sell his outside cloak and buy a sword. Instead of buying just one he had purchased two because of his great generosity. Now he smiled, thinking he had bargained well and that Jesus would be more pleased with him. He patted the hilts. He knew that the ordering of a sword had been a mystery to the other apostles at the dinner, as well as to himself, but he was positive that time would disclose the reason for it. He was both ready and able to use the implements of defense should the God-Man give the order. His toga was made of coarse brown linen and it hung clear to his feet. From time to time he glanced down at the God-Man's sandals. He was happy.

Looking up, he noticed that several disciples had entered through the main gate and were coming closer than he liked to the clearing in which Jesus loved to pray. He directed them to move farther down the hillside and to pray set apart from the Master, who wanted to be very much alone. He also cautioned them that regardless of any event that took place, or how long Jesus prayed, they were not to approach the God-Man at any time during the night. He tried to impress upon them that this was a most extraordinary time for prayer.

Meanwhile, Jesus and the two apostles stopped in a particular nook in the grove, and Peter hurried over to ask why they had decided upon that spot rather than the grassy one a few yards ahead, which he would have chosen. Jesus knelt on the ground and motioned for the three to follow His action. Quietly He said to Peter, "I have a surprise for you, but first it would be great wisdom on your part to pray in sorrow for the sins of self and the world."

They prayed silently, and then Jesus looked at Peter and continued, "With your permission I ask for a mortification from each of you. Someday you will understand the fine art of mortification, but for the present eat a handful of the dust upon which you are kneeling."

Peter nodded his approval in a dazed manner.

After the dust was eaten and their prayer ended, they imitated Jesus, who was digging into the earth with His hands, the carefulness of gesture indicating that here was buried a prized possession. Quietly Jesus said, "Beneath this earth we will find the incorrupt body of John the Baptizer. The angels brought it here, even though most people thought he was buried elsewhere."

A gasp of surprise came from the lips of the three men. Peter, in his vivaciousness, plunged his strong hands deep into the earth in order to hurry the uncovering of John's body. As he did so he exclaimed in eager enthusiasm, "This is wonderful—this is wonderful! What a surprise! Tell us, Jesus, how did the body get here? I assumed the angels took it to Heaven when You ordered them to remove it from the funeral procession near Herod's court. Has it been here all the time? Tell us, Master, if You will, how the angels carried it here without being noticed by anyone?"

Jesus answered, "I asked them to bring it here for proper burial, as I told you before when you were carrying it to the burial grounds in Capernaum. Angels possess the gift of agility as well as the gift that enables them to make visible substance invisible, although this is seldom used by them. However, they employed it in this case."

At last John's incorrupt body was exposed to their view. James was immovable and afraid to reach forth his hand to touch it. John the Beloved trembled as he clung closely to the robes of Jesus, who was kneeling closest to the grave. Peter was the only one of the three apostles who was not afraid, and he touched the body of the saint tenderly.

A heavenly fragrance of rose and incense came from it and permeated even into the surrounding hills, where knelt the loving disciples who wondered about its cause on the midnight air. They prayed with deeper sincerity and took the mystery of the phenomena as a gift from God. Their smiles could have been spoken words of understanding, for their hearts were saying, "Why shouldn't this happen? Jesus is praying."

The Master caressed the Baptizer's cold hands as they lay folded over his stilled heart. Tenderly He unclasped John's fingers, and reaching into the deep pockets of His own toga, brought forth the chalice He had used at the Last Supper. He had hidden it carefully in His cloak as He left the banquet room. Placing it into John's hands, He said, "John, here is your chalice and Mine. Keep it for Me. It gives Me joy knowing it is with you, and doubly so, because you were the last Melchizedek priest on earth when the flickering flame of the Old Law began to die. Someday your incorrupt body and this chalice will be found. During the last centuries, and at the end of time, it will be used in the Sacrifice of the New Law, which I have made a law tonight. I, Myself, will use it when I come to finish the last Mass on earth at the end of time.

"It is the one Adam made and used," He continued. "He made it at My Father's command out of simple clay, and while he presented it to My Father in the prayer of great contemplation to which he had risen after centuries of reparation and sorrow, the fire of My Father—Who is known as Light—fired it into burnished gold, which will never corrupt until time is no more. It has been handed down from generation to generation by one Melchizedek priest to another until now it has reached the crossroads of the Old and New Laws.

"When John was in prison and the hour of his death near, he wondered how he could offer the Clean Oblation Sacrifice according to the laws of Melchizedek, for it was the day of his offering. He was loyal to his obligations in life, and he realized through contemplative wisdom that he was the last Melchizedek priest on earth, and knew I would ask you, My followers, at the Love Feast, which I instituted tonight, to follow his order.

"The knowledge that you would receive the supernatural gifts was a joy to him, but in that joy he wanted to fulfill his obligation even at the last hour of his life. In the dark dungeon, and chained to the wall, he patiently waited for My assistance, for he believed I knew and understood his desires. I ordered mother to prepare the wine, unleavened bread, and the torch of fire for his needs, and then I asked her angels to take them to him, along with this chalice, which I have just placed in his hands. The angels freed him from his chains, and with their own assumed bodies they bent in a kneeling position and thus formed an altar for him."

John the Beloved asked, "Jesus, tell us something about the Old Sacrifice and its truths that were to foretell the inconceivable mystery of Thyself, which You have given us tonight."

"A few centuries after the beginning of time," the Master answered, "as the world understands time, and after Adam had offered his fixed life as a mortification for his sins, he was gradually enlightened by My merciful infusion of knowledge. His soul, illuminated through the gifts of prophesying grace through the prayer of quiet and the gifts of ecstasy, learned the mystery of My Incarnation and how My Father (Spirit) would become Living Man and take onto Himself man's ugly flesh to suffer and make sacrifice for the redemption of the human race.

"After many ecstasy flights he learned the love of prayer, and understood through the spiritual guidance of My Father that he was to be known as the first priest on earth and that he would offer sacrifices according to the will of God. One day, during ecstasy, God ordained him with special powers, which through sacrifice would unite the unseen world to reality. He was known as the first Melchizedek priest on earth and he offered the Clean Oblation Sacrifice. During one of those sacrifices he was permitted to see in a vision before him all the ages of time, even to the hour in which I gave you the Living Bread. In his understanding of that sublime gift, the Eucharist, he mourned because he would not be alive in this era to receive the New Law's Bread of Heaven.

"Because of his grief, My Father allowed him—from then on until death—to live in a partial state of ecstasy. Through his great graces he understood the gift of mercy and love, and how he could offer the merit of his sacrifice for the Living Bread to be brought to the world, for the animalistic nature of man did not understand mercy or love.

"My mother enjoyed the high spiritual heritage of being exempt from the Original Sin of Adam, which is common to all mankind. This was made possible through Adam's sacrifice of bread and wine in anticipation of the real Sacrifice which I have just given you, the offerings of all the other Melchizedek priests, the vows of the first-born of the House of David for over five hundred years to live the lives of virginity, and the anticipated infinite merits of My life now on earth.

"From the year of Adam's ordination until this hour, there has never been a season of time when a Melchizedek priest could not be found united in a prayer of sacrifice before God. There have been years when only one Melchizedek priest was in existence, but never was the golden thread of contemplation and sacrifice broken, or taken from the world, since the gift was first given to Adam.

"The fire, or torch, used on or near their altars symbolized My Father brought down to man's expression, or body, and way of thinking and acting in all things except sin, through His Divine will to be captured and held in the likeness of man's body. The incense thrown into the fire symbolized the prayers rising to Him through the Melchizedek priests and their friends. It was burned and consumed until it fell in ashes to the altar table as a sacramental, which could be used as a continuous blessing by the priests to the world.

"The unleavened bread they used was an outward sign, through faith, that God would become Man, and that He would institute the Living Clean Oblation Sacrifice through Melchizedek priests in the New Law. From Adam, until now, many priests have watched, through the grace of prophesying vision, the Clean Oblation Sacrifice of today, as if they were actually present in this hour, or in the ages to come. I would have you remember that in the grace of higher unitive prayer there is no time known as time, and everything is present with God and His friends who are so graced as to be caught up into the mystery of ecstasy. This grace and knowledge is, and will be, known as the Communion of Saints; for there is nothing hidden from the world in the wisdom of the saints.

"When a priest of the Old Law lifted the unleavened bread to the altar fire with tongs, his action taught the lesson that I was the only one worthy [when I was born] to approach so near to the Divine Fires of My Father. The consuming of the bread in the fire told symbolically of My death on the cross.

"The chalice of wine symbolized the complete human race, which could be made pure through the gift of transfiguration, which God, through My coming into the world, would make possible if people believed in the Commandments and the prophets who would bring them closer to Him through revelation.

"Sometimes in the Old Law Sacrifice the ashes were mixed with the wine and consumed, for the purpose of faith, to show that purification and transfiguration were possible for the human race. The prayer of the priests was that God would elevate the life of man to the perfection of conformity with the Divine Will."

Jesus then bent forward and kissed the brow of John the Baptizer. In a low tone He whispered, "John, you were a kind, most obedient priest. You kept the laws of obedience, which do not allow questions as to why I do this, or why I allow that condition in life. Your life was a perfect law in its conformity to My will. Many times while you lived I longed to console you, as would any good shepherd, but I knew you had found My Heart through the unitive way of prayer, and this was a greater consolation than if I had actually touched you in the manner of living life."

The Master then told Peter, James, and John to replace the soft earth over the sacred body of the Baptizer. After a moment's hesitation, Peter removed a handkerchief that he wore twisted into a narrow band around his head to keep his hair secure under the square headscarf, which men wore when they were not fishing, and smoothed it gently over John's peaceful face. The handkerchief-scarf was beautifully woven and embroidered by his wife, and was of brown linen with a tiny red ship sewn into one corner in memory of his fishing fleets. Jesus smiled at his thoughtfulness and blessed him for his care of the dead.

When the body was completely hidden from view once more, they scratched the words, "Saint John, remember us," on a shielding, overhanging, rock ledge with a small piece of flint. Jesus said, "It is holy wisdom to pray near the body of a saint. The nearness of his sacred tabernacle, even if it is only a speck of dust, is a sacramental of grace for people who venerate, or acknowledge, the goodness of that saint. And the saints' goodness, now represented as invisible power, is my Father magnified through them to the world. His direct nearness through a saint cannot be dimmed even in death."

CHAPTER 7

Watch and Pray

PETER, JAMES, AND JOHN knelt at the Master's feet while He sat on the low, projecting rock that overhung the Baptizer's grave. In answer to their questions, Jesus explained the great necessity of self-schooling the five senses, as well as disciplining the intellectual powers, which in time would not only lead them, but their friends also, to the gates of interior prayer.

He said, "Interior prayer, or we could call it the loving knowledge of God, will be the invisible ladder by which many people will understand the mystical union with God. But first, interior prayer will have to be earned, for it cannot be given as a gift from one human to another, nor can it be purchased. Therefore, the understanding will have to be schooled in the value of any subject the senses may touch upon, such as time, energy, pain, mortification, humiliation, knowledge, tradition, and heritage, both physical and spiritual.

"Interior prayer is a necessary goal for every soul on earth, for it is a reaching, as it were, for eternal life. When appreciation of the right use of creatures and of possessions is learned, souls are gifted with wisdom and the greater light of intuitive knowledge, which becomes another gift in the knowingness that we are never alone in life. God is always with us, listening to us, regardless of where we are.

"The soul tastes the love-nectar of silence with the possession of such wisdom, and realizes that it is a gift above all other gifts in regard to mental or vocal prayers, which are often said as lip service, or without full understanding of the words uttered. Unitive prayer is attained only after souls have analyzed phrases and words and have discarded the useless and the flowery and have changed long expressions into only a few words, else their prayers become as barriers to the flight of the soul in the way of simple prayer. When this way is mastered, a soul can be guilty of neither lip service nor idle words in any form, but will have put on the New Man and have been transformed more intensely into the characteristics of God the Father in Me."

Rising to His feet, Jesus asked if they had not noticed the wonderful peace and tranquility about them and the certain heaviness of their bodies. James and John smiled, for they had discussed that very subject while they walked through the garden gates. They had noticed their step was slow and heavy, while Peter's was impetuous. His hurried stride tired them both physically and spiritually, for to them it was a distraction to think of hurrying when Jesus was so near. Nothing else but His nearness seemed to matter—time and events were as nothing.

All three apostles were greatly interested in the unusual feeling of heaviness they now associated with their new knowledge of unitive prayer, and they asked the Master to explain its phenomena further.

Jesus began by saying, "The deeper you are in union with Me in life and in prayer, the more your senses die a mystical death. It can be said that the soul dies before actual death comes to both soul and body. The five senses become united as one in simple unitive prayer, and the intellect understands more than if the natural eye could see everything in life. That transition to the senses and the soul in flight to God usually comes over the body when it is least expected. Great lovers do not ask permission to give an embrace—surprise expressions are of greater worth. In simple unitive prayer a soul often knows My Father's embrace, which is a consolation above all other joys. Often, especially after the flight of the soul, the finite mind of man would rather remain silent than try to express the eloquence and the grandeur of God's gift, which is unintelligible in the sense of language. If the gift of silence has been mastered during a purification process and trial, for the greater love of God, the soul will find silence both helpful and beautiful, and the body will only speak when authority advises, for souls are often dazzled and left expressionless with the joys of My Father. They are often beyond any expression of finite words.

"Souls who are gifted with this way of prayer are often known as victim souls for My love alone. I address them as captains, for I have chosen many of them for certain missions on earth. In most cases it is quite necessary for them to have experienced the flight of the soul or they would not have the courage to venture far into the obedience of My will. Such victim souls are pillars of faith as well as gifts of knowledge to the world. Their way of life and merit for people is inconceivable, and oftentimes it is looked upon as foolishness by others.

"In the worldly knowledge of the five senses there are two kinds of prayer, which I will now explain. One is called 'watch' and the other, 'pray.' Both will be understood, in time, in prayer and work as the senses disengage themselves from any worldly want. These two titles of prayer have many expressions, and they will often be misunderstood by contemplatives.

"The word 'watch' means to give time and attention to a need of the world, through God the Father, in the experience known as bilocation. This experience may last but a few minutes, or for hours—all according to the will of God.

"The word 'pray' means simple prayer, which is prompted through the use of tradition and the heritage of books, pictures, and historical facts, and will continue through the ages to come much the same as in the Old Law. However, when a contemplative knows the word 'pray' in its higher sense, he realizes that it means ecstasy slumber, for reasons usually known only by My Father for the good of the world. Only My Father can lift souls to any of the higher states of prayer."

As Jesus gazed at His three apostles, He could see they were lost in the graces of profound truths that He had just taught them. This hour they would experience the knowledge of the words "watch" and "pray."

The Master continued: "It was mother's last request tonight that I remember Judas in My prayers. Now, will you watch and pray one hour with Me for the needs of Judas, and for the needs of any other priest who may follow his path in the centuries to come? With Me, you know, there is no time, and the merit you gain tonight may easily be applied to a priest who will live three thousand years from now—for indeed you are your brother's keeper. To watch and pray is to give your complete self into the care of My Father's will, without the slightest reservation as to the protection of your body during ecstasy or bilocation. Neither should you have the least concern over what anyone might say in ridicule. This calls for extreme trust. Are you willing?"

The apostles were awed with this request—they nodded their approval, and Peter said, "Jesus, You are the High Priest and You must teach us the way. Under a priest's protection, and following obedience, we have nothing to fear. When do we begin?"

Jesus smiled His answer and they followed Him into a thicker grove of trees. The night was very still, broken only by the clanking of Peter's swords. They stopped at a spot about thirty feet from John the Baptist's grave and knelt in the black shadows of a low-hanging olive tree. There Peter, James, and John offered prayers in reparation for the coldness of Judas and for his abrupt manner to the Master as he left the banquet room.

After a few moments, Jesus arose and left the apostles in meditation, which was the means of grace that lifted them slowly into the flight of ecstasy. Alone, the Master walked to the top of the hill, from where He could see more clearly the few flickering lights in the city below. Tears came to His eyes as He watched, for well He understood the numbers of souls there who were committing sin. Because He was God, He allowed an instantaneous vision of all men to be born in future generations to appear before His gaze. He hung His head in shame—particularly for the people of His own generation who had Him in their midst and yet showed such terrible ingratitude. Little did they realize that tomorrow He would die for them. Even many of His particular friends had gradually turned against Him because of His poverty and gentleness. He whispered aloud, "Greed is the coat-of-arms of this generation."

In the darkness beneath the olive tree, Peter looked with a startled expression at James and John. He could see the heaviness of their bodies because of their deep interior prayer, and how they swayed slightly as if they cared not what happened to them even though they were in a sitting position, leaning against a creek embankment. He moved to them quickly and tried to awaken them, but they were as though dead. He could not even lift their hands. Gently, he rolled them onto their sides into lying positions.

Standing over them in somewhat of a perplexed mood, he thought to himself, "They must be in the deep prayer of ecstasy. What is the matter with me? I should be with them. I know I have not kept my mind on the praise and the love of God, for I could not restrain my thoughts from turning to the Master's sandals, which I am wearing, and I couldn't keep from wondering whether or not He will feel the dampness of the earth without them. I do not want Him to suffer because He was so generous with me. Since He has given me authority, I will go seek Him and ask Him to wear them again. I wonder if He will question me for not following through with the deeper way of prayer that He desired for all of us tonight?"

Suddenly, the big fisherman felt very much alone. Kneeling, he prayed for guidance, for he believed he must hurry to the Master, and yet he was reluctant to disturb Him, for it was not unusual for Him to go away by Himself. He felt he should tell Him about James and John and learn whether or not they were all right. He started to rise, but found he could not. His feet were too heavy to move in conformity with his will. A chill of fear swept through him. In desperation he managed to crawl to the side of the Master.

Throwing his strong arms around Jesus, Peter clung to Him, saying, "Jesus, I am so afraid. Look—look at James and John—I cannot awaken them! Are they dead? Could they die in such a state of prayer? Master, just before they found their rest in ecstasy they said aloud, 'Our eyes are heavy like unto death.' I watched them for a few minutes and then I noticed this terrible weakness in my own legs and I crawled here. Now my eyes, too, feel heavy and I cannot keep them open. I'm afraid. This is not a natural sleep, for I am not drowsy. This has never happened before when I have come here with You to pray. Why, just think, Jesus, we have spent whole nights together in prayer and I found little or no difficulty in keeping awake. Lord, what is the matter with me? I want to stay awake and pray this hour with You."

Jesus smiled and placed His strong, protecting arm across Peter's trembling shoulders and patted his shaggy head. "Fear not, Peter," He said gently. "Do you not realize that My Father's will is lifting you into His embrace, and that you are only feeling the nothingness and the helplessness of yourself? Give Him His way with you without fear. I told the three of you that you would have a foretaste of ecstasy tonight. Remember, we are the pillars of faith in reparation for Judas, and for other priests who will follow his path in the ages to come. Ecstasy prayer and its discomfort are usually the price of reparation for such pillars of faith.

"James and John are now in the embrace of My Father. Do not trouble yourself about them, for that is My care. Come, let us go and see to their comfort."

Jesus arose from His sitting position and helped Peter to his feet. Arm in arm, they walked slowly to the slumbering apostles. Jesus blessed them, and pulling handfuls of long grass He formed pillows for them. Taking Peter by the arm, He led him back to the grove on the hill's ridge. As long as Jesus led Peter, the fisherman noticed it was quite easy to walk, even though he still felt the weight and numbness. After they had been on the ridge for a few minutes, they moved to the side of John the Baptist's grave. Kneeling there, they continued to watch the flickering lights of the city.

The Master said, "This hour I have called you, Peter, to be alone with Me in the prayer known as watchful. It is just another way of ecstasy, which I have already explained to you as the gift of bilocation. This type of ecstasy will be a means of real active prayer, in fact as active as if you had complete control of your body and will. Souls are often taken into this way of prayer, through God, to act as His actual instruments of peace, baptism, or any other way for the needs of the hour. Peter, will you watch one hour with Me?"

Trepidation and fear were in Peter's voice as he answered, "Yes, Master, but I am so afraid. Help me, and lead me into Your perfect way of love."

Jesus touched Peter's trembling hand as He said, "Courage, Peter, remember I will be with you. Never can this way of prayer be without My Personal Self present with the person called to do great deeds for the needs of the particular hour I may choose. Come, let us go into the city and watch the events of time in which Judas is playing such a terrible part."

Instantly, Peter was bilocated, with Jesus, into the city of Jerusalem. They found themselves invisible,[14] and, as far as Peter was concerned, powerless to act, within a few feet of where Judas stood in a large assembly hall before Annas and Caiphas, who were seated on huge lounging chairs, surrounded by all the ceremonial color and splendor of the courts of that day.

Caiphas was drinking heavily, and in a boisterous mood and voice he called to Judas as he and his friends from the party stood there

14 Bilocation can be either visible or invisible, according to the need.

escorted by two soldiers. Annas, a high priest of the Old Law and Caiphas' father-in-law, was visiting for a few days in Jerusalem. For the moment he said nothing. Even though this was a most unusual hour to call an assembly, or to discuss law, or to pass judgment on city affairs, it was deemed necessary because of the great numbers of conversions and a general uprising that centered about Jesus and His followers. Both Annas and Caiphas would stoop to any means to end this religious affair, for they were afraid of losing power and the esteem of the common people.

Seeing that his son-in-law was too befuddled to think properly, Annas stood up, and narrowing his eyes to mere slits, looked steadily at the unsteady Judas, who was drunk with both wine and fear. He saw a handsome man, tall, slim, and of dark complexion. The slothfulness and drowsiness from drink brought out impudent, arrogant words and actions that ordinarily were perfect. Annas' eyes shifted to Judas' friends, most of whom were ill-kept women. They were a deplorable looking lot to be ushered into the courtrooms of Caiphas. They eyed their surroundings uneasily.

Annas frowned, and asked in a commanding voice, "What about this report that you know the whereabouts of this Jesus Who is trying to take all law into His hands? I am told you are known as an apostle to whom He has given authority to govern people. Is this true, or does this authority deal only with the place known as Heaven? If so, what good will it do you now? I suppose you think you can predict the outcome of my life, and into whose hands I will fall. Do you know whether I will go to Heaven or to Hell?"

Judas turned pale. He was struck with the thought of Heaven, Hell, and judgment. He was about to admit that he was an apostle when he caught sight of the sneering expression on the face of Caiphas. He said nothing.

The storming voice of Annas continued. "Speak up, man. Why are you here if it is not to tell us where Jesus is at this hour? It is necessary for peace that we find Him!"

One of the women said in a low tone to Judas, "Come on, Judas, tell him where Jesus is hiding. You told us but we don't know the way. Why do you hesitate? He will pay you well. Bargain with him. Tell him that for thirty pieces of silver you will let him know about, and see, the Living Manna that Jesus gave you tonight."

Eyeing Judas critically, Annas asked, "What is this you whisper about Living Manna? God above, how far will this Jesus go in His sacrilegious teaching? It is time He was put to death. It isn't enough that He thinks He is the Messiah, but now He gives Manna to men, which our forefathers received only from Heaven by the angels and which the real Messiah will bring us one day!"

Striding across the room to a lectern, Annas picked up a purse of silver and dangled it in front of Judas. The ill-kept woman snatched the purse and whispered again cunningly to Judas, "Hurry, show Annas the piece of Bread which Jesus says is God, the Living Bread, and which has the promise of life everlasting for all who eat of it."

Judas took the Blessed Bread of Heaven from his pocket and gave it to Annas. Holding the Great Sacrament high above his head, the high priest and all the people in the courtroom broke into roars of hilarious laughter. Then Annas tossed the Sacred Manna to his pet dog.

Standing beside the lectern, Annas proceeded to give instructions, because Caiphas, who should have taken the lead, was drowsy from his overindulgence in wine. In a loud tone he shouted, "It is time we made an example of impostors such as this Jesus. We have had enough of His kind ordering people around and disturbing the peace for the last hundred years. Let us bring Him under the laws of justice, which make His crime punishable by death!"

Applause of approval and shouts of laughter filled the room as Judas was ushered closer to the lectern table. Annas made a motion of agreement with his friends and then he said, "It is now the eleventh hour and it is time for all of us to retire. See, Caiphas is already asleep. Judas, if I send a bodyguard with you, do you think you can bring Jesus here within the next hour? To bring this judgment about during the night will throw a light of grave importance upon the foolishness of such fanatical people and may help to bring His followers to a halt."

Judas assured Annas that within the hour he would have Jesus under arrest—provided, however, that Jesus did not use His power of persuasion in His philosophy of love over the bodyguards and thus win them over to His side. Judas knew well the power of this wonderful philosophy because he had seen the Master convert hundreds of people with His way of kindness and by the eloquence of His voice and words. He said, "I will lead the bodyguard to Him, but I will not be responsible for what His oratorical genius does to them or the use of the swords that Peter wears. Peter is handy with them and no doubt they are expecting a fight. Then, too, it is rumored that Jesus loves sports. Therefore, He, too, must know how to fight."

Annas stood up quickly and shook Caiphas awake. He told him of the plans and of the information that Judas had given. He then asked his son-in-law for suggestions on how to capture a man who possessed such powers over people. Conversing quietly together, they arrived at a startling plan that had never before been used in the history of the city. They would send twenty prisoners from the dungeons with Judas and the soldiers!

When this was announced, the soldiers and people were aghast. They asked, "What is this plan? Surely we have not heard correctly. Such a command has never been given before—it will be something to see!"

Several of Judas' friends hurried out to tell others, for this was an event as well as news. Those within the courts waited for further developments. Soldiers left for the dungeons.

Within a few minutes, twenty filthy, stumbling, bewildered, chained prisoners stood before Annas and Caiphas. Many of them had never seen the inside splendor of the court and were breathless with its beauty. Annas said loudly to them, "We are not going to kill you. Listen carefully to what I have to say. In the hills we have a hoodlum whom we must capture and we have conceived this plan of doing it. He is an outlaw just as you are—thus you will know His moods and way of fighting.

"We understand He has great mental powers, and it is claimed that He can overcome any man on earth with His oratorical and magical gifts. We are advised not to send our soldiers alone to capture Him, for we fear many of them have already listened to Him and no doubt have fallen into His snare. If so, they are afraid of us and will not confess their loyalty to Him. In this hour we trust no one.

"We have brought you here in order to offer you your freedom if you help bring this Man, Jesus, alive and unharmed to us. The stipulations are these. Every prisoner must return here in an orderly fashion with the soldiers. If any one of you attempts to escape and succeeds, the rest of you will face life imprisonment or death. For your own freedom you must watch one another. Many of you have been in the dungeons ten years and expect to stay there for life. A few of you face crucifixion. If you choose freely to go in search of this Man Jesus, our soldiers will accompany you and offer any assistance you may find necessary when you near the spot where He is hiding.

"We understand this trouble-maker has two swords, a bodyguard of three men, and is a good fencer. The soldiers will surround you at all times with lighted torches and will lead the way. This will keep you from attempting to escape. We are sending you on this strange command because we believe you want freedom rather than listen to this Man and His philosophy of love which, of course, cannot save you. We want this Jesus as a prisoner, and He must be brought to us within the hour. Judas, once His follower, will lead the way."

In wide-eyed astonishment, the prisoners gasped aloud, "Can this be true?" Freedom was theirs if they brought a man from the hills! They further questioned one another, "What kind of giant is He to give us this unusual privilege of freedom?"

A quick vote was taken and a spokesman answered Annas, "We pledge ourselves to bring this Man unharmed to you. We also pledge not to be caught in His snares. Therefore, we will return here in a body to receive our freedom."

The soldiers removed the iron bands from the ankles and wrists of the prisoners and ordered them to march four abreast through the halls to the doors and out into the streets. Judas led the way, and the soldiers walked to the side and to the rear. The strange procession began at a very slow pace, for the prisoners were not accustomed to walking and the soldiers wanted to preserve their strength in case a fight took place when Jesus was reached.

The people of the city had been awakened, as if an alarm had sounded, and they hurried quickly to the scene of the marching men, which added greatly to the night's confusion and fear.

CHAPTER 8

Jesus Prays Alone

PETER'S STRUGGLE TO AWAKEN HIMSELF from his watchful bilocation proved most difficult. It was agony to return to this way of life. He rolled his head in the Master's lap as Jesus touched him fondly. Kindly, the Master said, "Wake up, Peter, the hour is well spent. Return to the side of James and John and pray with them in the silences of deeper prayer while I pray here alone. It is better that I should continue alone. The Paraclete has not yet come to you, and as a consequence you would find My way of prayer most difficult to understand. If you should see Me in the prayer, which will be known as The Agony, you would, no doubt, wonder about the necessity of such suffering. I would spare you that occasion of doubt."

In great anguish of both spirit and body because of the bilocation knowledge that he had just received, Peter, wide-eyed, afraid, and angry, answered, "Jesus, let me go into the city and get Judas. Look, with these two swords I could easily slay him and then he would not be able to lead the enemy here."

Gazing calmly into Peter's angry eyes, the Master answered, "My impetuous Peter, have you not forgotten this is My hour in which to suffer for such sins as you would now commit—even in spirit to slay Judas? Remember I have often used the symbols of fig trees and fields of wheat as lessons for man. Now there is also a great lesson in your two swords, as well as the fulfillment of prophecy, which states that I will be reckoned among the wicked because I will be found with a sword.

"Remember before we left the banquet room I asked you to go sell your cloak and with the money purchase a sword that the Scriptures might be fulfilled? In your wonderful obedience and exuberant charity to Me you purchased two instead of one. Now, since you have two swords that will be found in your possession, allow Me to tell you another symbol story.

"Never use a sword, Peter, unless it is for the following reasons. First, for immediate self-preservation and second, for the security of a nation in case of another country's aggression. These two reasons would be considered in the eyes of justice as obedience to authority, to God, and to country. They also fulfill the Law of Charity, which states that no greater love does a man have than to lay down his life in order that another person, or nation, may have peace and life.

"I admire your loyalty and willingness to protect Me, Peter, but you must never have the thought of killing Judas, or any other person, in your heart, for with God the Father human thoughts are as real as spoken words and will be considered in the same degree at judgment, for sins are first committed in the will."

Bowing his head to the Master's knee in perfect self-surrender and shame, Peter wept bitter tears of sorrow. Jesus spoke kindly and softly of forgiveness, and then He and the fisherman walked together to the side of James and John, who were still sleeping in prayer ecstasy through which they would gain great merit for the growth of the Church.

As the Master was about to leave Peter with them, He asked, "Peter, who do you say I am?"

Astonished, Peter answered, "Lord, Thou art the Christ, the Messiah on earth as foretold by the prophets. I am sorry if my crude manners have led You to believe I had forgotten who You are. Jesus, allow me to speak in my new life of authority. You are the Christ!"

Jesus smiled and asked, "Will you pray in union with Me near James and John? It is necessary this next hour that I pray and suffer alone as human man. I will purposely, as I have done many other times during My life, forget My Divinity the better to suffer as man. It is My will, in My Humanity, to suffer the thought and knowledge of fear like unto that which you feel in regard to body weakness, loneliness, the world, and sin. The prophecy that I suffered all things must be fulfilled. This way of suffering that I have chosen must be fair and just to the minds of men or they will not dare become imitators of Me. They would boast that I could not understand their sorrows because of not having suffered.

"Peter, while I am in this great suffering, stay here with James and John and then I will be able to hear you if in sudden anger you decide to go after Judas. I trust you will heed My words, but well I understand the bilocation knowledge that you have received is both lasting and vivid. I would take you with Me, but you would not understand such depths of suffering."

Peter said, "Thank You, Jesus. I am consoled with Your command, and I think I understand the vagueness of Your desire. I will unite my prayer with Yours. Master, call me if You feel the weight and the anguish of Your humanity too great to bear—perhaps I can help You. Exercising the authority You have given me, I ask that You call me when Your sorrows are great."

Jesus answered, "I will call if it is necessary, but I assure you that to hear your voice will be enough. You must not come to My side. Already I feel My soul saddened nigh unto death. Watch and pray in the way of prayer that I have explained to you. Pray that the Tempter does not weaken your faith if you hear Me weep, for I know your spirit is willing, but your flesh is weak."

Peter fell to his knees as the Master departed from his sight, and he prayed aloud for guidance and understanding in this new mystery of prayer. He was afraid. He wished John would at least move his head, for ecstasy is like death, and it was all so hard for him to understand. Then he noticed as he tried to rise that his own eyes were becoming heavy in the deeper prayer of ecstasy. His body, too, began to feel heavy. His fear left him and he became determined to keep awake in a state of semi-wakefulness just in case he heard Jesus call. But gradually the divine sleep of prayer deadened his senses, and for a while his soul and body swung between the two worlds of life and death.

Jesus knelt again on the grave of John the Baptist and soon fell into the soul-agonies of actual prayer, while at the same time He saw real visions of the sins the people of the world had committed and were committing, as well as the sins of future generations until the end of time.

He was restless. He was already feeling the loneliness of prayer, and the human thoughts of the futility of His suffering as man pierced His heart. Tears of sorrow welled in His eyes as the first actual vision of people appeared before Him. Ah, if they only knew that He was watching! If men would only realize that God sees everything, that nothing is, nor ever shall be, hidden from His sight. If they only believed this sublime truth, God would be spared suffering, and life on earth would be a foretaste of Heaven.

Jesus arose to His feet in horror at the sight of endless murders. He was shocked and nauseated as He saw blood and terror. In His Humanity and fear He took a few steps in the direction of Peter and called softly, "Peter, are you with Me?"

Peter answered faintly as he tried to awaken himself from the sifting depths of divine slumber. "Yes, Jesus, I am with You, but my eyes are so heavy that I am nigh unto the sleep of death to the world. I will try to continue my prayers with You. Have courage, Jesus. How I wish the soldiers would arrest me instead of You. Is there no other way?"

Jesus answered, "Be consoled, Peter. I know your flesh is weak, but I also know your fighting spirit and its worth to our Church. You have consoled Me. I will return to My place of prayer. Thank you, Peter."

The Master shuddered at the thought of the hour ahead of Him as He knelt again near John's grave. Once more the veil of time lifted before His eyes. This time He saw a mystical sea, which was made up of all generations of people. Each generation seemed to roll toward Him as a huge, breaking wave. Each person mystically approached Him and He watched their individual deeds and words. As each one's sins struck with their awful force upon His soul and humanity, as if they were crashing breakers upon a shore, His body began to dampen with huge drops of perspiration. As each upheaval threw its force against Him, He felt its repercussions shake His body in a terrible strain of nausea. He was sick nigh unto death.

In a moment of bodily quietness, He watched the great ages of intellectual grandeurs and their beauty of life—then their terrible fall into the decay of faith through slothfulness because His Father had stilled justice and allowed kindness and mercy to reign through His humanity. All this was a terrible shock of ingratitude, and the huge drops of perspiration slowly formed into tiny streamlets, which coursed down His body.

Still another vision came, and now great numbers of people appeared as though dressed in their cloaks of heinous sins of nature such as murder, the killing of infants, and injustices to both young and old. For the God-Man's eyes to see these loathsome crimes brought on severe spasms of vomiting. His body rested heavily prostrate against the rock upon which He had leaned as He prayed. After each spasm of terrible vomiting, His arms were limp and lifeless as they hung over the narrow rock predella. He was so weak He could hardly lift His head, and His body trembled from its fatigue of shock at witnessing such terrible scenes.

Again He struggled to His feet and called, "Peter, are you with Me?"

Peter was slow in answering this time, for the deep sleep was overtaking him. His voice faltered as he said, "Yes, Jesus, I am with You."

Upon hearing the big fisherman's assurance, Jesus returned to His place of prayer. Once more the same type of visions appeared before Him. Ages after ages of terrible sins unrolled as if everybody's life were written in detail upon a scroll. This time He was very ill. Finally, He vomited blood, and the drops of perspiration over His body became mixed with a serum, like blood, as it oozed from His every pore. He moaned aloud in His dreadful agony, for His soul was torn between two emotions, gratitude and sadness. Gratitude because of the great numbers of saints mirrored before Him, especially those in the generations to come, and their heroic efforts and success to love Him in such a world of sin. At the same time He was sad because of the wickedness of man. Yet it was man whom He wanted to save through His sufferings.

Violent vomiting seized Him again, causing actual blood, this time, to exude from every pore as He watched sin as one complete mountain of injustice. In great anguish, fear, and loneliness He moaned as He called, "Peter, are you with Me? Come, I need you, I am so sick!"[15]

There was no answer. Peter was asleep in God's embrace of ecstasy.

A great fear of loneliness crept over the Master. He was alone! He was weak, ill, and nearly fainting! He wanted human consolation, and listened again for Peter's answer. Then, trembling, He looked toward the heavens as though searching for His Father's light of consolation.

15 Jesus' suffering as true man did not allow His reason, at this moment, to understand, or remember, the great effects of the deep prayer Peter was in.

Michael, the archangel, in the assumed form of a young man, the better to console Jesus in His Humanity, suddenly appeared over the hillside carrying a small, gold chalice. He knelt with one knee on the rock near where the Master was bent and exhausted. Placing the chalice on the ledge, the great angel tenderly raised the Master's limp head from the rock, His pillow, and held it gently between his hands.

Tears streamed down our Lord's face, then, seeing Michael, He smiled and thanked him for coming.

Michael said, "Ah, Majestic God, gowned in the clay form of man, Thy brilliancy, the Beatific Vision, is now hidden even from Thy thoughts for Thou hast willed it so. Never having had a body I cannot imagine Your suffering, nor how intense it must be. Courage, Master, courage. I have come to console You in Your loneliness—a task not easy for an angel—for how can a spirit who has never suffered offer sympathy? Jesus, Jesus, I must address You as man since You have willed this terrible hour. Allow me to say, 'All praise and glory be to Thy name, Jesus, on earth.'

"Must I remind You, through Your veil of tears, that You willed to become man as a redeemer? I know these particular thoughts of Yours, for even the courts on high have discussed the phenomena of Your suffering as man, and we know You have often said, 'Suffer more to save more.' As angels we do not understand suffering, but allow me in some way to console You. Please say something."

Jesus said, "Remind Me, Michael, more and more of Heaven and your joys."

Michael answered, "In Your suffering, then, try to think of the souls who have already lived and loved You. Think of the torments of martyrdom they have endured in order to love You for all eternity. Think of the millions of saints yet to be born, and how they will rise in glory because of Your suffering, now. Look up, Jesus, I will draw the curtain of Heaven aside so You may see how wonderfully happy the saints are there, and how they wait for Your hour of death so that they may enter into the Kingdom, which only Your death can open. Look, the mystery is unfolding!"

Michael helped tilt the Master's head upward, and Jesus gazed into a vision in which He saw all of earth's saints singing and praising Him for His mercy that had allowed them to know Him as God-Man. With such moments of joy and sadness before Him, He was overcome with a greater desire for suffering—a desire to suffer more in order that every person born in the world would know only the joys and the happiness that He felt in His Human nature at this moment as He watched the saints in their reward of eternal joy.

He announced to Michael (truly in His Humanity) that He wanted sin to cease, that He would end time at His crucifixion, and that His saints in Limbo would be liberated to the joys of His Father. He said, "If My Father will only allow Me to have the greater chalice of suffering that I now understand through this vision, I will suffer more and thus bring evil to an end. The human race will be brought to a stop and everyone up to this moment will enter into the Beatific Vision. I desire to save every soul who is lost to Him!"

In the God-Man's excessive love and charity for souls, He felt and expressed the folly of love that many saints, since Him, have experienced in their colloquies. Often, in complete abandonment, they have been heard to say, "Lord, if I can make Thee happier by trading my complete self for five souls who may fall into Hell, then let me offer Thee these souls, and let this nothingness of myself go into Hell. Just think, Lord, You would then have five loves instead of this one love of mine. Thou hast been too kind to me in life as it is by allowing me to know, love, and serve Thee."

In that mental anguish of the saints that often results in expressions of such folly, Jesus clutched the chalice and raising it high above His head said, "Father, not My will but Thine be done. Allow this chalice of My immediate suffering to pass from Me, and give Me a greater one, which will bring all souls to Thee, both living and dead, and at the same time bring about the end of time at the hour of My crucifixion. Allow Me to restore all things that have been lost to Thee! Give Me the larger chalice, which will permit greater sufferings now in this hour of agony. Give Me the greater chalice of loneliness tonight, and allow Me to die without further consolations from My mother, My chosen friends, or Michael."

Relinquishing His claim on the gift of colloquy, the Master fell exhausted across the rock ledge. The chalice dropped from His hands. Huge drops of blood dampened His toga, and particularly was His garment crimsoned near His Sacred Heart. Michael picked up the chalice, and touching its brim to the God-Man's brow caught at the trickling drops of blood.

Jesus prayed aloud, "Father, My soul is nigh unto death—nigh unto death. Please allow Me the larger chalice of suffering. Not My will be done, however, but Thine."[16]

Michael took the chalice, which was partly filled with the Master's blood, and disappeared into the light of Heaven. Again Jesus was alone and in such terrible agony of soul-suffering that He actually hovered between life and death. At different times His agony was most severe—His bloody perspiration and awful sickness continued until Michael once more returned. Holding the chalice toward the Master, He said, "I took the chalice of blood to Your Father, and there before Him I pleaded Your petition and hope for the greater chalice."

Jesus was so exhausted that He could not move or raise His head. Michael knelt beside Him and continued caressingly, "I plead with You in Your agony to remember how the prophets of old foretold that You would suffer *all* things. Remember that You were seen by one great prophet as You carried Your cross, and in that agony You spoke to him in, and through, the mystery that with God there is no time. Please, Jesus, speak to me that I may know You hear me."

Jesus said, "Tell Me, what is My Father's will?"

Michael answered, "In order to suffer all things, You, too, must know the disappointment of not having a petition granted, even though You think it would be merciful and just. Throughout Your life all Your petitions to the Father have been answered immediately. The lame walk, the deaf hear, the blind see, and even the dead have risen. And we must not forget that through Your life sinners have been converted and that great numbers are still talking about the mystery of water changed into wine. Little do they realize that it was a changing mystery to show all people that they will represent the water at the future Love Feasts and You, the wine. At the Consecration they, too, will have a foretaste of the Transfiguration by receiving You in the Bread of Heaven. That mystery was only to show them the visible soul-change

16 Jesus did not complain about the agony of His Body or Spirit, but rather, that terrible suffering of His Soul, which first receives the effects of the five senses. Man's sins were expressed to Him through, and on, His senses, which caused His Soul (human intellect) to become emblazoned with charity, pity, and love for man.

in the body of man. Master, do You realize You have given man everything in this era and that he may live Your complete passion before the curtain of death strikes? What is this great gift but an outward sign of Your infinite love and devotion to him?

"To this minute, the Father has always answered You, but if this petition for the greater chalice were granted, the prophesies would not be fulfilled. Many people, questioning whether or not You were the Messiah, would ask if You suffered all the prophesied events. Others would boldly accuse You of not suffering all things because You had every petition answered at the will of Your Second Nature, and that You did not know the anguish of a soul who feels that his petitions are not heard according to human will and desire.

"It is the will of Your Father that all prophecies be fulfilled. You must even suffer this apparent denial of Your petition. You are not to have the greater chalice. The Father chooses, in and through the love He has for You, to have more, and greater, saints in the generations to come, even though many other people lose their souls because they will not cooperate with grace.

"Jesus, don't weep. Remember, great imitators of Your humanity will make You glad. Would You deny Your friends the joy of being One with You for all eternity? Here, You have this smaller chalice—take it into Your hands and the touch of reality, after such suffering, will make conditions and time clearer to Your human mind. Be comforted, Jesus, for Judas is near the garden gates. Your hour has come!"

Extreme weakness again caused the Master to fall over the rock. For another few minutes His limp body seemed to have fainted. Then, in obedience to Michael, He arose from the ground. He bade the great angel goodbye until tomorrow, and then walked slowly toward another type of suffering.

CHAPTER 9

The Sword

AS THOSE ENGAGED IN THE MANHUNT moved through the streets of Jerusalem, Annas sent several guards of the Sanhedrin court to search for witnesses to testify against Jesus. Money was to be paid them if necessary, and they were to be brought to him immediately. His plan was not only to listen to their accusations, but also to prompt them in powerful word-expressions according to the Scriptures. Then he set five in the morning as the hour of the court, even though this was a most unusual and even unlawful hour in which to hold an assembly, but he was afraid of a sudden uprising of the people, for a majority of them believed this Jesus was the real Messiah.

Meanwhile, as the parade headed toward the place where Jesus prayed, loud, boisterous laughter and jesting concerning the Master was brought into play by the soldiers in order to instill courage in the prisoners, who now began to show signs of fear and fatigue. Up until that moment they had been overjoyed in the fresh air of the night, and the excitement was as good as wine to their senses as they shouted to their friends of their promised freedom, which they wanted above everything else. They swore that nothing Jesus could say would sway them from their promise to capture Him.

Then they began to wonder again about the Master, and to ask what manner of man He might be. Was He strong and vicious? Would

He be swift in action in a fight? Did He carry a sword or a club?

Many of the people who followed the parade were in a gambling mood, and they shouted their bets as to who would win, the prisoners or Jesus. One prisoner asked gruffly of a passerby, "Tell us what this Jesus looks like. Is it true He is a giant who uses both clubs and swords? It is said He bought two swords. Does He fight alone, or does He have a gang of friends to protect Him?"

A sharp, commanding voice answered, "Oh, you won't have any trouble. He doesn't know how to fight and He will probably be unarmed, with the exception of His tongue. Watch out for that, for it is like a piercing sword, and He calls His way of talking the word of God."

Another man voiced his opinion, "It is said He is immaculate in His personal neatness and has uncalloused hands, so you have nothing to fear. I wager He is afraid to fight. You know the usual weakness of self-styled preachers. Don't fear His strength. Rather fear His philosophy of love, which can harm you to the end that you will become as little, weak children. If this happens, He may run for His freedom. Love and meekness seem to be His doctrine. His followers are for the most part women."

This answer brought loud shouts and laughter from the jeering soldiers and prisoners. One soldier shouted, "We want a king of power and wealth when the Messiah comes. This Man is but a Nazarene—nothing good has ever come out of Nazareth! Hail to the king of power who is to come. Down with this Jesus!"

As Jesus saw the soldiers' torches near the entrance gates of Gethsemane, He hurried to Peter, and patting him on the head, whispered, "Peter, poor Peter, you could not watch one hour with Me. But don't worry, for in My suffering as man I fully understand the willingness of your spirit and the weakness of your flesh. If I had not suffered just now as True Man I might in justice scold you by asking, 'Could you not watch one hour with Me?'"

Then, once more in the full memory of His Divinity, He said, "Come, let us go, now, to meet the enemy who is just outside the gate. I do not have time to explain their evil designs. Let us allow James and John to continue in their ecstasy sleep, for they are earning great merit for our needs at this hour. The soldiers will not find them if we hurry down the path. Come, the torch-bearers for Judas are close."

As they left the grove, Peter suddenly stopped and stared at Jesus, for His toga looked as though it had been sprinkled with blood. In the light of the full moon he could see the gray pallor of the Master's face and the drying streamlets of blood, which had coursed from His brow to His chin. The Messiah was ill!

Jesus calmed Peter by saying, "It is all right. I am not suffering now. The sweat of blood came on Me as I watched the sins of the people and the far-reaching effects they will have on the generations to be born."

Trembling, and without speaking, Peter hurried to the nearby creek, and dipping the hem of his cloak into the water, he washed the face and hands of the Master quickly. Then, kneeling before Him, he removed Jesus' sandals from his own feet and said, "Lord, in the power of authority that You have given me, I dare speak a command to You. Lift Your feet that I may replace Your sandals. You have suffered enough without going barefoot any longer."

Jesus obeyed meekly, and as He moved His left foot forward to receive the second sandal, the New Ambassador continued, "Your feet must be very sensitive now that they have suffered bleeding. My, I am sorry for my past offenses. Little have I realized the terror of sin, and its balance made possible through penance. Help me, Lord, that I will never offend You again."

Embracing Peter, Jesus kissed him and whispered, "Peace." Together they resumed their walk to meet the intruders. Peter was now barefoot.

Tall torches sent shades of flickering light across the prisoners' faces as they marched through the gates of Gethsemane. They smiled in the hope of their freedom. Then a noticeable still in the air seemed to settle over soldiers, prisoners, onlookers, and the hundred or more of the Master's closest friends who had gathered, with His disciples, hoping to come to His defense if He gave the command. All that could be heard was the dull clanking of swords bumping against the wooden clubs held by the prisoners.

Nearing the grove of trees, they saw Jesus and Peter standing on the hillside. Judas whispered to the soldiers that he would run ahead and kiss the Man they wanted.

As Peter watched the crowd come out to get Jesus, he grew angrier and angrier. His face was colorless and his knuckles white as ivory as he clutched nervously at his sword hilts. Jesus, noticing this, quickly but gently pushed the weapons back into their sheaths saying, "Peter, do not use the sword. If I needed help I would call on My legions of angels. My sufferings are not yet over. Remember I am to be crucified. Keep your peace."

"Yes, Jesus," Peter answered, "I understand. I am sorry I am so easily angered. Teach me to follow Your way of peace."

"Have courage, Peter," Jesus said.

Judas and the soldiers were close at hand. In a friendly manner, as though he were joyous, Judas ran and embraced Jesus, and in doing so, kissed Him on the forehead.

Smiling at him, the Master asked aloud for all to hear, "Judas, why do you kiss Me? The soldiers and your friends know who I am. So, too, do My disciples who have followed you here, as well as those who are already here in prayer over the hillside." Then scornfully, "You are quite the foolish actor, Judas. Stand aside and let your friends have Me."

The prisoners raced ahead of the soldiers, and as they were about to take hold of Jesus, He stepped forward into the light of their torches and asked in a clear voice, "Whom do you seek?"

The prisoners dropped back a step astonished, and with clumsy, stumbling movements several fell to the ground. In their embarrassment, which was only natural on such a mission, they tried to answer, but their confusion caused them only to stare at the Master as if they were mute. Once more Jesus asked, "I say, whom do you seek? May I help you?"

In great fear several prisoners spoke as though with one voice. "We are seeking the Jesus of Nazareth. Is it possible You are the Man Caiphas wants?"

Jesus smiled and approached a little closer to them. "I am Jesus of Nazareth," He said.

Two prisoners stepped closer instantly and grasped His arms. A loud cheer of triumph arose from the crowd. When all was quiet, Jesus said to the multitudes of His disciples, "Friends, return now to your homes. It is written that I have not lost one whom the Father gave Me. If you obey Me now, you are among those He gave Me. My own know My voice."

Hundreds, in obedience to this command, departed from the hillside and roadways without murmur, or complaint, and many were overcome with sadness at thus leaving Jesus and their beloved Peter alone with the enemy. The soldiers and prisoners were aghast and unnerved at this display of obedience, for it seemed as though the entire crowd was leaving the scene of capture. Boldly one soldier pointed at

Peter and asked, "Why doesn't he leave with the rest of Your crowd? Is he not one of Your disciples?"

Jesus answered, "He is One with the Father and Me. His power is so great that if he should ask Me to kneel before him I would obey. He exercises his own judgment and authority as to whether or not he should leave Me."

The soldiers and prisoners were shocked and did not understand His words. In their confusion, the prisoners began questioning one another, "They told us this Man would not fight, yet look at Him. He is already covered with bloodstains! With whom has He been fighting? His look and manner are not one of anger. Can He have been fighting Simon with the two swords? Do you think Simon took them away from Him before we arrived, knowing this would help Caiphas? Is Simon's silence a means of aiding us with this cunning prisoner? Perhaps Judas and Simon are working together. Is that why Simon does not leave?"

Looking closer at the swords, a soldier exclaimed, "These swords have not been used, and the only mark of blood on Simon is on the hem of his garment. What does this mean?"

One prisoner now said boldly, "Let us see whether or not this Jesus will fight!" He lunged forward and spat full in the Master's face. The spittle ran down His cheek and dripped from His chin. This was too much for Peter. Before anyone could stop him, he brought a sword into action and cut off the prisoner's ear, and with it the flesh of his cheek that matched that portion of the Master's face touched by the spittle.

Peter then froze in fright, for suddenly he realized what he had done. He dropped his sword and ran down the hillside. Several soldiers and prisoners pursued him. He was overtaken at the gate and there a terrible fight took place. Peter's strong fists quickly knocked three prisoners and one soldier unconscious before other soldiers brought their swords into play. Peter surrendered.

During this action, which held the attention of the soldiers, prisoners, and people in great fear and expectation, Judas looked at Jesus beside him. The God-Man had not tried to run for His freedom, as Judas and the others had expected He might under just such conditions. Rather, He enjoyed the fight and found it difficult to stifle a chuckle.

Judas was both startled and spiritually awakened at the Master's sense of humor. He was seeing Him as true Man and God at the same time. He looked again to make sure of what he had seen. Yes, it was there. Truly this Jesus was a real man! And Judas now believed also that He was the real Messiah! How he wished he could shout his sorrow to all the people and tell them of his terrible mistake. How he wanted to embrace Jesus and plead his sorrow, but he was paralyzed with fear and terrified at the thought of the sin he had committed with the Blessed Living Bread. He turned violently ill and bent over the edge of the roadside, unnoticed by the excited crowd.

Then, because he was sick all over himself, he quickly removed his clothing and wrapped his body in a large linen sheet that one of the disciples had left behind when he returned home at Jesus' command. In terrible pain, he remained huddled and hidden behind low-hanging shrubs along the road not far from the gates of the garden. When he thought no one was looking, he attempted to run, but the soldiers caught sight of his strangely wrapped body and his suspicious actions, and dashed after him. Catching hold of the linen sheet, they jerked it from his shoulders. In pain and fright, Judas ran naked into the forest of shrubs across the roadway. The soldiers laughed, but did not recognize him.

Meanwhile, Peter had been pushed, at the point of a sword, to the side of the Master. Neither spoke, but they exchanged glances of kind understanding. There the Divine Master stood, between two prisoners who held His arms locked behind Him.

All looked in awed silence at Malchus, the prisoner whose ear Peter had severed. This man had often acted as a servant to Caiphas because of his good behavior, which had merited a degree of freedom for him. Now, he lay writhing in agony in a pool of his own blood, bleeding to death. His jawbone and teeth were visible to the spectators, who tried to soothe him. However, they soon turned away from such a terrible sight.

Suddenly, both soldiers and prisoners became hysterical with the thought that now they could not all return to Caiphas as he had ordered. If Malchus died, the prisoners knew they would forfeit their freedom and would no doubt suffer crucifixion, or death in some other way. Stunned, they watched Malchus roll and moan in his agony, and remembered their pledge that they would all return to Caiphas unharmed.

A great fear seized the prisoners, and they realized that perhaps their only chance to live lay in their escaping into the grove and becoming lost in the night. But on second thought, they realized their clubs would have no chance against the swords of skilled soldiers.

Seeing their uneasiness, one soldier shouted angrily to Peter, "You will be crucified for this. I am sure that if most of these prisoners were not your friends they would kill you!"

The soldiers watched the prisoners carefully, anticipating a break for freedom, their swords drawn and ready. They realized only too well that if an escape were successful they would, in turn, be thrown into prison, and perhaps would suffer death for having failed to bring Jesus to Caiphas.

Frightened, Peter stood beside Jesus and the angry mob. He realized that his mistake in cutting off the ear of Malchus had been an act of disobedience to the will of Jesus, yet he asked himself, according to his authority as ambassador, did he not have free will to act in defense of the Messiah?

Although Jesus was held fast by the two prisoners, He spoke to the soldier in command. "If I save the life of Malchus," He asked, "and restore his ear as good as new, will you give Simon his freedom?"[17]

This question brought a laugh of scorn from the prisoners and the soldiers alike. "Why," they exclaimed, "that is impossible. Malchus is near death now from bleeding. Your silly talk about such healing power proves You are crazy. It is no wonder Annas has gone to such extremes to capture You."

However, at a word from the commanding officer, Jesus was allowed to walk in freedom toward Malchus. With a twinkle in His eyes He looked at Peter and said, "Pick up your sword and put it into its scabbard to stay. Peace be with you, but remember, you will not always have Me with you to correct your mistakes—such as putting ears back on people."

Kneeling beside Malchus, Jesus spoke quietly, His words for the suffering man alone. "I am going to replace your ear," He said, "and take away your pain. No doubt, through your own free will, you will now become a devout follower of Mine, for you will recognize that this miracle is only something God can do. But, to save the other prisoners from further dungeon life because of your conversion, and in the case you speak of loyalty to Me, I ask you to accept the cross of silence that I will give you. You will never speak again in this life. Now, when I replace

17 The people did not know Simon was now called Peter by Jesus and the apostles.

your ear and when the pain ceases, which will be immediately, I ask you to act quite unconcerned. Do this to insure the freedom of your fellow prisoners, for many of them are not guilty of their accused crimes."

Bending still closer, the Master continued, "Do you believe that I am the Messiah?"

Through eyes of great suffering and weakness, Malchus simply looked at Jesus with an expression of love, which told clearly of his new feelings. He embraced the Master and whispered, "Jesus, I believe now." This gesture was mistaken by the soldiers and prisoners to be a wild gesture caused by a spasm of pain. Malchus had spoken his last earthly words. From that moment until death his tongue was silenced.

As the Master searched for the dust-encrusted ear that lay near His feet, Malchus writhed once more in terrible agony, throwing himself here and there on the ground near the knees of Jesus. The soldier in command said loudly, "Hurry, can't You see he is dying?"

Finding the ear at last, Jesus sternly commanded the wounded man to lie still as He put the severed member once more into place and smoothed the flesh across the jawbone. Instantly, the miracle was wrought! The crowd was stunned and could hardly believe their eyes as they watched Malchus rise to his feet without pain. Silently, he walked to his place in line with the other prisoners, who exclaimed in awed wonder and examined his ear and the faint, pink scar that was the only visible mark of the wound now evident upon his face. Then they looked at Jesus and said, "Are You the Messiah?"

Jesus did not answer.

Malchus listened to the questions and then hung his head in order to hide his great interior joy—he believed, and knew, this Man was the Messiah.

Jesus was a dreadful sight. His own blood, from the bloody sweat of The Agony, was still damp on His clothing and now the dirt and the blood of Malchus was added to it. This would certainly cause Annas and Caiphas to believe that He had put up a terrible struggle before surrendering. Indeed, He would be listed among the wicked! With these thoughts going through His mind, Jesus smiled at the prisoners, who were so bewildered and frightened by all the events. Rather than show any gesture of friendliness toward Him, they seized Him once more and bound His hands. They were afraid of His magical powers, which they could not explain, and they wanted their earthly freedom much more than the thought of faith, or life everlasting.

Jesus was forced to walk backward on the return march to the courts of Caiphas. Thus He faced Malchus, who wept all the way because of his gratitude, love, and pity for his God. The other prisoners thought he cried because of pain, and they chided the Master for performing only half a miracle. Malchus tried to make them understand by gestures that he was not suffering, but failed. They did not realize that he could not speak.

In order that there might be an atmosphere of courage and victory about them before they arrived at the courts, and to show the people on the streets how fearless they were, the soldiers and prisoners spat on Jesus and hissed all manner of evil words as they struck Him in the face and then dared Him, if He was a prophet, to tell whose fist dealt the blow.

Thus the victors reached the city. Shrill trumpets sounded from the high walls of Caiphas' court, where soldiers stood on watch. Only Annas and a few people he had bribed to testify against the prisoner faced Jesus when He was brought in. Caiphas had retired. Annas gave the returning prisoners their freedom, and they hurried at once into the streets of Jerusalem, free men.

Nothing was said between Annas and Jesus. They just looked at each other and then Annas ordered the Master to be led to the dungeon hall below the court rooms, where He would be kept until the Sanhedrin members assembled.

These members had been alerted, but many of them were still asleep, having given orders to be notified when Jesus was captured. However, this was not necessary, for the shouting and the cheering in the streets as the prisoners were released awakened them.

As they dressed quickly in their togas of authority, they hoped fervently that Annas had found witnesses who would testify against this Jesus. In that way their job of condemning Him would be over quickly. Surely, they thought, there would be no difficulty in obtaining a verdict, for the mere fact that Jesus could cause such a commotion at this hour was enough proof that He was dangerous. Thus, He must be dealt with in a most severe manner before He managed to get all the people in Jerusalem to follow Him.

CHAPTER 10

The White Rose of Consolation

THE GUARDS KICKED AND SLAPPED JESUS in a most atrocious manner as they took Him to the subterranean cell. Again, in order to test His gift of prophecy, which seemed to interest them more than anything else, they asked, "Whom do You say struck You?"

Jesus did not answer.

Angered by the Master's silence, they pushed Him down the narrow stone stairway and brutally shoved Him from side to side against the stone walls. Then they threw Him into a dark cell-room, where there were twenty other prisoners. As the door closed, they jeered, "This Man thinks He is God. See what you can do to break His will before the Sanhedrin meets and brings Him to justice for such blasphemy!"

Many of the prisoners were new there, and their awed expressions told of their foreknowledge of Jesus. These were silent in fear as the others openly expressed their disbelief and hatred for anything pertaining to God. They pushed the Master and spat upon Him and threw Him to the slimy floor. As He knelt in the mud at their feet, their loud expressions of hatred nauseated Him. Pulling Him erect once more, they pushed and buffeted Him again and again, shoving Him from one to another, trying to make Him confess He was the Living

Messiah since He would not deny it. They wanted to hear Him say the words that were called blasphemy.

Without raising an arm in defense, Jesus fell at last exhausted over the limp body of an elderly man who lay moaning in his death's struggle of old age in a dank corner. Steadying Himself, the Master knelt tenderly beside him. Taking him into His arms and stroking his face tenderly, He whispered, "Have courage now—remember life ends for all. Do you know God loves you? I know you have waited with countless others for His coming. Because you have done this, you are a believer in God and should have nothing to fear."

The old man nodded and answered, "Yes, I have waited for the coming of the Messiah." Then feebly he asked, "How did You know? I have never talked with You before."

Jesus said, "You will soon understand, and this I promise you—you will recognize the Messiah's presence here on earth before you die."

Another old prisoner shouted, "If You are the Messiah, heal him instead of offering him such nice promises. We dare You to do such a thing here in the dungeon. Stand back, men, and watch a miracle!"

There was a moment's silence, and then as nothing happened the prisoners laughed boisterously and pulled Jesus from the old man. But now the steady gaze of the Master quieted them. They began to recall all they had heard about His miracles, and truthfully they were afraid they might actually see one. A few of them even trembled, for the meaning of the word *miracle* was not new, nor unbelieved by them. Had not another sort of miracle been taking place right there every night for years?

Almost with one accord they looked upward toward a high dungeon window. The dying man whispered to Jesus, "Every night at this hour someone lowers a basket of food and wine to us through that window. I wait all day for a taste of the wine, for it is the only heat I have for this poor, broken body of mine. We do not know who the Good Samaritan is, whether it is man, woman, or angel, for we know that no one is allowed through the guards at the gate entrance."

One of the other prisoners turned to Jesus. "You tell us who it is," he said. "If You are the Messiah that knowledge should be known to You."

A hush fell as yet another prisoner said, "Be still—it is time!"

It was obvious that the prisoners lived for this hour. Surely it was a consolation and a blessed hour. All of them listened, and heard, the quiet shuffling of footsteps outside the window. Slowly and quietly a small basket containing food and a flask of wine was lowered by a rope into the many uplifted hands.

The contents of the basket—roast meats, nuts, dates, and bread—were divided among them, Jesus and the dying old man excepted. As they ate, the Master arose and walked over to where the rope hung limply against the damp wall. Tugging at it gently, He called, "Turan, lower a potion[18] for a sick, dying man."

Stunned and astonished, the prisoners fell back against the wall and looked at Him. Then for the first time they heard the voice of their benefactor. A woman answered, "I will see what I can do. It is getting late, but I will hurry."

The prisoners began to ask one another, "Who is this Man to have His commands obeyed like this? We have called and begged for our friend to speak to us but without success. He calls only once and is heard. Who is He?"

One prisoner asked Jesus slowly, "Do You know this woman you called Turan? Who is she?"

"I know her very well," Jesus answered. "She is indeed a Good Samaritan. I know her most secret thoughts."

Now the prisoners were afraid—afraid that this mysterious Turan, who surely must be a friend of Jesus, would learn how they had treated Him and as a consequence discontinue her gifts of mercy, which had been their very life and hope.

One man suddenly grew very pale. "Don't you know who she is?" he gasped. "Haven't you ever heard that name? She is Annas' daughter, the wife of Caiphas!"

There was a complete silence.

After a moment, Jesus nodded. "Yes," He said, "she is the wife of Caiphas. She is also a devout worshiper of God, and because she loves God she has learned how to be merciful."

Now they were more frightened than ever. They pleaded with Jesus to pardon them and begged Him not to expose their actions to Turan. Jesus assured them He would say nothing. "Do you know why she is merciful to

18 Narcotic.

you?" He asked. "She doesn't know any one of you. Then why do you think she risks her health and time giving to you who have never helped her?"

The prisoners shook their heads.

"She understands mercy and kindness because she has prayed much," the Master continued. "She knows that each act she performs in life for her fellow men, regardless of who they are, earns a jewel for her eternal crown. She knows, too, that she will die someday and that she will live again in Heaven with God. Then she will receive the crown of jewels made possible through her earthly acts of mercy and love. These acts are living prayers, and God calls them gems of compassionate mercy. Compassionate mercy is actual work—the doing of something for the poor and suffering.

"Showing mercy is one path that leads to God's kingdom of everlasting joy, and Turan has found it. Death will one day strip you of these clay bodies, and then your spirits will gain their freedom as only such freedom was known before the fall of Adam. How do you think you will look in the darkness of spirit without a single jewel that you could have earned while you had the chance? Jewels must be earned—that is the reason of life. God the Father rewards well and most faithfully the least little favor accomplished in life. Why, even in this dark prison you can store up jewels by showing mercy and kindness to one another. Why do you wait longer before you start to build treasures for your eternal joys? Turan has shown you the way."

Frightened until he trembled, one prisoner asked, "How can God hear us when we are already so wicked and have never thought about mercy and Heaven? He hears only the good people and those who worship in the synagogues. How can we lay up treasures in Heaven when God does not hear us? Remember, we are in prison."

"God is everywhere," Jesus answered, "even in your hearts. He is in this dungeon and at the same time He is in all the world. Nothing is impossible with Him—He knows no bounds and is all-powerful. Remember He is Spirit. Why do you try to restrict Him even with a thought? Try living for Him—even here you can gain merit and eternal freedom.

"Did you know that God in His Humanity said, 'Blessed are the merciful, for they shall obtain mercy?' Think about those words, for in them lies a tremendous promise and gift. Rebuild your lives around that beautiful foundation of truth, for it is a way of living close to God while you are yet on earth. Never forget how you have enjoyed the gifts Turan has given you. She sustained you in health and gave you moral courage because you lived for that one hour in which she came to you—all because she dared to do good for the love of God. Remember, she did not do these perilous deeds of mercy because she loved you—rather she did them because she knew she was pleasing God. Follow her way, and in little things become coworkers with God, doing good to souls."

One prisoner said, "You talk with wisdom and as if You had great authority. Could You be the Messiah we have looked for? You are here because You claim to be God. Let us hear Your own statement. Won't You show us a miracle that we may believe?"

Jesus answered, "Whom do you think I am?"

The man said, "I think You are the Messiah. No other living man could have convinced me of God's mercy as You have. Also, I would like the Messiah to be like You."

Most of the other prisoners just looked baffled and afraid. How terrible if He were God—for they had struck Him!

A soft step and a rustling was heard at the window above. Slowly a flask, filled with a thick green syrup made especially for the dying, bumped against the wall as it was lowered into the dungeon. All eyes were on Jesus as He took and, raising the suffering old man against His knee, gave him to drink. His pain was eased immediately. Then the Master embraced him and said, "Since you know you are dying, I am sure you want to do so in the good pleasure of God. Tell Me that you love God."

The old man answered carefully and shyly, for he was not accustomed to the expressions of love, "Yes, I guess I do love Him. Anyway, I believe there is a God."

Jesus continued, "Do you believe the prophecies that say God will suffer on earth in order to bring about the redemption of men?"

The old man answered, "Yes, the Messiah will come someday. I have waited so long. You are a good man; do You know when He will be here? What is this I heard the men ask—whether or not You are God? You are not God—because You are in prison. God could not sin, which would bring about an arrest. If He were so unfortunate as to be here, through a misunderstanding, He would no doubt perform a miracle and thus make His escape. He would help us, too, for many of us are not guilty of the crimes for which we have been accused."

Jesus did not answer. He arose and took the empty flask to the table, whereon dangled the end of the rope just as He left it. As He was busy adjusting the rope once more around the flask there suddenly appeared, on the table, eighteen white roses.

Immediately the air was filled with their sweet, clean fragrance. It was as if all earth's flowers were gathered there. The men were awed, but then after a few minutes they began to handle and to caress the exquisite blooms and to say, "These are roses—but roses like these have never grown in this country. Where did they come from? And look at the stems—they are fully two feet long. And the dew—it is like fresh rain!" Lonesome and hungry for the touch of rain and the smell of earth's warmth, they hugged the roses and gazed in wonderment at Jesus. They had asked for a miracle—was this it?

The Master broke one blossom from its long stem and took it to the dying man. All about Him the prisoners were exclaiming, "There can be no doubt about this miracle! Of all things, roses in a dungeon! We expected some sort of action to take place, but nothing like this. We have never seen roses such as these! This Jesus is surely the Messiah, for only God could make us talk now of roses and love when only yesterday we talked of murder. This is the miracle the old man asked for. Are we going to be fools and not accept it?"

One man said, "God has been merciful to us—we haven't seen a rose of any kind in years and now we can touch and breathe them. God is wonderful, and wonderful are His ways. This miracle shows us our stupidity, for if Jesus had healed the old man we would have said He used magic or trick powers of the mind, but God wished to save us from that blasphemy. Just think—through a simple rose we are compelled to believe this man, Jesus, is the Messiah. We have the living God right here in the dungeon with us!"

They all knelt around the Master as He caressed the old man, who was beginning his sleep of death. They pleaded, "Lord, we don't know what to say to You or how to act in Your presence. You are so human. Teach us what to say." They kissed His feet and continued, "Jesus, redeem us. Jesus, save us. Take us from this prison. Give us freedom. Make us worthy disciples and give us courage to proclaim Your mercy and kindness to all the world."

Jesus said, "It is the law of the land and the will of man that you are here. Even though I have the power to take you from this dungeon I will not do so now. I respect man's free will, as well as the laws of a country. However, remember that prayer often changes the tide of life for one as well as for many, and that changing tide is often another miraculous gift from God."

They all became quiet then, and knelt beside the old man. Jesus said, "Here, take this rose in your hand, for it is the rose of consolation for you. It is white because My Father loves purity, and it is thornless because I have not yet died to redeem man. When I am crucified you will be redeemed."

Raising himself upon one elbow the old man gasped, "Then You are the Messiah, the Christ? My God, what have I ever done to deserve this?"

"I am the Messiah," Jesus answered quietly. "I told you that you would see Me before you died. Here I am beside you and ready to walk spiritually with you through the portals of death. Death is but a shadow made clearer with freedom—it is just the passing of time. Be not afraid."

The old man died smiling.

The prisoners, now acting as though they were little children, threw their arms about Jesus, and some of them even wept while others said, "Jesus, Jesus we cannot part with You. Allow us to escape and we will try to save You from crucifixion. Please let us help You! Is it absolutely necessary for our redemption that You die?"

Quietly Jesus assured them that it was. However, He said that in three days He would rebuild the temple, and He taught them that the word *temple* meant His body. He said He would raise it from the tomb as though He had never died nor suffered, and would again live among them on earth for forty days.

They asked eagerly, "Will You come to us here? Will You be invisible, or will You be arrested again? Will we know You after You have arisen?"

Jesus answered, "I promise I will come to you here in this dungeon room and I will eat with you. Keep constant in your prayers for My Father's glory to be known over the earth during the Resurrection. I will come to you at this early hour of the morning. Remember, I love you and will protect and redeem you."

After covering the old man's body with a cloak, the prisoners returned to the table and silently arranged the roses in the flask for their wonderful friend Turan. They were childlike as they thought of her surprise and joy when she pulled them over the window edge.

Meanwhile, Turan was worried over the passing of time. It was nearly dawn. Suddenly she began to wonder how that Man in the dungeon had known her name. Curious, and yet filled with the fear of being found out, she leaned forward and whispered into the dark depths below, "I would like to speak to the one who called me by name."

"Yes, Turan, it was I," Jesus answered. "Thank you for your great kindness to us."

Leaning further over the sill, Turan asked, "How did You know my name, prisoner? No one else is aware that I come here. How did You learn about me? I must know—it is for my protection that I ask. And I would like to continue with this mission of mercy."

"Turan," the Master answered as all the prisoners watched and listened, "the Messiah knows the hearts of all men. I know your heart and soul and your least little thought. You are the wife of Caiphas—and I know that he is not aware that you come here. Fear not, for I will soon take you to your heavenly home with Me."

"Turan, you have a withered eye, which has given you much pain. Within a few minutes it will be cured. I bless you with a miracle of perfect sight because you have been merciful to My friends."

Turan, almost overcome with both fear and joy, answered as if she were speaking to herself. "Only God knows I come here," she gasped. "Truly You are the Messiah! Are You the new prisoner—the One they call Jesus the Impostor?"

The Master's answer came back to her out of the darkness. "Yes, I am Jesus of Nazareth."

A faint cry escaped Turan's lips as she strained to catch a glimpse of the Master, and for a moment Jesus was transfigured into His true light of glory for her benefit and the prisoners'. All were speechless and numb with the beauty and the knowledge that came to them intuitively.

As the heavenly light dimmed, Jesus called, "Now you had better lift the rope, Turan. Hurry for your safety."

Obeying His order, Turan pulled the rope toward her. Jesus and the prisoners smiled as they watched the flask filled with roses disappear upward over the bumpy black wall. Then they heard her whimper of great surprise.

Quickly, Turan gathered the roses into her arms, carefully concealed the basket and flask in the folds of her gown, and ran from the prison window.

Outside the prison walls and into the streets she hastened, and then she remembered the Master's promise that her eye would be healed. She believed, but her thoughts were above miracles at that moment. She wanted to save this Jesus from being crucified and to tell everyone in the world that He was the Messiah.

Knowing that the Sanhedrin would send Jesus to Pilate for His final sentence, she hurried to speak to Claudentia, Pilate's wife, who was her half-sister. Perhaps if she told her, and Pilate, the happenings of this morning, they would listen and stop this terrible execution.

On she ran, then pausing for breath, she mused again about how Jesus had known her name. It was incredible! Yes, she was certain He was God. She hurried on happily along the dark path, and as she went one white rose touched her withered eye. Instantly she was cured!

It was a gray, dim dawn as she hurried up Pilate's pavilion steps. She knew that at that very moment her husband must be confronting Jesus. What was he saying to Him? She prayed he would be merciful and find no fault in Him.

Within the hour she was ushered into the living quarters of Claudentia and Pilate, and hurriedly she began her story. Awed by her healed eye, they took the roses and caressed them. As they listened, they realized that guards would not allow a prisoner to take roses into his cell. And if that were so—where did such flowers come from? Like the prisoners, they recognized that roses of this species did not grow in that country nor had they ever seen any like them. Truly this must be a miracle. Well they understood the philosophy of miracles and they believed God could do all things. Hadn't He made the world?

When Turan had finished her story, Pilate said with great deliberation, "As I awakened this morning, Claudentia told me about a dream she had during the night and she begged me not to listen to the Jews in regard to this Jesus. She wanted me to have nothing to do with the case, particularly if the death sentence is demanded." He frowned. "Now, with what you have told me, I'm afraid to act in the authority that I have. However, I promise you and Claudentia that I will try every way possible to prevent a crucifixion.

He paused. "Knowing the Jews as I do," he continued slowly, "I believe there will be no change of mind on their part. They will not ask for this Jesus' release, which is a custom of this yearly celebration, as you know. I have little doubt but that they will demand our worst criminal, Barabbas, instead. Their minds are too filled with revenge and hatred to do anything else.

"Already this morning I have heard crowds assembling in the courtyard calling for a crucifixion. I must ask both of you to give me your pledge of silence in regard to this discussion. This you must do for my protection. Also Caiphas must be considered. How his temper will flair when he learns about your visits to the prison, Turan!"

As Pilate left the room he muttered, "I must truthfully say that never before have I heard of a false, self-styled Messiah performing such a miracle as the healing of Turan's eye!"

He was greatly worried and wished he had never heard of Jesus. What a decision he had to make. He must judge whether or not a mere man was God—and he found himself inclined to believe that this Man was!

CHAPTER 11

The Sanhedrin

BEFORE THE GUARDS ARRIVED to take Jesus to the Sanhedrin, the prisoners—in their new and great love for Him—bathed His face and hands and tried to freshen His robes, which were badly soiled from the dust and the mud of the dungeon floor.

They were barely through when they heard rhythmical marching feet come to a halt outside the prison door and knew the hour had arrived. It was a sad parting, for they realized this was their last earthly glimpse of the Messiah before His terrible crucifixion. Kneeling before Him they clung to Him as though they were frightened children, and begged Him to remember His promise to visit them after the Resurrection.

The Master smiled and assured them He would not forget. At that moment the door opened and the guards entered. At sight of the prisoners keeling about Jesus, weeping and praying, they became violently angry because the Master was not hated as they had hoped. The pushed Him roughly out into the corridor, and then turning to the prisoners cursed them and spat in their faces. On their part, the prisoners begged the guards not to have anything to do with the crucifixion lest it be to their condemnation. The guards were astonished at this united oration of love from men who only yesterday were considered the most wicked and the most loathsome types of humanity in Jerusalem. They left the prison cell quickly.

Roughly, they buffeted and slapped Jesus as He walked up the narrow stone stairway toward the main floor of the courtroom.

Even though it was early for hearings, the assembly hall was a scene of hurried activity as caretakers busied themselves with the last-minute dusting of benches and tables, and the lighting of hundreds of candles and oil lamps. Charcoal fires were also set aglow and incense burned in shallow trays above the embers, in order to take away the musty odors that clung to the dampness of the luxurious draperies and heavily-cushioned chairs.

As each candle and lamp was lit, the room appeared more and more glorious and quiet in its mystifying depths of age and hidden history, which breathed from the stone floors and the columned arches and from the worn velvet and gold-threaded tapestries. The magnificent colors of these age-old fabrics were bright with a sheen of gold enhanced with blue and black as each thread appeared to dance to the flickering fires beneath the incense trays. These trays, themselves, seemed alive as their curling vapors rose into the nothingness of the courtroom's silence. Hanging from every wall were priceless collections of antiquity, as well as great arrays of war trophies. In the dim corners deeper colors shimmered from every conceivable ornamentation. Jewels and gold nuggets recast their captured fires and winked as though they were sleepy serpents. The caretakers smiled as they watched the phantasms made by their hands, as if they were artists using fire for brushes against the black canvas of time.

A hundred richly carved stalls, which could serve either as couches or chairs for members of the Sanhedrin, stood along one side of the rounded room. About thirty feet in front of the stalls were three highly ornamented thrones, which ordinarily faced a sanctuary at one end of the stalls where visiting high priests prayed, burned incense, and offered the bloody sacrifice for sin.

Directly in front of the center throne stood a large lectern. On it was a scroll of laws pertaining to Jerusalem, and on top of that lay a folded garment of gold cloth, which was to be worn by the officiating high priest. It was the custom that the high priest dress himself in this robe and tear it vehemently from neckline to hem when the Sanhedrin gave a final decision. Thus the people knew a law had become final.

A shrill trumpet sounded and slowly four great, massive doors opened. Ten trumpeters, two abreast, led a solemn, colorful, majestic procession into the room. Immediately behind them marched twenty elders, men of age and wisdom whose minds were enriched with great learning about the laws of the land. Fourteen scribes followed them. These were writers and doctors of the Law of God as given to Moses. Bringing up the rear were the ceremoniously dressed high priests, better known as the Council of the Jews, numbering thirty-six, and comprising the greater number of the Sanhedrin. These were dressed like the elders, but were considered men of greater knowledge and, therefore, walked in a group by themselves.

The high priests took their places in the stall-enclosures with stateliness, dignity, and pomp. Now, Annas, Caiphas, and one other visiting high priest entered and took their seats on the three thrones which, for the hour, were turned to face the council.

Because of the hour and the unusualness of the whole court routine, three other high priests personally ushered Jesus into the hall. They smiled with the knowledge that this Man must be made a spectacle of, and jested with one another about their eagerness to begin their persecuting attack. So anxious were they that they did not even wait until they faced Caiphas to begin. As they walked toward the thrones one high priest said in a loud voice, "If You are the Christ, tell us of authority, and we may save You from death. Why do You admit such claims to the common people? If You are authority, then You should seek authority. Wouldn't that be in keeping with the law?"

Jesus did not answer and kept His eyes straight ahead.

One of the other high priests asked, "If You are the Messiah whom we look for, why do You come here as a prisoner? Let us hear You confess that You are the Christ."

Jesus smiled faintly and then said in such a low tone that only the priest who spoke last heard His words, "If I tell you, you will not believe Me—and if I question you, you will not answer Me, nor let Me go. But henceforth, whether you believe it or not, the Son of Man will be seated on the right hand of the power of God."

The high priest stopped as though brought to a sudden halt by a command. He scowled at Jesus and hissed the single word, "Fool!"

When at last they reached the thrones, but before Caiphas could ask a question, this same high priest shouted, "Art Thou, then, the Son of God? Answer us yes or no!"

Jesus said nothing.

Caiphas, in all his regal splendor, arose and demanded, "Jesus, art Thou the Son of God?"

As the Master was about to reply, loud, excited voices arose near an entrance. All turned to look as soldiers brought in the witnesses—three men and two women—who were to testify against Jesus. The color and pomp on every side seemed to frighten them as they were led to a position in front of the thrones.

Caiphas lost no time in questioning them, but many of their answers were so contradictory as to time and place that they were quickly dismissed. Caiphas was embarrassed and his face red with rage. To hide his terrible mistake, which the false witnesses had implied through their stupidity and ignorance, he once more demanded loudly, "Art Thou the Son of God?"

Jesus answered calmly and in a firm voice, "You, yourself, say that I am."

Annas, raging with anger, jumped to his feet. Caiphas turned to the Sanhedrin saying, "What further need have we of witnesses? We have heard it, ourselves, from His mouth!"

While a servant dressed him in the garment of gold cloth, the council whispered together and then gestured that they had reached an agreement. Caiphas walked to the lectern and after staring rudely at Jesus and pointing at Him, said, "He blasphemes! He says He is the Son of God and that is understood to mean that He thinks He is the Messiah!"

A silence of expectation filled the room, and then the rending of Caiphas' robe could be heard. Its swish, the sound of silk falling to the floor, brought a sigh from all those present. A verdict had been made a law. Loud, hilarious shouting and laughter arose on every side as soldiers and a few high priests bound Jesus with heavy cords and led Him to a small room just outside the main room to wait until the crowds disbursed. From there He would be taken to Pontius Pilate, the Roman governor.

CHAPTER 12

Pilate

COLD AND UNFRIENDLY were the glares, and vehement the verbal expressions of hate as Jesus left the great hall of Caiphas. Six Jewish soldiers were in charge of Him, and as they descended into the roadway their attention was drawn to the slow, uneven rumble of a cart as it bounced and bumped over the cobblestone street. The thud, thud, thud of the wooden wheels, together with the loud squealing hogs from within the cage-like vehicle, attracted the attention of the townspeople and soldiers alike. They watched with disgust and indignation as it went its way toward the open street markets. Suddenly, it came to a halt. The owner, a little old Roman man, angry and cursing, chased several Jewish children away who had been amusing themselves by poking the swine with long, sharpened sticks.

At this moment Jesus and the soldiers were about three hundred feet from the cart. As the soldiers watched the proceedings they conceived a terrible plan, which they lost little time in putting into execution. Since they all felt nothing but disgust and hatred for Jesus, why not make Him ride with the swine to which He had lowered Himself? They believed a liar no better than swine, anyway. This great humiliation—a Jew in a hog cart—would prove to everyone the gravity and the contempt with which they hated an impostor.

One soldier said as he pushed the Master forward, "Ride in full view of Your public, swine! This will be quite different from the time

You rode through the city on an ass and were cheered as the hero of the hour!"

After much bargaining, the old Roman accepted five pieces of silver, and Jesus was pushed into his cart, which was a low, two-wheeled wagon with a fenced-in platform that measured about three feet by six. On top of this cab, or cage, were tied boxes filled with noisy chickens and geese. With three large hogs already in the cart, Jesus had little room in which to stand. He was forced to straddle one of the beasts, and in a bent-over position steadied Himself by holding onto the dirty side bars, which were about ten inches apart.

The driver, constantly scolding and cursing his small donkey, got the cart once more under way. The passersby jested and laughed at the strange parade with its squawking geese and squealing swine. It made quite a scene. Many Jews shouted, "Come see what becomes of a degraded Jew Who thinks He is the Messiah. Look, He is riding with His equals—only the swine are sinless. Let this be a lesson to our children!"

The soldiers marched immediately behind the cart, and as the parade moved through the streets the children resumed their game of poking and sticking the swine with their sharp sticks. Their shouts and laughter told of their delight as the clumsy jumping of the frightened hogs nearly overturned the cart. From time to time Jesus was thrown to the floor or caught behind, or beneath, one of them. He was covered with terrible filth as each time He rose and steadied Himself. This terrible misery was brought on by undisciplined children, who were cheered by their parents and bystanders.

The older children were brazen and impudent, and they struck with green willows at the white knuckles of the Master as He clung to the bars of the cart. Other children spat upon Him, and then laughed and shouted all manner of indescribable words about His bent and dirty body. They said, "So You are our King? Are You the Holy One we have waited for? If You are the Christ why don't You ride with the high priests instead of with the swine? It is said You cast devils into a herd of swine—are they with this lot? Look at You! Could a God be so dirty? Would a God stand for this treatment? Where were You born? Who is Your mother?"

Further along they met larger groups of still more children, who formed a dancing circle around the cart. As they danced they shouted, "Come look at the Christ. Come look at the Man Who claims He is God. Look, He can't help Himself—He doesn't have any power. The miracles we heard about must be lies or He would get Himself out of this dirty cart!"

Jesus' eyes were filled with tears as He gazed upon the parents who cheered their children's behavior. He addressed them saying, "Pray for your children. If they will do this in their youth, what will they do to you in later life? Also pray for yourselves, for while your children are with you, their minds and hands are the same as if they were yours. You are the governors of their souls, and at death you will be judged according to the example you have given them through your own lives."

Upon hearing these words, many of the parents raised their voices in wild protest and scoffing, and commanded their children to stone Jesus. Within minutes a hundred rocks, and more, raced through the bars into the cart. The swine were again frightened and tried to find shelter. The Master was tripped and thrown to the floor.

Some distance down the street, a heavily veiled woman pushed her way through the crowds and up to the cart. Reaching through the bars she touched Jesus gently and whispered, "Jesus, I am with You. I am Mary of Magdala. I'm sorry Your own people are treating You like this. Forgive them, Jesus. O, if I could only help You!"

She walked along, then, trying to console Jesus each time He fell. Her words of sorrow and self-humiliation of devotion rang through the crowd as she cried aloud, "Jesus, forgive them—forgive them!"

Angry women, curious to know her identity, tore the veil from her head and gasped when they saw how young and beautiful she was. Tears streamed down her face. Then one woman recognized her, and pointing a finger, cried aloud for all to hear, "She's Mary of Magdala. A few months ago she was a harlot who had fame and fortune in Herod's court until this Jesus came into her life!"

The woman's words of scorn and bitterness aroused the people against Mary. She, too, was then spat upon and scratched with sharp sticks as the children turned their attack upon her.

A man shouted at Jesus, "Do You know this woman? To have won her charm You must be a miracle man! Tell us Your secret of how to attract women of such fame and beauty. If You are God You will tell us!"

Another man pushed Mary aside and asked scornfully, "Did this miracle man pay you well to put on this act? How much did He give you?" Then he turned sneeringly to Jesus. "Tell us how You got her to follow You and we'll set You free from the cart!"

Jesus did not answer, but He smiled at Mary and blessed her as He extended His hand over her. At that moment the children began to dance once more about them and to chant, "Mary, the harlot, loves Jesus—Mary, the harlot, loves Jesus!"

The attention of everyone was now upon Mary. She smiled and was more than glad that the sticks and stones fell upon her now as she clung desperately to the cart, utterly unmindful of the soldiers' and the people's commands that she leave the street. Her only thought was to be near Jesus.

The hog cart was brought to a halt in front of the Roman tribunal. As Jesus stepped down, the soldiers turned and directed Him with the points of their swords, for He was too filthy to touch with their hands. He smiled at Mary Magdala and at a few other friends in the crowd, courageous in His manmade degradation. Then He turned His eyes heavenward and stood erect and silent. The people followed His gaze but could see nothing. His expression of calm devotedness even frightened the soldiers, and they began to wish they had not made Him a victim of the cart. For the first time they realized they should never have taken such authority into their hands. Their orders had been only to march Him to the Roman court. They became afraid and confused. Pushing Him to the curb of the building, one of them picked up a scrubwoman's kneeling-rags from a door stoop and draped them over His shoulders in a futile effort to cover up what they had done.

A friend handed Mary of Magdala a wet towel, and with it she washed the Messiah's face. Then Jesus was ordered to enter the building. Near the entrance sat a beggar woman with a basket of unsold rose wreaths. Not having a home, the poor creature slept in any open doorway, and now that she had been suddenly awakened at this early hour, she acted out of habit and held up a withered wreath, asking the soldiers to buy. Taking it from her rudely, one of them plucked off the withered petals and placed it on the Master's head. Now the Messiah was clothed in brilliant red—scrubwoman's rags—and wore a crown of briars. In this deplorable condition He was taken to Pilate.

Pilate and his men smiled when they first caught sight of Him, and then a death-like silence came over them. Indignation flared in Pilate's dark eyes. Never before had a prisoner from the Jews been brought before him in such dress and filth.

He shuddered and wondered what had come over the Jews. Their culture had always bound them together in a closeness unequalled in any other race. Never had they turned against their own. This seemed unthinkable—and he realized he must act carefully and diplomatically if their anger and indignation had reached such a point of hatred. He was afraid, yet he knew he could not tolerate such disloyalty and mockery. Pity rose in his heart as the Master stood silently and with downcast eyes before him.

Quietly he ordered Jesus taken into an anteroom and His crown and mock clothing removed. Another toga, a clean one, was to be placed over His own.

After this command had been carried out, Pilate went to Jesus, for he wished to question Him alone. A half hour later, the two walked together on the high pavilion porch from where they could be seen clearly by the crowd beneath.

A wild display broke out immediately. Pilate waited until the shouts and the demands for a crucifixion had died down, and then pleaded with the people to think about what they were doing. He told them he felt certain they had been mistaken in their verdict and reminded them that Jesus was of their own race. Then, showing impatience, he raised the tone of his voice and said he, himself, believed Jesus innocent of any crime. They should realize that a man could not be put to death for believing He was the Messiah. This Jesus had never harmed nor killed anyone. Above hatred they must remember justice.

He asked them to recall how Jesus had prayed and healed their sick, and pointed out that anyone could rise to great perfection and power through the habit of prayer, to which they could testify. If that power were put to good use, why condemn a person for faith?

A man hurried up from the crowd. "Your honor," he pleaded, "do not make a final judgment until you have heard how far this Man's teachings have spread, and how He has persuaded the people to believe in Him. If this continues, you may lose power, for we fear a general uprising here in the city. The whole Roman Empire is in great danger. We do not accept Him as our king, for surely such a one would be a man of dignity, power, and wealth. This impostor has stirred up trouble in Judea, and beginning from Galilee even to this place!"

When Pilate heard the word *Galilee* he turned to Jesus and asked, "Art Thou a Galilean?" He smiled with relief and satisfaction as he realized the Master lawfully, then, belonged under Herod's jurisdiction. At least it was off his mind. He sent for a group of soldiers quickly, and ordered them to take Jesus to Herod, who happened to be visiting in Jerusalem at the time and was staying not a half-mile away.

Herod was exuberant and grinning when he heard, an hour later, that Jesus was in his building. He had always hoped someday to meet and to question this miracle man, for he was keenly interested in magic and wanted to see a phenomenal happening. It would be very interesting as entertainment only, of course, for he had no belief that Jesus might be God. Perhaps he could bribe Him into performing a miracle. He toyed with several silver coins in his pocket, knowing well how far the poor would stoop sometimes for money.

But when Jesus was brought before him, He simply stood erect and gazed silently into space above Herod's head as if He were not listening to a word. Herod's enthusiasm turned to bitter contempt when the Master would neither speak nor work even the smallest miracle to satisfy his curiosity. In order to mock the high priests who sent Him, he had Jesus robed in a bright toga of many stripes and marched him back to Pilate.[19]

Pilate was talking to a group of scribes and high priests, whom he had assembled in order to learn more of the prophecies in case the necessity arose for further defense when the Master returned. The soldier in charge spoke to him a few minutes, and then Pilate addressed the people, saying, "I have found no guilt in this Man, and neither has Herod deemed a death sentence necessary or he would have ordered me to make such an announcement. Again I say, nothing this Man has done is deserving of death!"

By this time the crowds had grown into the thousands and, because they were indignant with Pilate for not following their will, they began to shout loudly for the release of Barabbas. Their chant sounded and resounded like rolling thunder. "Crucify Jesus! Release Barabbas! Crucify Jesus! We want Barabbas! We want Barabbas!"

---

19 See Luke 23:11.

Pilate, seeing that he had failed to please the people and fearing that a riot was in the making, took a basin of water and washed his hands, saying, "I am innocent of the blood of this just Man. See to it yourselves."[20] He knew they would understand the symbol of the washing.

A great cry came back to him. "His blood be on us and on our children!"

In one last effort to save Jesus, Pilate ordered Him scourged, hoping this would arouse the indignation of the Jews and thus stimulate their usual sense of loyalty.[21] He well knew the hatred they had displayed on other occasions when one of their own was to be scourged by a Roman.

For a moment they were silent as they watched the soldiers remove the Master's striped toga. Now He stood before them in His own seamless, soiled garment that His mother had hand-woven for Him. He looked at it caressingly—memories were sweet—hadn't He wound the spindle when she wove the linen? It was a comforting thought and cooling to His soul when all around Him the hearts of men were filled with wrath and hatred.

The soldiers led Him toward the scourging arena, which was several feet from the pavilion, and as He went, He heard the water from Pilate's basin splash onto the pavement. He smiled and whispered in prayer, "The water in the basin of My heart will empty for you, Pilate."

---

20 See Matt. 27:24.
21 See Matt. 27:26.

CHAPTER 13

Death of Judas

A FEW HOURS AFTER THE BETRAYAL in the garden of Gethsemane, Judas, dressed in a clean toga, hurried to the courts where Caiphas judged Jesus. Huddling near the outside entrance in order to hide from Peter should the big fisherman see him and wish to vent his wrath upon him, Judas stayed in the shadows of the oil fire over which Peter warmed himself. He shuddered as he listened to the applause that came from the great hall, for well he understood its awful meaning. Poor man, he had believed Jesus would be imprisoned for only a short time when he made the bargain for the silver—now he knew the truth. The Master was condemned to die!

Judas became frightened and began to feel the weight of his crime as the trial ended and Jesus was sent to Pilate. At the same time, he raged with silent indignation at his friends and at Caiphas. He pushed aside a guard and hurried to Annas, who stood beside the lectern table laughing with the other high priests over the clever way they had handled the judgment of Jesus. Wide-eyed, frightened, and knowing the futility of pleading forgiveness in such a place of law, Judas fell at Annas' feet as though fainting from exhaustion.

Holding aloft the small bag of silver coins, he cried aloud for all to hear, "I have sinned! This Jesus whom you have just condemned to death is God on earth. He is the Messiah! He is innocent of any crime!

I have betrayed the Messiah, and you have helped me in the judgment of God. You took advantage of me when I came to you drunk. Here, take your thirty pieces of silver. God forgive me for what I have done!"

Throwing the silver at Annas' feet, Judas fell on his face and wept hysterically. Annas kicked the bag away and said sternly, "What is your sorrow to us? See to it yourself—and ask your God, Jesus, to forgive you, since you now seem to believe in Him to this extent of fear that has come over you. Go search for Him; He is not dead yet. Why do you come here to us and plead your sorrow when you believe He is the Messiah who forgives sins and loves the sinner? We have heard of His doctrine of forgiveness and love. Is this not what you claim your Jesus does?"

Judas walked unsteadily to the door and there paused, clutching at a heavy drapery for support, as Annas continued, "Why don't you wait and see whether or not your Jesus rises from the tomb on the third day as He predicts? The prisoners in the dungeon below believe His words, and all night they have sung praises to Him about the Resurrection. Why don't you join them? I give you permission. Then if He comes as a ghost into the dungeon ask Him, yourself, about your sins and the condition of your soul. Or would you be afraid to face Him now that you believe you have betrayed Him?

"We have learned through various means of persuasion in the torture chamber, that your Jesus has made all sorts of promises to the prisoners. Why, they believe they will soon have their freedom for He will open the dungeon. Of course, any thinking man would know His promises are ridiculous and impossible.

"Just suppose He does rise from the tomb—tell me—how will He gain entrance to the dungeon, when I have it so heavily guarded? Wake up, Judas! Be a man of civic interests instead of one filled with such childish fear.

"And then there is the utterly fantastic story of miraculous roses appearing in the dungeon, which were pulled out by a woman who had lowered a rope. If there is any truth in this story, and we learn who the woman is, she will die for disobedience of the court laws. But of course there is no truth in it—all these tales are miserable lies or imaginary flights of fancy, which often come to men in dungeon darkness."

Annas suddenly grew still as a thought raced through his mind. How could this man Jesus predict with such exactness and certainty that He was going to die? If He were that accurate, then what about His prediction that He would rise on the third day? Annas shuddered. He tried to discredit the thought by continuing to address Judas. "We have you to thank," he said, "for the overwhelming success of exposing a false god. Just think, this Man nearly overpowered Jerusalem! You are the city's hero to have captured such an invader who used neither sword nor army. Now, begone, Judas. Get yourself out of the court."

Annas and his followers burst into laughter as they saw Judas turn pale with sorrow and then red with anger. Once more he became violently sick and staggered from the room. Running from the building he disappeared into a nearby thicket of trees and shrubs.

When his paroxysm of vomiting was over, he wanted only to be alone in order to cry out his storm of tears in bitter regret over the folly that was upon him. As he wept he became afraid that the women to whom he had told the story of the First Clean Oblation Sacrifice would openly ridicule Jesus at the crucifixion. He shuddered at the thought of facing his own mother and father. What tears she would shed and what anger his father would display! He became hysterical once more, and so intense and ungoverned were his piteous cries that he rolled and kicked in the dust beneath a low-hanging bush.

Back in the courtroom, Annas was angry over Judas' actions, and he expected Caiphas to feel the same way, but instead, his son-in-law was pale and wore a sudden, shocked look. Great drops of perspiration stood out upon his brow.

"What makes you stand like this?" Annas asked. "Are you ill? Are you afraid? I would suggest you arrest Judas for throwing the money at us. It was an unlawful act, you know, and he could be judged and jailed on charges of contempt. Come, sit down. What is the matter with you?"

Caiphas could not answer. Annas shouted angrily, "Judas has done this to you. Send your guards after him. You look like you've seen a spirit. Your expression makes me think this Jesus-nonsense has converted you, too. Your fear seems to match that of Judas. Speak, man, speak!"

Caiphas finally managed to talk slowly and fearfully. "Annas," he said, only loud enough for the older man to hear, "I have just talked to Turan. Her withered eye is completely normal and she can see—she is cured! And neither does she have any pain. She had with her the white roses the prisoners told us about. They were not telling lies. Do you realize that your own daughter, my wife, was the woman who lowered the baskets of food to them and lifted out the roses? You made a promise to the Sanhedrin that if she were caught she would be put to death. She is my wife—what are we going to do?"

Annas steadied himself against the lectern and finally managed to whisper, "Do you suppose this Jesus is the Christ? My God, if He is, what have we done?" Caiphas did not answer. "It can't be!" Annas continued at length, and pulled himself together with an effort. "But we shall have to do something about it. If Turan has received a miraculous cure and if the credit goes to Jesus—if He is acclaimed for His nonsense about the roses, we may have to forfeit our judgment of Him. We'll just have to keep this quiet and hidden. Are you sure her eye is cured?"

Noticing the curious glances thrown in their direction Annas said abruptly, "Let us not discuss this any further, now. We don't want to arouse curiosity."

His composure outwardly restored, Annas ordered the guards to pick up the thirty pieces of silver, which were scattered over the floor. When this was done, he addressed the few members of the Sanhedrin yet in the hall. "Whether or not we can use this money is your decision. What shall we do with it?"

One elder answered, "It is ill-gotten money. Therefore we cannot accept it for the city treasury. Death has been purchased with it. It is the same as if it were cursed!"

Caiphas, still shocked and trembling, forced a note of boldness into his voice as he said, "Yes, it is the price of blood. What does the Sanhedrin say on this matter of decision? What do you suggest we do with it?"

A gold-clothed priest answered, "It is not lawful to put it into the treasury as has been said. I suggest the court take it and use it to buy a burial field for strangers who die in Jerusalem."

A servant, knowing that another decision had been reached, dressed Caiphas in a robe of gold cloth, and immediately Caiphas tore it from top to bottom and let it drop to the floor. Another opinion had been made a law. A potter's field was to be purchased.

This finished the business to be transacted, and within a few minutes the last member of the Sanhedrin had left the hall. A mystifying quietness was now between Annas and his son-in-law. At last Annas said, "If what you have told me is true, we must forbid Turan to speak of it to anyone until this Jesus is put to death. It is the only way to save ourselves. We must insist and seek for His death now above all other obligations. I feel sure Pilate will follow out our plans."

Raising his voice, the old man almost screamed, "Caiphas, we can't be wrong! In spite of a miracle He must be an impostor!" More to reassure himself than anything else, he repeated the popular belief. "He can't be the looked-for Messiah, for we expect one with power, wealth, and prestige and not a silver-tongued orator who speaks about kindness, charity, and love as the means of gaining life everlasting. I believe when the real Messiah comes He will bring His heavenly powers with Him and will conquer the world and order it in a pattern that will favor us, His chosen tribe. All things such as miracles and love will then have their places in the new quieting process of law. But first He will wage a war and subdue nations. Can you imagine this Jesus going to war? He is too fanatical about love and peace!

"This is my day to offer incense in the temple, and when I do so I will plead for the real Messiah to come to us. After that we will discuss this matter in greater detail, but in the meanwhile, tell Turan immediately that she must not be seen or heard!"

Outside the great hall, Judas still knelt in the thicket weeping uncontrollably and praying for his sins. His excessive grief caused his throat muscles to swell and tense so that momentarily, in hysteria, he gasped for breath. He became terribly frightened and imagined devils were tearing at his throat because of his sins. Stumbling to his feet, he ran from the thicket to his home and there to the synagogue, hoping to receive some consolation from the presiding priest who would offer incense there that day.

Laboriously, as one about to faint, he managed to reach the front of the synagogue and to kneel beside the incense table. There he begged forgiveness from God until the rising fumes of incense caught his senses. Looking up he was shocked to discover Annas officiating. The old high priest was now in a prayerful mood of solemn piety, but inwardly he was still frightened about Turan.

Judas, oblivious to everything about him, including custom and order in all things and especially that of worship, took this moment as an opportune time to kneel again at the feet of Annas and beg God's forgiveness through him, the priest.

Annas, in all his radiant garb, nervously motioned Judas to go back to his place of prayer and to be quiet. He was embarrassed and confused. Judas asked if he had not heard what he said. This disobedience unnerved Annas, and his uneasiness grew as Judas openly persisted in begging for God's forgiveness and Jesus' release.

Annas tried to quiet Judas, but became frightened when he realized the poor fellow's actions were those of a madman. He pulled constantly at his throat muscles and at Annas' robes as he begged him to scatter the devils through his priestly powers.

At length Annas whispered, "Be quiet and I will bring a scapegoat from the pens when I have finished here. Then you may confess. Even though this is not the time of year for open scapegoat confessions, I will allow you this privilege because you think devils are near you.

"After you have confessed your sins, as we lay our hands on the beast's head, you must take him to the hills and there lose him, or drop him over a cliff. He must be destroyed. This will be a sign that your sins are also destroyed and forgotten in God. A goat's death, or his becoming lost in the hills following confession, symbolized forgiveness of sin. Quiet now, and I will see you later. Offer your troubled soul along the rising incense."

Annas could hardly continue with his prayers, for he imagined the invisible finger of Jesus pointing at him. Suddenly, as though touched with grace, in good conscience, he could no longer deny that Turan had been miraculously healed by the Master. Now, to further disturb him, Judas was a bother and a worry. He even wished the former apostle would get himself lost in the hills until after Jesus' death, at least.

The offering of the incense came to an end at last, and Annas reluctantly went with Judas to the pens. A servant of the temple brought out a huge ram as they waited at the gates, and both priest and penitent placed his right hand on the beast's head, his left hand over his heart to symbolize truth and sorrow, and Judas openly confessed his sins. As he knelt in silent thanksgiving, Annas stood nearby, the long, fifteen-foot leather halter strap in his hands, one end of which was fastened to the ram's neck-band.

It was a dark, cloudy morning and the fog had not yet lifted as Judas left the temple. He was very calm for a few minutes, but fatigue soon overcame him. He found pulling the stubborn ram up a narrow mountain path a trying feat that was beyond his strength. The top, with its accompanying deep ravine, seemed far away. At times the animal would do nothing he wished it to, apparently wanting only to take time out to eat or to romp. In his impatience, Judas redoubled his efforts to pull the beast, then unexpectedly the animal would run ahead of him, or pull, or bunt him along. All of this was terribly exasperating to his tired nerves. Soon he was in tears and tearing again at his throat muscles for breath. Perspiration began to roll from his body and presently he fell exhausted to the ground. His fear of dying in the hands of devils frightened him into crying aloud as he struggled back to his feet, "O God of Israel, God of my father, forgive me. God save me from Thy hand of Justice!"

Again and again the scapegoat pulled or bunted him along the mountain path, which was now close to a deep, rocky ravine. Judas' nerves were spent, and he finally lost control of the ram altogether as they reached the top. At this highest point he tried with all his strength to push the animal over the edge, but the ram playfully scurried away to safer ground and stood looking at Judas as if he planned to push him to destruction, instead.

Tired, Judas rested as he watched the animal and toyed with the leather strap that was circled many times about his hand. Slowly the ram ventured toward him and before Judas quite realized it, nearly pushed him over the edge. Judas jumped to his feet in sudden fright, and in doing so, let fall the strap.

The ram stopped sideways to the ledge and Judas realized his chance had come. As he darted forward he accidentally stepped into the strap circle, however. At the same moment the ram, for no apparent reason, whirled and jumped over the rocky ledge. This jerked the strap tight about Judas' ankle, and before he could save himself he was dragged after the plunging beast. In their quick fall together, the halter strap caught over a projecting rock in the wall of the cliff and there Judas swung head down, like a pendulum, his neck broken, on one end of the strap, the goat on the other.

No one saw the freak accident, nor did anyone know the hour of misery Judas spent in his penitent soul as he tried to push the stubborn animal over the mountainside.

For several days Judas' body hung as it had plunged to its death. Weather changes of fog, rain, and sunshine made it bloat from natural gasses until finally it burst asunder and his bowels gushed out.

Two mountaineers found the body as they searched the hills for lost sheep. They cut it down and took the halter to the courts of Caiphas in order to report their finding. There, they merely left word of their discovery with an attendant and the halter strap as evidence. When Caiphas heard the story of the man who hanged himself, he ordered his soldiers to bury his body in the new burial grounds set aside for strangers.

Annas later recognized the halter. From the evidence he, too, thought Judas had committed suicide and was happy to tell his son-in-law about giving him the goat and the strap. Caiphas laughed heartily and commanded two of his soldiers to search for one of Jesus' disciples and to present him with the halter as a reminder that one of his Master's chosen friends had committed suicide by hanging himself with it.

A few days later these soldiers found the apostle James and told him the news. They also told him of Caiphas' threat, namely, that death in the same fashion would be visited on any of Christ's followers who refused to forget Him.

Later that night, when James was praying for the soul of Judas, he was caught up into the realm of silence in ecstasy. There he understood that Judas had gone to a place of his own.[22] Judas was a priest of God and Jesus had said to him, "Thou art a priest forever." James now understood that the word *forever* meant *in the glory of God in the Eternal Kingdom*, and that the sublime mark of the priesthood, as golden light, could never be dimmed, nor taken away from a priest, regardless of his individual sins or weaknesses.

Considering the high rank of priests as other Christs on earth set apart from all men, God allowed Judas to go into a place of his own. Even his purgation was set apart—different from any other person's place, or suffering for sin. Since Purgatory was already occupied and known as Limbo, he could not be alone there. God, therefore, at the moment of his death, created a place of suffering in the very lowest part of Purgatory known as the place of perdition. Spiritually it is between Purgatory and Hell and the priests who, like Judas, are so unfortunate as to enter there must remain until the end of time—actually lost for the duration of time. They are the Sons of Perdition, and the prayers of the faithful cannot reach them, nor can they in any way help themselves. But no priest can ever be lost in Hell because he is another Christ.

---

22 Acts 1:25 (Editor's note: see CCC 1031; cf. 1472).

CHAPTER 14

The Scourging

AS JESUS WAS LED AWAY from Pilate to the arena in the patio of his court, Mary of Magdala hurried to the home of John, where Mother Mary rested and waited. A half-hour later the two holy women were on their way to the scene of the scourging.

As Mother Mary stopped for a moment to allow Mary of Magdala to rest, she said, recalling her last hour with Jesus, "I promised my Son I would not offer any word of restraint to the crowds, nor to any of the men who will aid in the crucifixion. I want to help Jesus all I can, and the best way is through silence and calm, which is known as interior suffering. Because I know you love Him, too, I ask you to follow my way of forgetting self today. If we are calm, Jesus will suffer less anguish because of us. Let our calmness prove to Him that we understand the plan of redemption."

Mary of Magdala could only nod her head in approval. Then they went on their way once more to the scene of sorrow.

The terrible scourging was about to begin. The soldiers removed the Master's seamless garment and threw it across a bench. His undergarment, a loosely folded cloth, was fastened more securely with a rope tied around his hips. In this nearly naked condition He was marched to an upright column, which was about five feet in height and at least seven inches in diameter, and which stood in the center of the arena. The soldiers bound His wrists together with leather cords and then fastened the knot to a large, copper ring on top of the pole. At regular spacings of about five inches, the height of the pole, were inlaid heavy copper bands with rings, through which the bridles of traveling camels were often tied.

Five hired scourgers sat on a bench nearby. This particular day was considered as a day of sport by the Gentiles and as a holy day by the Jews. However, the pagan rituals and the general commercialism of the times had swung a majority of the Jews from their traditional rituals and they found delight in the pursuits of the Gentiles.

As the half-drunken scourgers awaited the signal to begin their brutal work, they joked and scoffed at Jesus and gulped great quantities of wine. They bragged openly how, with vicious vigor, they would scourge Him who claimed to be the Jewish God. To demonstrate their strength they cracked their whips over the smooth pavement. This rhythmical slapping of the lashes attracted a playful dog, and as he came closer a single stroke killed him instantly. Pulling the limp body to the feet of Jesus, one scourger sneered, "If You are a God why did You allow this dog to die? You, Yourself, have taught the people about mercy—then why didn't You save this hound? Are You worth the death of a dog?"

Spitting, the scourger laughed and continued, "This is the first time in my life I have been asked to whip a self-styled God. What next will the courts offer us to do?"

The Roman soldiers, after seeing that the Master was securely bound, departed from the arena, leaving Jesus to the mercy of the hired scourgers. These men now went immediately to their knees, throwing dice in order to determine who would lift his whip first. It was the custom for each scourger to strike his victim eight times, each man attacking a different part of the sufferer's body. The lawful number of strokes, according to Roman law, was thirty-nine lashes, with one extra for full measure.

The Jews and hundreds of Romans who had followed the hogcart stood in the crowded archways and on the second-story windowsills. Most of them were anxious to see how the Impostor, as they kept cheering Him, would act under the ordeal of the whips.

A shout arose as the first scourger took his place and lashed his whip across the back of the Messiah's knees. With each blow the mighty whip left its dark blue, circling impression. Within minutes the Master's blood trickled down onto the gray-white pavement. The Jews in the crowd cried tauntingly, "You fool, strike His body. Whip Him! Why are you so stupid? Why do you keep your scourge at His knees?"

The scourger struck with greater force and said, scowling, "I'll bend His knees. Watch and see this Jesus, your God, kneel and plead for mercy. The other men may whip Him as they please, but first He will bow before me!"

Again the whip whistled toward its mark, but this time Jesus, Who was free to move about the pole within a limited radius, stepped aside and it missed.

At that moment, Mother Mary and Mary of Magdala entered the great arch that partly overshadowed the arena and were met by one of the Master's disciples, who told them Peter was in a room close by. Mother Mary smiled, for she knew he would not be far away, so sincere was his loyalty. Before her eyes beheld her Son, she hurried to him.

Peter was on his knees beside a couch in uncontrollable grief, his face wet with tears. He clung to Mother Mary as she sat beside him, and as he wept he told her of his failure and utter inability to help Jesus. He cringed and trembled each time he heard the whip in the arena outside slap across the body of his Master. He hated the roar of the maddened people and buried his face in the folds of Mother Mary's gown.

Mother Mary tried to console and calm him as she dried away his tears. She talked to him about the will of Jesus to redeem man and how, having become Man, He wanted to die according to man's dictates and powers. She reminded the big fisherman that regardless of how powerful God was, He would not go against man's free will, be it exerted in doing either good or evil.

Peter became calm slowly, and in a sudden burst of hope pleaded with Mother Mary to use her great gifts and power to stop the scourgers—surely it would be enough for Jesus to suffer the crucifixion alone.

There were tears on Mary's face as she patted Peter's shaggy head—he had removed his headdress—and told him gently of her promise to her Son. She told him, too, that he must try to be a consoler and not a restrainer.

As she rose to her feet she asked him to go with her to the arena and together they would watch the terrible events. Noticing a brightly striped toga hanging on the wall, she suggested that he borrow it, and disguised thus he would not be recognized. However, Peter declined—

he could not bear to watch. He would rather remain hidden in the room to pray and to listen.

Mother Mary returned alone to Mary of Magdala, and side by side they entered the arena and stood holding each other's arms as they gazed for the first time upon the scene taking place there. Their eyes filled with tears as they watched the great blue welts on the Master's body rise, break, and bleed. They shuddered as they saw Him tremble with pain and shock.

The scourging was a slow process because after each blow the scourger took a bow and listened for applause as if he were an actor on a stage. At the seventh blow Jesus' knees began to bend toward the pavement. Now the cheering crowds were nearly out of control and their expressions were blasphemous. The Master slumped to the ground.

This horrible accomplishment was a signal for the first scourger to stop. As he threw his blood-covered whip down he faced Jesus, spat upon Him, and said, "This is indeed a sight—a God kneeling before me! Now do You think You are the King of the Jews after they have allowed You to be whipped? What do You think of them? Why don't You plead for mercy before it is too late? Confess to the people that You are an impostor and You may still save Yourself!" He laughed and drank from a bucket of cool water.

Jesus did not answer. He looked kindly at the man and smiled. In his words there had been a trace of mercy and Jesus loved him for it.

The second beastly scourger took his bow. The people shouted, "Finish this self-made God of Israel. Hurry His death. Why take Him back to Pilate? End His blasphemous life! Let Him die here! Kill Him—His life is in your hands. Kill Him for us!"

Mother Mary and Mary of Magdala shook in each other's embrace as they watched this second unmerciful scourger crack his whip across the shuddering shoulders of Jesus, who was still kneeling on the pavement. The Master's low moans, which now became audible, brought nothing but laughter and scorn from the crowd. A voice called out from a balcony, "Don't strike Him across the neck, prolong His agony! People are coming from distant cities to watch this scourging. A runner just informed me that hundreds of His followers are on their way here, scandalized. They must see to believe that He who healed their sick and raised their dead is Himself bound and whipped. They are all asking: 'Would God in the Flesh allow this?' I say prolong His agony and let them see the Man who claims to have great power. Let them see a Messiah suffer. Let them see that He cannot save Himself!"

When the scourger heard this, he struck with less vigor, but his strokes were lost count of and they became multiplied into many little stinging jabs. As each one cut across the Master's torn shoulders, small particles of His Sacred Flesh fell from the knotted leather whip-knots to the pavement, which was now covered with His Precious Blood.

Upon seeing this desecration of His Flesh, Mother Mary asked her angels silently, in their invisible way in the spiritual life, to come pick up each particle and bring it to her. While she prayed she unwound a beautiful, sheer scarf from her head and neck. As it hung from her shoulder it formed a cup in the curve of her arm. She was a living ciborium, the first of this kind of tabernacle on earth.

As the particles of His Flesh were brought to her, she and Mary of Magdala, gazing upon the torn fragments, were caught up into rapture and there they saw all earth's ciboriums, in God's way of visions, stretching out in an unbroken row before them—reaching out into the ages—even until the end of time. Within this experience of holy delight, the two women bowed to the majesty and the mystery of time, the Sacred Flesh in the ciboriums, and the mercy of how God fed His children upon Himself, the Living Bread.

Meanwhile, Peter must have been praying that something happen to the second scourger, for suddenly he became ill. Bending forward in a cramped position, he sat down suddenly on the bench and handed his whip to the next man in turn.

The third scourger was a most repulsive-looking man, and the expression of his voice was both contemptible and hateful to the ears of the good people who were forced to listen to him. Sneering at Jesus, who now hung limply by His wrists, he kicked at Him and snarled, "Speak, You swine! Haven't You anything to say?"

Not in answer, but to question, Jesus asked, "What would you say if you were in My place?"

The executioner replied loudly, "If I were in Your place I would beg for mercy before it is too late. And if I were the God of the Jews, as You claim to be, I would curse the one who struck me, and then I would destroy the world."

Jesus answered, "I am not pleading mercy for Myself. But because I am Your Messiah, I am pleading that My Father of Justice will be merciful to you and to the people whom you represent. Do you know it is written that I must die? It is My will to suffer the trials that circumstances place before Me. I am eager to return to My heavenly Kingdom.

"It will also be written that if I be lifted up in your heart I will draw all things to Me. I want you to become a savior of men and not one who beats them into despair. Now that I have answered you, hurry My hour of death. I am ready to die for You. I must not waste time in pleading forgiveness for you."

This answer unnerved the drunken scourger, and as he lifted his whip his foot slipped on the wet pavement and he fell face down in the Master's Blood. For a moment, as though stunned and shocked, he lay motionless. He both saw and watched a miracle—invisible angels gathered small particles of the Master's Flesh and took them to a woman standing in the archway. Aghast, he watched the particles fall, as though by their own power, into the woman's scarf, which she held across her arm. He saw her smile—and yet understood she was in great sorrow. He marveled at her beauty and courage. She didn't appear frightened, but he knew she, too, could see this tremendous happening. Raising himself to his knees in order to see her more clearly, he said in bewilderment, "This Man must be the Living Messiah. Why He just told me He would be lifted up. Look, His Flesh is being lifted up before our very eyes!"

Realizing that other people did not see the miracle, he screamed hysterically, and pointing at Jesus continued, "He is the Messiah! O, God in Heaven, what have I done? This Man is the Christ! Kill me instead of Him. He will rise from the dead as He has said. I know because I have already seen His power in lifting up the particles of His Flesh. He can rise on the third day. Fall on your knees and worship Him!"

Struggling to his feet, he lifted his Master's bowed head and went on tenderly, "Jesus, Jesus, forgive me."

Reaching for the bucket of water to offer the Messiah a drink, he saw a reflection of the Master in its cool depths—but it was not the kneeling Jesus at the column he saw, but His Majesty as King. He stood as though paralyzed with shock.

This infuriated the crowd. What was the matter with him? The next scourger struck the bucket from his hand and instantly a terrible fight began. The two men fell to the pavement and rolled and tumbled here and there. Wild cheers arose from the crowd at this turn of events. The whole flagellation became a raging fight among the spectators, who either fought physically with one another, or engaged in loud disputes.

Mother Mary and Mary Magdala removed their outside cloaks and used them to soak up the Precious Blood from the pavement. As they came near to Jesus they whispered tender words of encouragement and then returned to their places in the archway.

Over and above the terrible unrest on every side, came the voice of the scourger who had seen the vision. "I tell you this Man is the Christ!" he screamed. "I have just seen a miracle. Hear me—listen to me! This Man is the Christ! He is our King. Look, when I peer into the water of this bucket I see Him as King. Come look for yourselves, and see that I tell the truth!"

A storm of laughter came from the crowd as they told him he had had too much to drink. He didn't realize that no one else could see that particular vision, and as a consequence he continued his fruitless coaxing.

At that moment the fourth scourger snatched the whip and struck again and again at Jesus in a most heinous manner. With the other hand he reached out and pushed the bucket of water to the ground. As his whip lashed across the face and chest of the Master, Jesus' body convulsed with pain and He threw Himself backward in an arc from the pole.

Instantly the first two scourgers seemed to freeze. Both distinctly heard Jesus say within their hearts, "Come follow Me."

The third scourger fell to the pavement in fear and adoration. Covered with the Master's Blood—even a few drops splashed into his mouth—he cried, "O God on earth, what have I done to You? Forgive me—forgive me!"

The crowd began to press forward to see what was taking place. Never had they seen such confusion. Some of them became frightened and even proclaimed that this Man must indeed be the Messiah.

The fourth executioner stared into the water bucket in complete amazement, for now he, too, saw the vision of the King. At his feet writhed the third scourger, who was struck suddenly with a heart attack. Within a few minutes he died with the words: "Jesus, I will follow You!" upon his lips.

Angrily the crowds took the fourth scourger—who now was both deaf and dumb from shock—and imprisoned him in a room. They could not understand what had happened to him, and shrugging their shoulders they said he must be mad. The third scourger they believed to have died from over-exertion.

By this time the fifth scourger was in a terrible mood of anger and fear. He pushed the people back from Jesus, and whipping Him viciously across the face and neck, shouted, "There is no God—there is no God! This Man is not the Messiah or He would not be scourged. Look, He cannot save Himself!"

Peter could not help but hear that terrible cry from the courtyard, "There is no God!" Unable to stand his interior suffering any longer, he threw the brightly striped toga over his own and adjusted the Oriental headdress, which came down closely over his face. Bending over as though crippled, he hurried from the room.

Reaching the arena, he saw the scourger raise his arm to strike the Master again. Leaping forward he snatched the heavy whip from his hand and hurled it up and over the two-story building. Then he jumped upon the startled man's back, and with his weight bore him to the ground. Burying his strong hands into his hair he began to smash his ugly, brutal face against the pavement.

At that moment the shrill tones of trumpets announced that the soldiers were coming back for Jesus.

A little revived, the Master struggled to His feet. With a most wonderful smile He whispered, "Peter, you are courageous, but I thought I taught you differently. Do you not remember the swords? Hurry away, for I cannot bargain with the men on your behalf this time."

Tears of gratitude filled the big fisherman's eyes as he fled obediently. So quick had been his attack that no one recognized him. As he went he said to himself, "It was worth the fight to see the Master smile. I am glad I did not restrain myself."

Reaching a lonely nook, he rested and for the first time noticed blotches of Jesus' blood on the hem of his toga. He had discarded the borrowed one as he ran. Conscious of having such a gift upon his clothing, he was frightened. Reverently, he bowed his head to the earth and in adoration kissed the sacred drops.

He tore the hem into little squares, which he tied together with a bit of cord and secured it about his neck underneath his vest. Then he hurried on to find James and John, whom he had ordered earlier to purchase a tent from a tent maker named Saul, who would later be called "Paul." They were to pitch it close to the top of Calvary so that they could hide in it and yet be close to the Master during His crucifixion. Buying a tent from a Roman citizen would be less suspicious than buying it from one in the Jewish community. It would be dangerous for the Jews to know they were going to be present, or even near, the scene of execution.

Once more the Roman soldiers led Jesus before Pilate, who still raged indignantly against the disloyalty of the Jews. The Master's own brown toga had been placed over His shoulders and the cord adjusted, thus hiding most of His terrible wounds. On His head He wore a crown of thorns formed from briars, placed there by soldiers who were not officers of the day. This was pushed down, like a cap, over His brow. One long, terrible thorn pierced through His left eyebrow and blood from it coursed down His face. In this awful headdress as a mock king, He stood before Pilate.

Pilate stepped backward, shocked. He regained his composure quickly and, pointing at Jesus, said to the crowds at the bottom of the pavilion steps, "Behold the Man!"

A shout, as if it were a groan, rose from the multitude. "Crucify Him! Crucify Him!" they answered.

Jesus was a piteous sight. He was bent forward in exhaustion, His eyes were closed, and the piercing thorn through His eyebrow had caused that eye to swell completely shut. Pilate hoped the sight of Him would cause His people to relent, but the cry "Crucify!" rose from the air instead, and he shuddered. There was nothing more he could do. The Master was led to the top of the pavilion steps, from where He would descend later to the street below to pick up His cross.

Mother Mary and Mary of Magdala remained in the arena, busy wiping up the sacred bloodstains with what linens they could procure. Then they proceeded quietly in the direction of their home. Hurrying through the streets they heard the loud screaming of the people calling for the crucifixion. Neither spoke of this, nor of the verdict.

In the little house, Mother Mary unrolled the torn linens, and into their folds she placed the precious particles of her Son's Flesh. Carefully, Mary of Magdala sprinkled each particle with spices and then they rerolled the linens, along with the Messiah's original swaddling clothes, which Mother Mary had kept.

Taking the bundle into her arms, Mother Mary said, "After the crucifixion, you and I will go to Bethlehem for a few hours and there bury this bundle deep into the floor of the stable where Jesus was born. I want to give this gift to the world. From out of its hidden depths will flow many sacramental graces, as if it were an invisible sunburst spreading across the earth to touch the people. It will be a perpetual sacramental."

CHAPTER 15

Jesus Carries the Cross

FROM OUT OF THE DEPTHS of Jerusalem's main dungeon came the prisoners' voices chanting, "Jesus, Jesus, Son of God, save us!"

The sound of hurrying feet could everywhere be heard, for the hour of the crucifixion was near and it was something not to be missed, especially by those who thrilled at the sight of suffering people.

One woman, the wife of Dismas, unnoticed by the crowd because of her heavy veils, hurried in the opposite direction from the pavilion steps where the crosses were laid for their victims. She was on her way to visit her husband and attempt to cheer him in his last hour on earth in the dungeon just outside the city walls where he waited, with Rachel's brother Gestas, to be crucified.

Her eyes filled with tears as she neared her destination and stopped in the street to listen to the chant, "Jesus, if You are passing by, save us!" She began to weep heavily, for the emotional strain of hearing men's helpless voices pleading for aid from two different prisons within the last half hour was almost more than she could bear.

Composing herself as best she could, she descended the ladder into the dungeon, and as she did so, she heard Gestas' angry voice reproaching her husband and the other prisoners, for believing Jesus to be the Messiah. He said, "I tell you, if there is a God, He is Yahweh. I do not believe in this Man you call the Christ. You are all hypocrites to the One True God!"

Neither the prisoners, nor Dismas' wife, realized then that the Jesus scheduled to be crucified that morning was the Messiah to Whom they prayed. Many men were named Jesus. Dismas' wife had been occupied with the affairs of her family and with visiting the prisoners, and as a consequence had found no time to learn the immediate events of the day.

Gestas was surly, and he jested unmercifully at the good woman as she embraced her husband. Pretending not to hear him she talked happily about their children, twin sons about nine months old, and an eleven-year old boy who was a cripple. The pranks of the younger children had brought many smiles and laughs to the prisoners during the past months, for Dismas' wife had recounted many of them.

At last the hour came to an end, far too quickly. Dismas' wife told her husband she would be waiting for him, with the children, at the bottom of Pilate's steps, where he would see them before he picked up his cross.

Then she climbed up and out of the dungeon for the last time.

Two hours later she arranged a straw mat for her crippled son as she had promised, and his grandfather, who had been carrying him, placed him upon it. The child's anguished cries of pain could be heard even above the din of the crowd.

At that moment, loud cheers came from the people. They pointed to a cloud of dust, which appeared some distance down the street in the direction of the dungeon. In a short while they were able to see Dismas, Gestas, and Barabbas approaching. The three men shuffled along clumsily, kicking up the powdery dust until they were encased in a fog-like dusk.

The sudden, bright sunlight had blinded Dismas, and he staggered and stumbled from one side of the road to the other. He fell helplessly from time to time, and the people laughed and spat upon him. Because of his blindness, they chose him as a victim for their sport, buffeting him from side to side, trying to make him, in his darkness, lose his way. His wife hurried to meet him. Holding him in her arms, she comforted him and led him through the middle of the street, where his step would be sure. He wept as he leaned upon her for he was sick and afraid. Quietly she cleaned his face of perspiration and spittle.

Presently, they stopped and listened to the crowds calling vehemently for Jesus to be crucified and jeering at the idea that He was

God among men. There He was standing beside Pilate at the top of the pavilion steps.

Stunned and angry, Dismas pushed his trembling, shocked wife aside and said scornfully, pointing in the direction of the steps, "Is this Jesus the One you told us about? Is He the Miracle Man?"

The people about him answered, "He's the One Who claims to be the Messiah. He's going to be crucified with you. You should feel honored. Imagine a God Who cannot save Himself—that's a laugh!"

Dismas clutched angrily at his wife's arm and demanded: What does all this mean? Is it He to whom we have prayed and hoped for our deliverance? Answer me!"

She could not. The people laughed and made great sport telling Dismas what a fool his wife was along with many other wives who believed such tales. Dismas' wife remained as though transfixed, her eyes upon Jesus, who still stood in final conversation with Pilate. He didn't seem to be frightened, nor too grieved.

In deep sorrow, Dismas went down upon his knees on the straw mat and embraced his children, who were crying and afraid of the angry, hissing people. Helpless in his temporary blindness and pain, he huddled over them. Then as his wife knelt weeping beside him he said, "We should have continued praying to Yahweh. Why did I listen to you? Now our children will always question about the true God. See what you have done! This is something they will never forget. My disgrace is nothing compared to what you have brought upon us. Look at the celebration for a crucifixion! There has never been any greater. No doubt history will record it and our children will never live it down!"

Striking at his wife and pushing her away, he indicated his son and continued, "If this Jesus performs miracles why does our boy lie here crippled? If He is God He should know you have taught us about Him, and in gratitude He should heal this helpless child. Challenge His goodness. Make Him prove Himself with a miracle for our boy and I'll believe in Him. Woman, how can you be so blind as to believe in a Man who cannot save Himself? Speak! Answer me!"

His wife could not. She wept bitterly as Dismas now stood erect and shouted, "Jesus, I do not believe in You even if my wife does. She is a fool! I want these people present to know I do not believe You are the Messiah so that they can teach my children accordingly when I am dead!"

A hush mantled the crowd. All eyes turned toward Barabbas as he stepped toward the pavilion. He was a beastly looking man who weighed nearly two hundred and fifty pounds. Very short in stature, he walked with a slow, deliberate step, his long arms dangling limply at his sides. His mouth was partly open and he drooled as he grinned at every woman whose eye he could catch.

He mounted the steps and turned to face the people. He seemed to enjoy his popularity, and made the most of it by posing and smiling and frightening the children as he waved and shouted his greetings to Jesus. In a heavy, booming voice he thanked the Master for taking his place. He, Barabbas, was the people's choice.

This free, evil man then turned and walked again through the crowd. Women screamed as he approached with his slow, possessive step, for none of them in Jerusalem would be safe alone now that this human beast had been set free. Hundreds of men, especially Gentiles, began fighting with the Jews because they had liberated him without thinking of the safety of their women. Open fistfights broke out, and Barabbas grinned as he watched men of both races fall exhausted to the ground. He spat upon them.

Meanwhile, Pilate seethed with anger as he looked at Jesus. Upon hearing that an unlawful number of lashes had been given Him through the carelessness of the soldiers in charge, he ordered them imprisoned. This order carried out, he left the pavilion.

Jesus descended the steps to the street. As He neared the last one, Dismas' wife ran toward Him, pleading, "Please help my husband and son, who is the cripple at Your feet. I cannot forsake the thought that You are God. I must cling to that hope. Even though You are condemned to die with my husband, I know You are God!"

Dismas shouted angrily, "I do not believe You are the Messiah!"

The order was given at that moment for him, and Gestas, to pick up their crosses. Instead of watching them, Jesus listened to the little mother. He smiled as the crippled boy reached forth his hand in order to touch His feet and said, "Help me to get up and walk as You commanded the old man at the gate. I know him—he told me about You. Jesus, I want to walk."

Dismas' wife added her voice to his. "We have prayed so long to You. We know You are the Man-Christ promised to us by the prophets. But now You are going to die. Jesus, how is it possible for You to do this when You are the Messiah? I cannot understand, yet for some reason I do believe You are the Anointed One. Jesus help us!"

As Dismas shouldered his cross he curled his lip at Jesus and snarled, "See what You have done. Since praying to You I have even lost my eyesight and am denied the sight of my sons before me. If You were God, surely You would have mercy on me, and would have hidden the sun beneath a cloud so that I might see. Is it right of God to forget us? I know the true God is displeased with me, therefore He has sent this added curse of denial and suffering."

Jesus, stifling a sob, answered, "My hour is over."

Dismas walked away beneath his cross and the Master, with the kindly gesture of a light caress over the children's heads, blessed them. Tenderly He took the twins into His arms and embraced them. Dismas' wife hurried after her husband and again pleaded with him to have faith in Jesus, but he pushed her aside as the soldiers hurried the prisoners and the procession along.

Staggering with grief, she returned to Jesus. Taking the twins from His arms, she noticed their clothing was now smeared with blood that had oozed through the Messiah's toga. Not realizing the wonderful sacramental gift the Master had given her, she smiled, her expression telling Him it was all right that the children's clothing had been soiled. Immediately, however, her attention was drawn to her other son who was weeping, not because of physical pain alone, but also because of losing his father. He begged for him to come back. Piteously the little mother besought Jesus to help them.

Three unknown prisoners, very old men, carried their crosses after Dismas and Gestas. The people laughed at the old fellows and made bets that they would not live to reach the top of Golgotha. It appeared they, too, were victims for the sport of the day, but no one seemed to know them or anything about them.

The slow, uneven sound of the crosses scraping and bumping over the rough paving stones and hard earth revived many sorrowful memories of the ancient past in the minds of old ones present, who still came to watch the scenes of death. Many recalled, with tears streaming down their faces, how certain loved ones had also walked that dreadful path. Others expressed hope that one day the practice of crucifixion would be abolished by law.

Within a quarter of an hour, and only a short distance from where the procession started, a break took place. A low moan was heard and one of the old men fell beneath his cross and rolled and tossed in the agony of a sudden death. He was kicked to one side brutally. There was no one to mourn his passing.

Meanwhile, Jesus picked up His cross. Much to the dismay of the soldiers they discovered it would not do at all. Handmade, it was much too short for a man of Christ's stature. They sought quickly for another one, but finding none, hurried down the street toward a young tree that had been felled not long before. Trimming the dead branches away, they started to pull it to the side of the Master. A voice said from the crowd, "It is written that the Christ would die on a tree!"

Jesus said quietly to Dismas' wife, "My hour is over but there is another coming."

The poor woman raised her eyes to the Master in thanksgiving. As she did so she noticed He looked at one of the twins in particular as He continued, "Soon I will take this child with Me to My Father's Kingdom." His eyes moved to the other. "This boy will be one of My successors. Someday, little mother, you will understand My words. You are most courageous. Blessings on you!"

Dismas' wife was breathless, bewildered, and at the same time so grief-stricken about her husband that she could not comprehend the vastness of the Master's meaning and promise. Smiling graciously through her tears, she stood aside as the soldiers returned.

The log that they placed near the Master could easily be spanned by a man's two hands. One end of a four-foot rope was tied about it and the other around Jesus' waist. By this time, the main procession was some distance ahead and the soldiers jested about having a parade of their own. A young man dropped back at that moment to tell them that another of the old men had died.

Many in the crowd who had preferred to remain near Jesus now surged forward in order to see his death. As they did so, they pushed the Master and He stumbled over the log. Everyone laughed.

The soldiers now tied two short branches, each of good size, to the tree trunk. Later, on Calvary, they would convert them into arms for the cross which, this time, would not be too small.

Jesus lifted the log and steadied it on His right hip. Then He started on His way to death.

The crowd was uproarious and many bets were made that He would die before He reached Calvary. Had He not suffered and lost much blood during the scourging?

CHAPTER 16

Jesus Is Nailed to the Cross

AS THE PROCESSION WOUND ITS WAY through Jerusalem's narrow streets, the outward signs of the Master's enemies became more and more vicious as they struck and cursed Him. Loud, boisterous women hung from second-story windows and small overhanging balconies and cheered wantonly each time He fell or stumbled over the rough, jagged pavement. Drunken women in the streets made every effort to further His torments by jesting and prodding the soldiers with their fingers as they hurried the condemned Man along at the points of their spears.

Here and there other groups of women danced forth from doorways and formed lines across the street in order to stall the procession. They glared in mocking glee as they even fell against the crosses to make them heavier for the prisoners.

Under such jarring and added weight, Jesus stumbled and fell again. This time He was in front of the building into which Judas had hurried the night before to tell his friends about the Living Bread. The women who had been at the party were waiting in a group for Him. As He lay at their feet, they drew bits of sopping bread from their wine cups and, in an ugly pretense of acting, coyly dropped them into one another's loathsome mouths saying, "This is my body. I will give you Manna. Here is your Living Bread!"

Others took up a chant, pointing and laughing at Jesus as He struggled to rise from the mud. "Look," they said, "here in the street lies the Bread of Heaven under a log. Look at the Man who claims to be Life Eternal. Doesn't He think we have any sense to try to make us believe that? Would any of us exchange places with Him? Even His disciples have fled lest He ask them to take His place, or help Him to carry the cross. Look! His Heaven is in the mud!"

One man close to Jesus said, "Son of David! That is a great title You have chosen. Why don't You follow us in our philosophy and teach eat, drink, and be merry, for tomorrow we all must die? There is no proof of an eternal life. How can You say there is when Your own race has treated You like a dog? Deny all Your teachings and maybe the Gentiles will fight for You. Speak!"

Jesus looked at him without a murmur. Bowing His head in silence He prayed for Heaven's light to flood this man's intellectual disbelief.

Once more He went His painful way. Presently He reached a corner and was about to turn it when His feet slipped on stones upon which onlookers had been pouring water. The ground came crashing up to meet Him. How they shrieked with laughter! Some had watched the women with their wine cups and bread and now they took up, and added to, that sacrilegious act by placing pieces of wine-sopped bread into their own mouths and spitting them upon Jesus.

What a disgraceful, unkempt sight they made of the Messiah! The bread clung like cotton balls around His brittle wreath of thorns, and many jested that He wore white and pink roses as a crown.

Rising slowly, Jesus shouldered the log and tried to hurry from the frenzied crowd as they lashed Him with both tongue and whip. Then He smiled as He caught sight of Mother Mary standing just ahead of Him. She stepped nearer, determined to caress Him regardless of the punishment that might be inflicted upon her as a result.

Jesus allowed the tree-log to roll to the ground as He received His mother's embrace. Her fingers loosened the crown quickly, and in doing so she brushed some of the wine-sopped bread away. His weary head, for a moment, leaned against her shoulder.

Angrily, a soldier pushed Mary aside as Jesus whispered, "Mother,

Tabernacle of the World, all men must seek and love thee as My mother, for knowing you they will learn more of Me."

He fell again. He seemed so weak that the soldiers began to fear He might not live to be crucified after all. They had bet on Him, and as a consequence now looked about for a means of help.

Their eyes encountered a dark-skinned man, Simon of Cyrene, hurrying toward Jerusalem, displaying no interest whatsoever in the festivities of evil around him. They called him and when he paid no attention, two of them caught his arms and brought him back to Jesus. Roughly, they commanded him to pick up the log and help this criminal along.

Simon scowled and snapped, "I'm not a Jew. Why should I be forced to help Him? Why do you choose me out of these thousands of people to help in your evil parade? I'm in a hurry and don't want any part of it. I don't want to help in a crucifixion."

A soldier struck him across the mouth and ordered him, in the power of Pilate, to pick up the log. Simon obeyed with great reluctance and placed it across his shoulders. In that second he and Jesus looked at each other and the Master smiled. Simon shuddered and then chilled, as though filled with joy. What did this mean? His feelings were most unusual. Ordinarily he would be angry at such a situation, but instead he felt like smiling and singing.

Suddenly he remembered where he had seen Jesus before. He was the Man who had befriended him when he was suffering from hunger in the desert months ago. He had stopped to talk and had even cured him of a withered arm. He had told him then to befriend everyone, that it was God's will, and never to mistreat even his enemies. From that time on Simon had tried to live up to those words in thanksgiving for his healed arm. It was no wonder that he had not wanted to take part in a crucifixion.

Simon's smile told Jesus that he remembered and, in gratitude, now wanted to help Him carry His cross. The heavy log became light as paper! Simon's smile grew a bit broader, but he gave no indication to the soldiers or spectators of what had taken place, continuing to walk as though the log were heavy. Well he understood that this was just another of the great miracles Jesus was capable of performing. Why, even the chiefs of magic in the dark countries could never match this Man's powers!

One of the Master's disciples stepped from the crowd and walked beside Simon. "You are helping the God-Man," he said quietly. "He is the Messiah and you will receive many gifts and perhaps eternal life for what you are doing. Don't fight against this crucifixion, for our ancient prophets have told us for hundreds of years that God would be crucified. Because you have been chosen to help Him, your name will be known and taught until the end of time. Tell me something about yourself so that I may relay it to the higher chosen men."

Being a good actor, Simon never once ceased to pretend that the log was heavy, hoping not to have any further punishment brought upon the Master. Jesus stumbled again and was about to fall when he caught Him in his strong arms. Shouldering the log and supporting the Master at the same time, he believed with his whole heart that this Man was the true God.

He whispered, "Jesus, will You be my God? To whom shall I go when You are dead? I have known You such a little while, but I believe You are the Messiah of the Jews."

The Master answered, "I am your God. Allow My tears to touch your face the next time I fall and I will baptize you, Myself. Then, when I am dead, search for a man known as Simon, the great fisherman. He will instruct you and give you the Food of Heaven that I have left to the world."

Slowly they continued their walk to Calvary. As the people went on spitting upon Jesus and mocking Him, Simon said consolingly, "Don't listen, Master, don't listen to them. They don't know who You are! Allow me to suffer all these outrages You must listen to, and I am sure my relations and friends will join with my thoughts for You. I want to protect You. Would that I could die for You!"

A little further along, as Jesus seemed to have recovered a bit of His strength, the soldiers pulled Him from Simon's protective arm and forced Him once more to carry the log alone. Simon walked to one side and very close to Him. It was not long before the crowd caused Jesus to fall still another time, and Simon went down beside Him. He rubbed his dark face against the Master's, which was wet with tears, and as he did so, Jesus said, "You are My son. You are Mine. I have given you the gift of tears."

The soldiers hauled Simon to his feet and pushed him into the crowd, for they could not help but notice the way he and the Master looked at each other. As Jesus lay in the fired dust of the hillside, He heard Simon's loud, booming voice telling of his sudden belief that He was God. He also told about his arm and about the miracle of the log. Jesus smiled silently at his courage and love.

Simon's talk of miracles rekindled the minds of many listeners, and they wondered again about the condemnation they were bringing upon themselves and future generations if this Man were God. They became frightened and confused, and many wept and went in search of the scribes to ask about the prophecies. Many Jews, clustered in groups, took back the offer that their children suffer because of this crucifixion. Kneeling, they asked Jesus to forgive them. His eyes both blessed and granted their request.

Turning to one of these, the Cyrenean asked where he might find Simon, the big fisherman, and was directed toward Mother Mary, who led a little band of people up the hill. As Simon watched, many of those who had just taken back their promise, ran and joined her group.

Meanwhile, Jesus still lay in the dust. A woman darted from the doorway of a house some distance from the path and, kneeling before Him, unwound a headscarf and with it dried His face of its perspiration and spittle.

The Master smiled. Then she was pushed away, but all heard her say, "I still believe You are the Christ, and that You will save my husband and cure my son!"

She was Dismas' wife.

Jesus answered, "Fear not, little mother, I will do as you have asked. Be at peace."[23]

At last, Jesus, Dismas, and Gestas approached the spot of their execution. The hill was hot and dry and their bodies glistened with perspiration. Quickly built stores, stalls, and concessions of all kinds lined the road. Jews and Gentiles alike were busy hanging tapestries for shade. They wished to watch the crucifixion in comfort. Arabian flies swarmed about horses and people, and their sting was comparable to a burning needle piercing the flesh. In clouds they settled over Jesus and stung deeply into His scourging wounds and became matted in His eyes and thorn-wounds.

Upon seeing how the Master suffered, many women wept and, with their children, tried to brush the flies away, but the soldiers pushed

---

23 "Veronica" is a title. It means a person who is always instant in prayer: "True Image."

them back. Jesus said, "Weep not for Me, but for your children, who will only know Me through the eyes of faith and your teaching. Bless you, mothers in the world, for you are torch-bearers and tradition will live through you."

A loud cry arose a few moments later as a trumpet announced that the prisoners had reached the summit of Calvary.

Events marched more swiftly now. Jesus was seized and stripped roughly of His brown, seamless garment. The tree branches, which were approximately four feet long, were wedged tightly into the main log with an ax, and were held in place by strips of rawhide and large nails, forming a huge Y. The Master's cross was ready.

Slowly and willingly He lowered His weary Body upon it. He extended His open right hand until it rested upon an indentation in the tree branch made by a soldier pressing with all his weight upon a spear. He was ready for the first nail to pierce His Sacred Flesh.

Mother Mary knelt near the lower end of the log, and she shuddered and closed her eyes when she saw the large, square nails. Tears streamed down her face, but she made no sound. Then she heard the blow of the mallet. She opened her eyes to see a half-drunken man wield the hammer again and again. It missed the head of the nail and smashed savagely into her Son's hand. His beauty was now crushed, open and bleeding, revealing bare bones as part payment for the sins of men.

He writhed and moaned in a low tone. "Mother," He said, the words escaping from His lips, "help Me bear this pain. Remind Me with your smile of courage the cause of this suffering, and the good it will bring, lest for a moment, in anguish of soul, I forget the world. This I must not do, Mother, because you are still in the world with My friends."

Rough, gnarled hands grasped Jesus' left hand, and pulled it toward the indentation in the left tree branch. It did not reach. The pull was increased so greatly that His arm was dislocated. Then the thudding hammer was heard again. The nail was driven through His left hand.

In anguish, Jesus' head rose and fell against the wood of the cross, which drove the thorns in His crown deeper into His head than ever. Mother Mary hurried to His side. His face was now ashen-gray and His eyes beginning to look glassy with shock. Yet He whispered, "Thank you, Mother. My greatest pain is to know you are watching the brutality of men. It will take centuries for the majority of people to overcome the beast nature within them, and it will be accomplished by grace which, in turn, will teach kindness, love, and devotion to all men. Great ages are coming, Mother, great ages are coming."

Again, Mother Mary was thrust aside. A soldier used an ax to chop a few chips out of the log, toward the base, into which they pushed the Messiah's heel. As the nail was being driven through His foot, His foot slipped from the niche, and the nail pierced the bark of the tree. The soldiers decided to use one nail to hold both feet at the same time.

With one quick jerk they yanked the Master's foot from the nail. Then His feet were crossed and a long, rusty nail was placed over the instep for the final pinioning. Jesus closed His eyes and said, "Hurry, men, with My death!"

With shuddering violence, faster than driving rain, the huge nail shattered its way through His Sacred Feet into the center of the tree.

As the soldiers adjusted the ropes with which to raise the cross and slide it to the hole into which it would be dropped, Mother Mary fell upon her knees beside Jesus. The soldiers agreed to allow her to remain for a few minutes.

In great anguish of spirit she embraced her Son, and in doing so her arms also embraced the wood of the cross. Then she kissed Him over His Heart. He said, "Mother, do you realize what you have just done for the world?"

Mother Mary shook her head.

The Master continued, "You have kissed the first crucifix on earth. Through your willing surrender and obedience in not coming to My defense in any way, you have this instant gained for all your adopted children, until the end of time, the grace to know that at any moment during their lives when they kiss an improvised cross and think about these hours, I will make their kiss equal in merit to their actually kneeling now beside you. With Me there is no time."

Mother Mary was hurried away. The sound of the soldiers' shovels removing earth from the hole in which the cross would stand, was rhythmical and seemed like the prancing of horses' hooves. Other soldiers stood at attention with uplifted spears, as if these weapons were some sort of triumphal banners. The diggers looked up from time to time and jested at the cries for mercy that came from the two thieves, who were now gasping in convulsive agony on their crosses to which they were tied.

The flint-hearted men, in a terrible gesture of mock mercy, used their spears to pick up skeleton heads of newly uncovered animals, which had been buried in the hill. The heads, filled with moving worms, were deliberately held to the faces of the suffering thieves. These poor men shrieked and swooned in horror as the living insects left the recesses of the skulls and crawled into their new living flesh.

When this atrocious fun grew tiresome, the skulls were tossed toward the Master's head as He lay on His cross on the ground. The stench from them added to His already agonizing torment. Swarming flies covered Him like a blanket.

Between taut ropes the first crucifix was raised between Heaven and earth. Slowly the holy cross was brought into an upright position at the very edge of the hole, which was about three feet deep and three feet in diameter, and was then slid heavily, and with a terrific jar, into it. The soldiers lost control of the ropes, and the cross fell forward against the rim of the hole with such jolting force that Jesus' hands pulled from the nails. His body bent forward and His head crashed against the earth. His feet held.

Almost as quickly as He had fallen, He was pushed back onto the cross after it had been tilted backward, and His hands were tied, this time, to the cross-arms. Nails were driven through His wrists. Thus six nails were used in nailing Him to the tree, but only three actually held Him.

Slowly, the cross was worked into a vertical position and held there. Small pieces of wood and rocks were stomped tightly about its base and the hole filled with soft earth. A soldier placed a ladder at the back of the cross, and nailed a sign to the top which read: THIS IS JESUS, THE KING OF THE JEWS.

Mary of Magdala fled from the crowd and knelt at her Master's feet, which were about six inches from the level of the ground. She covered His poor, wounded feet with her beautiful hair and in this way kept the flies away from them. It was at least an hour before she moved from this position of sorrow and adoration.

CHAPTER 17

Peter's Ecstasy

THE HOUR FOR GOD'S DEATH HAD ARRIVED. The greatest drama on earth was about to be staged. The world and the people seemed to be in a state of utter confusion. Even the elements showed revenge by the silent language of heat that poured down in streams of blustery vapor, striking the spectators as if they were streamlets of stinging rain. It was hot and dry everywhere. Men and women panted for breath as they sat in the shade of their tents or knelt under awnings.

Over a hundred tents nestled close to the three crosses that stood silhouetted against the blue, diamond-dusted, heated sky. People had lived on the hill for several days for this, their hour of entertainment. The scene was satanic in its color, and the brilliant tents seemed to wither in the slow, creeping breeze like a writhing snake of many hues and stripes.

Disguised in Gentile togas, Peter and James, led by an unknown disciple, walked unrecognized through the crowds to the tent that had secretly been prepared for them. They would be near Jesus, at least, in His sufferings even though they had to remain hidden or face imprisonment. Their faith told them that the Master would know of their closeness and devotion.

The tent was about fifty feet in front and a little to the left of the Messiah's cross. Peter entered and saw that he had full view of the three crosses from the front opening. Every few minutes the soldiers wedged and packed more dirt and stones into the soft earth around the bases of the crosses, which seemed to move away in sympathy as the anguished muscles of the men struggled against the wood that held them.

Watching the terrible agony and listening to the steady thud of the crosses in the loose earth caused Peter to prostrate himself upon the ground, where he wept like a whipped child—he was helpless to protect the One he loved.

Steadying himself, he clasped at the tent flap and prayed aloud in a whisper, "Jesus, Jesus, let me suffer in some little way with You on the cross that You may suffer less. Lord, only You know the depths of my sorrow when I realized, after grace had fled, that I had so terribly denied You. My suffering is great, but, Lord, how much more is Yours, since You are God, and can see into the hearts of men to be born and hear not one voice deny You, but perhaps a million say, as I did, that they do not know You? Jesus, let me suffer in reparation for them. Take me, Lord, mystically into You that I may ease Your pain!"

As his prayer ended in a sob of anguish, Peter was caught up into ecstasy. Through that gift of God—a soul suffering the pangs of spiritual union—spirit with Spirit, before death, he saw from the Master's position on the cross the generations to be born into the world from that hour until the end of time. Each generation rose and fell like ocean breakers before the feet of Jesus, and in those spiritual mists he visioned the forms of men, women, and children talking to the Messiah. They, too, begged for the privilege to relieve Him of suffering. Would He allow them to suffer in their members?

The Master answered that He would allow them to be sharers in the plan of redemption. Through grace He taught them, regardless of their state in life and its circumstances of pain and strife, that they could, at will, unite their sorrows and joys with the pattern of His life and thus become incorporated with His will that He suffer for man. With an act of will they would thus become engrafted in Him and make any circumstance in life His will, in union with Him.

Other men, women, and children, in each mist of time, turned away their head when He tried to address them. They represented the minority of people who could not bear to see suffering or want to understand its meaning, as Jesus called them by name from the cross. As His plea went unheard and they continued to turn away, Peter begged them mystically to stop and at least look at the bleeding feet of the Messiah. The tide turned, all through the effect of grace Peter had earned for them, and they listened and dared to lift their eyes to the feet of the Master.

Aghast at what they saw, they pleaded, "Lord, allow us to suffer with You. Share with us Thy pain while we live on earth. Allow us to suffer in the members of Thy feet. Give us bruises, scars, and even amputations—all this, if You will suffer less. Anything, Lord, according to the circumstances under which we are born, we will offer in union with Thy suffering feet."

Jesus smiled, and Peter felt within his own soul, hidden in the heart of God on the cross, the relief of pain in the Master's feet.

Jesus whispered to him, "My friends shall be graced to suffer with, and for, Me. The suffering charismata will appear to them in many forms, such as afflictions of shedding blood, amputations, swellings, and many others too numerous to mention now. Certain effects of pain, even in this hour, have ceased in My feet. I am suffering less, but in and through them, I will suffer all things. Their bodies will be My other borrowed body. Together we will suffer all things even to the last hour of time. Well they understand My words: 'You are your brother's keeper.'"

In vision's light of understanding, Peter then watched thousands of his people moan under their crosses. Many limped, while others crawled into their respective paths of life in time.

Mystically he lifted his voice again, and thousands more dared look upon suffering. Their eyes seemed to hold fast to the bleeding knees of the Master. They asked that they, also, might shed their blood for Him, any way He allowed, under the circumstances of life.

Many other groups of people looked compassionately at Jesus' outstretched hands nailed to the cross. They knew, in the plan of will incorporated with the Master's wish, that they would suffer pains of the hands. They were glad.

Scores of others bowed in solemn quietness as they gazed fearfully at the sufferings of the Master because of His crown of thorns. They, the unseen generations who would merit through this suffering, prayed to be courageous because that pain was most terrible to accept and to bear.

Great moans arose from the sea as people had a vision of the blindness of Jesus as blood trickled into His eyes from the piercing thorns. They asked pleadingly to suffer all manner of blindness if He would only continue to see the vision of time and allow His gaze to fall upon all the peoples of the world.

Mystically, Peter watched them stumble then, and grope in their pending blindness. They walked into every path of life. They smiled, knowing they had allowed the Messiah to prolong His vision while He suffered on the cross.

As the vision of the suffering crowds dimmed, Peter noticed an equal number of people beneath the cross just looking at the Master. They had not voiced petitions that would entitle them to suffer the crucifixion pain. They seemed to be transfixed as they watched the crowds in their mystical paths of suffering. Suddenly, these non-sufferers cried aloud as if with one voice, "Jesus, if all these people suffer Thy life in their members according to the laws of the crucifixion, who is going to comfort them? You have given the gifts of suffering to both young and old, and to others the interior suffering of just watching unrepentant sufferers. Look at their anguish. Many are now around the thieves' crosses. Many hearts are breaking over the wrongs, the injustices, and the suffering of Dismas and Gestas. You have given these people some of Your interior sufferings, mourning, shame, and loss. Are they not Your garden agony sufferers? Look how their souls are afflicted and tormented with doubt and hope and then loss, which could lead to despair. Surely they are the ones who relieved Your soul when You complained in the garden that Your soul was nigh unto death.

"Now we stand as another body of people asking: 'Lord, isn't there anything we can do in the merit of Your crucifixion to console the people of the earth in body and soul as they suffer for You, or in the loss of despair? Allow us to be acting angels of mercy that they may continue to live and to suffer until You call them in death. We are not asking for personal suffering, but we do ask to follow Your life in another pattern. We would like to give hope and joy and comfort to the sufferers. Allow us to live Your life up to this hour, for it was composed of hope, consolation, mercy, and love.'"

Peter heard Jesus answer, "My friends, walk to the other side of the cross. See the nails? They have pierced through the wood. Back against these nail-points, and your weight holding to the nails will steady the cross for Me. The other side of the cross was left vacant just for you. I would have you know that when you steady a friend's cross in his life of suffering, whether it be an interior cross, or the easing of body pain, you are steadying My throbbing cross. Come, stop My cross from thudding and jarring loose in the soft earth and you will lessen My pain from the crown of thorns.

"Then, My cross-steadiers, in our closeness we will talk about pain, joy, and sorrow. With Me, and through My eyes, you will see death, birth, and new life through the mystery and the power of grace because of your cooperation and knowledge of My cross. Hurry, My friends, the cross is thudding as I twist and writhe in agony, either on this cross, or in My many other friends. Come, we need your steadying hand.

"Look, even My sinless mother feels the earth's reverberations as the cross trembles in its moorings. This thudding is the nearest to actual suffering that she understands, for she is free from Original Sin. However, she mystically understands pain in the knowledge of My Human Nature because we have had the exchange of hearts. Thus she is better able to understand the free will of man and the different circumstances of life in which he is born and which may lead to good or to evil. Help Me, through you, to lessen even this echo of wonderment and pain in her, My Heart's Tabernacle. I promise all cross-steadiers that I will be with them when they writhe in their death's agony. I will come to them in My Humanity as I will appear after My Resurrection, and I will console them as they have consoled even the least of My children."

The cross ceased its thudding. Peter watched Jesus look heavenward, where were assembled countless numbers of angels, the future guardians of all those souls who in vision a moment before had asked to be cross-steadiers. A smile spread across the Master's face and He prayed, "Father, I thank Thee for the willingness of human hearts to suffer with Me in My passion of solicitude, pain, joy, charity, kindness, and death."

Then in the life of vision's majesty and power, Peter stood alone before Jesus. Having seen the wonders and the beauties of the heavens above, the big fisherman asked aloud, "Lord, Heaven's view gives You joy and brings a smile to Your face. Lord, don't look down this way again—keep Your eyes on Heaven's glory. Allow me to help You keep Your smile of joy and peace. Allow me and my successors the suffering that You would experience now if You were to watch the rest of these souls beneath Your cross as they turn away from You."

Into the depths of his soul Peter heard the Master whisper, "I will leave all souls from this moment in your care, but in order that the Scriptures be fulfilled, that I suffer all things, it is necessary, with your permission, that I cast My eyes down toward Hell and watch from its brink a soul hurrying into its destruction. Peter, I want to spare you and your successors that suffering of the flesh, for I am sure its sorrow would kill your souls. Only My flesh could stand the pangs of a lost soul and bear to hear how he turns in awful revenge and accuses Me of abandoning him, when in truth he abandoned Me."

Peter answered, "Your will be done that the Scriptures be fulfilled."

He watched Jesus lower His head, and then the Master shuddered and repeated the accusing words of the lost soul who was saying at that moment, "My God, My God, why hast Thou forsaken Me?"

Trembling in his ecstasy with God, Peter pleaded, "Jesus, I know I am not worthy to die as You are dying, by crucifixion, but since I have seen Your greatest sorrow, the final departure of a soul, and how he accuses You of forsaking him, I must use my authority and ask You never again to witness such a scene, but rather allow me and my successors that scorn of a revengeful tongue. Grant this petition, O God the Father—allow me to be crucified head down, that my eyes may be nearest those who are lost to You."

Tears streamed down the Master's face as He answered, "You will be crucified head downward in the symbolical manner of lowering your head. Your crucifixion, and the soul crucifixions of your successors, will merit grace for souls, even on the brink of Hell, to hear your words. Many will return to Me."

Now, to go back to the time when Peter was first wrapt in his ecstasy. The wife of Dismas, still dazed and in deep mourning, knelt beside her children on the pavilion steps. A woman traveler emerged from the crowd and tried to comfort her, saying, "My name is Rachel and I am the sister of Gestas, who is being crucified with your husband. Is there anything I can do for You? Don't cry. I know your cross is greater than mine because Dismas is your husband while Gestas is only my brother. Your grief is greater still because you have two hearts to mourn within you—one the heart of a wife, and the other the heart of a mother. Even now your little ones tear your heart with questions regarding your helplessness. Because I haven't any children to bear the stigma of a father's crucifixion, allow me to comfort you and to help you."

Veronica shook her head. There was nothing anyone could do. She was inconsolable.

Rachel suddenly gasped aloud with shock and surprise as she caught sight of Veronica's headscarf. "Where did you get that?" she asked. "Look, the Messiah's face is imprinted on it. Did you paint it?"

Veronica turned deathly pale. What was this Rachel saying? She hadn't noticed any image on the scarf after she had used it to dry the Master's face when He had fallen so heavily that time. And Rachel had come from another direction and so could not have witnessed that act of kindness. And there had been no time for anyone to have drawn a picture of the Messiah.

Veronica trembled and was afraid to lift her hand to remove the scarf. She asked, "Are you jesting? Is this your way of helping me over my grief by giving me a shock?"

Gazing steadily into Rachel's eyes, she slowly removed the veil only to drop it with a gasp. Yes, she could see the image—Jesus' face on three different places!

Her eleven-year-old son took hold of the veil excitedly and exclaimed, "It is the Messiah's face! These pictures were not here when I unfolded it for you this morning. How did this happen, Mother?"

Reaching for the scarf, Rachel said, "Let me see to make sure it is the Messiah's face. Then, frowning at the boy, she asked, "How is it possible you recognize the Master, agonized and covered with spittle as His features are? This is the way we saw Him on the hill carrying His cross!"

Veronica answered, "It is a miracle because when He stood here His face was not like this. This scarf shows His agony. It must have happened when I knelt beside Him and dried His face. Now I know that He is the real Messiah among us. Let us hurry to save Him!"

Rachel nodded with some hesitancy, for the word "miracle" brought to mind the heavenly tones of the pearls. Then hastily connecting the history of the pearls with this Jesus who was being crucified, she said aloud, "Surely He must be the Messiah. He was born in my stable. No one on earth could perform this miracle but God. The three images on the veil must mean the truths John the Baptizer taught when he used the term 'Trinity' in regard to God being Three in One!"

Veronica became more than excited. "Tell me all you can!" she begged. "I, too, have heard about a certain holy man named John, a baptizer in the Jordan. Is it he of whom you speak? Is he a hermit? Have you heard his orations on the actual coming of the Messiah? Hurry, tell me about him!"

Rachel sat down on the steps, holding and caressing the scarf. She wondered whether or not there might be a phenomenal mystery revealed through it, such as what took place when she held the pearls and thought about the beautiful woman and her Son Who had been born in her stable.

Deciding to put the veil to a test, she removed a pearl from a pocket, and holding the headpiece toward the crippled boy, said, "Kiss the image and at the same time I will pray upon this pearl. I believe Jesus will cure you as I meditate upon His birth in my stable near the inn. Hurry, kiss the image, and say that you, too, believe He is God!"

The lad obeyed without hesitation. Immediately his legs were straight and strong. In his ecstatic delight he ran in circles, shouting at the top of his voice, "Jesus healed me! See, I am cured! I can walk—I can walk! Jesus who hangs on the cross is the Messiah! He cured me!"

Those moments were breathless and joyous for all who stood near the little boy. A few people, realizing at last the grave mistake made in condemning Jesus, ran frightened through the streets, calling to friends and neighbors that they had crucified God and now surely the end of the world would come. God's wrath would be upon them.

Rachel was speechless. She just stared into space. Veronica shook her and drew her attention to the truth of what had happened. No one could doubt it. She repeated slowly the Master's last words to her, "My hour is over, but another is coming."

Rachel smiled and drew from her pocket the little purse containing the rest of the pearls and quietly told Veronica their history. As she did so they could hear heavenly strains of music as though it came from them. The two women sat on the step breathless and speechless with the reality of truth before them.

Scarcely could Veronica answer as her son tugged at her dress saying, "Hurry, Mother, let us go to Calvary and show Jesus and my father that I can walk. See how I can run! I can run! It is fun! Hurry, mother! Maybe the soldiers will take them down from the crosses now that I can walk!"

CHAPTER 18

Jesus Dies

IN THEIR NEW CONVERSION OF CERTAINTY that this Jesus was the Messiah, Veronica and Rachel embraced each other, wept, and laughed. Their joy was beyond the expression of words, and their first intention was to hurry to Calvary, believing this miracle would stop the crucifixion and put everyone to shame and penance.

The grandfather of Dismas' son took one of the twins and hobbled toward home, smiling and happy to think that he had played even a small part in the great event. Had he not cared for the three children while Veronica hurried after Jesus and dried His face with her veil?

Dismas' wife and Rachel took turns carrying the other twin as they hurried toward the three crosses on the hill. Joyously, the little cured boy scurried ahead of them—only to stop and beg them to walk faster. People gasped in surprise and fear and exclaimed their sudden belief in the Messiah when they saw him fully restored to health.

Some of the hateful women who had tossed wine-sopped bread at Jesus fainted as they recognized him and heard him shout, "Jesus cured me! Come follow us—Jesus is the Messiah!" Shocked and afraid, others dropped their wine cups and ran to hide. Old people hurled stones after them.

Men turned ashen gray as they knelt in the streets to beg God's forgiveness, saying, "I wish I were not living in this age. We are in a measure guilty of killing God. We have everything to fear now. Why were we born in such confusing times?"

The news of this latest miracle became widespread within a few minutes. Hundreds of people who were not interested in the crucifixion, as well as many aged and infirm, came into the streets when they heard of this new procession that told only of joy. They wanted to see in order to believe, and upon observing the dancing, happy child rather than the hopeless cripple crying in pain, they, too, were suddenly converted and knelt to pray for pardon. Their remorse was great, and in prayer they asked God's mercy on Jerusalem. They wondered about the scribes, and asked one another how the judges would take such a humiliation.

These people were the Master's latest converts, made possible through the bravery of one woman and her son who dared to sing and call aloud the truth.

A little further along, Veronica and Rachel stopped to rest near the doorway from which Veronica had hurried to dry the face of Jesus. Men and women crowded about them, asking for the full story of what had taken place. Veronica reenacted the event and unfurled the scarf for all to see.

Rachel exclaimed in a loud tone, "I believe this Man Jesus is the Messiah!"

Thousands cheered, and as the two women resumed their way they took their place in the procession of new converts. They would see and believe Jesus now as He hung on the cross.

Walking side by side, and taking turns carrying the infant twin, Veronica and Rachel grew very tired and wondered whether or not they would have strength enough to climb the steeper part of the hill. Rachel said, "I am going to ask Jesus for a second miracle. Let us talk about it and maybe we will forget ourselves. My brother never knew your son, and therefore he will not realize the contrast of sickness and health, which these other people have seen. It will take another miracle to convince him, I am sure, for he is a very stubborn man. He will probably say we are pretending this to save him from death."

Veronica answered, "Perhaps the old people who are following us will sway him. They are rich in wisdom and courage and will not be afraid to talk even to a condemned man. Let us rest again for a moment."

As they paused, Rachel prayed softly, "God, please listen to our prayers for Gestas. Answer us according to the measure of glory it will mean to You if he is converted. Hear us, God, as we sit here in this hallowed street where just a little while ago You gave a miracle to the world for all time. It can never be forgotten, for too many have seen the veil.

"As I meditate on Thy holy birth in my stable (once more she took the worn purse from the folds of her dress), and hold Your grandmother's pearls, please allow the miracle of music to come forth into this street that everyone may hear and lift their hearts to Thee. The music, and the fact that souls hear it, will tell me there is hope."

Almost instantly hundreds of people looked heavenward. "What is this strange music we hear?" they exclaimed incredulously. "It is not of the earth. It must be God's answer that He will hear us, and forgive us our misjudgments and hate." Tears of joy streamed down their faces as they hastened along the rocky path toward the top of the hill.

Veronica and Rachel were the only ones who knew the deeper mystery of the heavenly results brought to them through meditation and the pearls that they had started to call "beads." All they could say was, "God is wonderful—God is good!"

Peter awakened slowly from his ecstasy and two of his disciples, kneeling beside him, took hold of his arms to steady him as the reality of the terrible scene before him disrobed him of the ethereal light and knowledge that he had enjoyed in the serenity of God's peace. While he was yet clothed in some effect of this joyful serenity, however, his happiness was as a leaping deer and he was without care. If the disciples had not held him back, he would have run to the cross to further continue his talk with Jesus.

Stopped from leaving the tent, he thanked the disciples for their care and then he pointed exuberantly to Dismas' son running up the hill, calling, "Father, Father, I'm cured! Jesus beside you on His cross cured me! See? I can walk and run like other boys. Ask Jesus to take you down from the cross. He can do anything. He will save you. Quick, Father, ask Him!"

Peter smiled through the tears that coursed down his cheeks and tingled with the joys of Heaven as he watched the crowd of old people streaming after the boy singing and shouting, "Jesus is the Messiah! We have seen a miracle on this boy. Take Jesus down—take Him down! He is God with us!"

The soldiers, high priests, and unbelievers about the top of Calvary lifted their voices in anger. "He is not the Christ!" they shouted. "He is being crucified. It is too late to take Him down. He is about dead. God, as you call Him, is dying. Don't you realize that if He were God He could not die? Be on your way—go back to the city!"

One high priest, attired in a brightly striped, flowing garment, addressed Jesus saying, "If Thou art God, take Yourself down from the cross and show these people Your powers!" Then pointing at the Master and looking at the people, he continued, "Just look at the crowd who follows Him! They are the weak, the sick, and the fanatical. They haven't any better sense than to believe. Come down, Jesus, and even I will believe!"

When nothing happened, he commanded the soldiers to break up the throng. "Away with you!" he bellowed at the top of his voice, "Go away from Calvary! Can't you see He can't come down? He doesn't obey me and I am a high priest. Why should He do anything you command?"

Soldiers on horses herded the people away as though they were cattle. A few died from fatigue and excitement, while others were injured by the prancing hoofs.

As Dismas' son held out his arms to his father for a last embrace before he, too, would be hurled back, Dismas suddenly received his eyesight, as well as the great grace of mind-lumination into the mystery of the God-Man on earth, even though his body convulsed with pain.

The boy looked at his father in such suffering, and was horrified. He stood transfixed, staring at Dismas' eyes. He was shocked with the knowledge that man could take such suffering and laugh about it. Gently, his mother came and stood beside him, taking his cold hand into hers. The boy pulled away, and embracing the cross and his father's feet, cried, "Father, come down off the cross! Everything is all right now. Everyone knows this Jesus is the Messiah!"

Dismas looked at his son and answered, "Yes, He is the Living Messiah. He is your God. Go embrace His feet instead of mine, and ask Him to allow me to die with Him. It will be an honor. I don't want any change in plans. I must go with Him all the way. Hurry, He is about to die. Don't mind the soldiers, go!"

As his son obeyed, Dismas called out in a loud, anguished voice, "Lord, remember me when You enter into Your kingdom!"

Jesus smiled. He felt the child's fingers caressing His feet as he knelt alongside Mary of Magdala. Turning His head toward Dismas the Master answered, "You will be with Me in Paradise today!"

Then Dismas, suddenly graced to become an oratorical gem, preached to the crowds from his pulpit, the cross. Between moans and sudden convulsive reactions of his taut muscles he said, "People of Jerusalem, especially you who would crucify innocent blood, behold this Jesus is Your Messiah. He is the Christ! He is the *Refugee from Heaven!* He left His throne and joys of ethereal majesty to become One in the flesh like you. He is glad to go back to His Kingdom, for He was only a refugee here, and few people knew Him as the Christ.

"It was because of the Father's mercy and love for us that He became clothed in our humanity of ugliness and discord. We can look upon Him and not be consumed with the light of His majesty. We can touch Him and not be burned with the fire of spiritual substance, like our fathers in the desert who followed the Pillar of Fire, yet could not approach It. That Pillar of Fire was this God-Man without the shroud of our flesh, which serves as a temperer for our very senses.

"Only God could cure my son. Look and see the miracle for yourselves. Look at Jesus and tell Him you believe!

"It was prophesied that the Christ would die. Where is your trust in the prophets? Look, the God-Man is raised between Heaven and earth. Hurry, embrace Him, it is your salvation. He came to us and gave us everything, but we refused Him. I was one with you, then, but now I believe, and I want to die with Him. Imagine, I am going to die with God! Even now He will forgive you. Ask Him! He has forgiven me, and already promised me a place with Him in Paradise. Hurry, go to Him before He breathes His last breath. Think of the countless people to be born who will envy you this opportunity to embrace the cross and to hear Him speak!"

Dismas, filled with grace, turned the minds of the majority who heard him, and the Master watched hundreds kneel in adoration before Him. In that throng were Jews, Gentiles, scribes, a few high priests, and a small number of soldiers. Their cries of sorrow touched His heart and He cried out in His anguish of pain, "Father, forgive them, for they knew not what they did!"

A great many other people, too proud to believe, ran down the hill and hid themselves in the city. They were confused and afraid of the sudden conversions. Who was safe, even among relatives, since this strange turn of events? Who could tell who might be imprisoned or stoned? Consequently, they secreted themselves and trembled with the thought that if this Man were God, the wrath of Heaven would surely fall upon them. They were not safe now from either the world, the people, or the law.

Many remembered tearfully how Pilate had wanted to free Jesus and not judge Him, nor be guilty in any way in His death. How they wished they had had the courage to defend rather than scream "Crucify! Crucify!" with the maddened crowds. What would they do now, and how would they explain to their young that they, themselves, had taken the blame, and even called the guilt down upon their children? Pilate had made their views a law—they were afraid!

Other people, in groups, walked the streets weeping, and crying aloud, "God of Heaven, forgive us if this Man Jesus, who is being crucified, is the Anointed One!"

Rachel wept alone beside the cross of her brother. His revengeful, scurrilous words to her were vehement with hatred. His terrible utterances in regard to his sufferings were unspeakable. He spat upon her. In vain did she try to console him between his loud, cursing breaths, which were fast and labored. He became exhausted, limp, and dying. She took that opportunity to speak to him again, pointing to Dismas' son, saying that his cure was a miracle.

Gestas pulled his face into an atrocious snarl. Once more he spat at her and shouted above the voice of Dismas, "My sister is a witch. Only witches could believe this Man is their God! Ask Him if He believes in music coming from pearls as she does!"

A hush spread over the throng. What was this about pearls? They had never heard of them.

Gestas continued, "She knows all the witchcraft you people believe to be miracles. Why don't you crucify her? She's as bad as Jesus. She is a mockery to the one true God—if there is such a thing. This Man certainly isn't God, and I don't believe there is One!"

Veronica beckoned Rachel to come to the cross of Jesus, and there quietly introduced her to Mother Mary. Immediately they recognized each other and were joyous even under those sad conditions.

Embracing Mother Mary, Rachel said, "I have searched so long to find you!"

At that moment both Gestas and Dismas cried aloud, maddened in their fight with pain. Rachel looked pleadingly at Jesus and begged Him to save her brother.

Jesus answered, "Rachel, I cannot, in justice, resist a free will. Man must come to Me of his own free will or his worship and loyalty will not be pure and true. Free will must be exercised in order for man to gain merit and prove to himself which master he is following. He cannot serve two masters. I am the master of Heaven and the devil is the master of Hell. I can beckon, and coax, and appeal to the five senses, through which man gains knowledge, but other than that, the foundation of faith, I am helpless to sway his free will. However, you must remember that I have said: 'You are your brother's keeper.' Rachel, do you have the desire to do anything within your power to save Gestas?"

"Lord," Rachel responded fervently, "if there is anything I can do, allow me the privilege of trying."

"Would you freely give your life doing reparation for him?" Jesus asked. "Your acts and deeds would be a constant petition before God, which might gain the grace for your brother, in his judgment, to pray an act of sorrow—especially because he has seen Me and not heard My words. Grace for this type of person is most difficult to earn. It would be easier if he had never heard of Me, for now his sin is triple. He has seen Me and refused My Light, the Father within Me. He and I are One. I am the Light of the world."

Rachel pleaded anxiously, "Lord, is there time? He is dying. Teach me the way. Tell me Your plans that I may follow. I will deny myself anything to save his soul. If I love him this much, how much more then must You love him."

Jesus said quietly, "A soul's judgment may last several days according to earthly expressions of time, even after death has been pronounced over the body. In that timeless time of judgment a soul may be saved through repentance earned by the deeds and prayers of a loved one, or through several holy souls living for the same common good. If you choose to follow a life of reparation for Gestas, you will indeed be following My life. I have said take up your cross and follow Me. I am the Good Shepherd Who left the comfort of ninety-nine friends to go in search of one lost sheep."

Smiling with new hope, Rachel answered, "Lord, I will do anything You ask. Gestas was such a good little brother to me. Often he gave me his last crust of bread when I cried for more. I shall never forget his kindness before he turned to deeds of hate and revenge. O, if only he knew his God were beside him!"

The Master's eyes searched those of Mary Magdala, and then looking at Rachel he addressed them both, saying, "Love each other. Your former dislikes are a heritage ritual that does not graft easily into each other's moods. Charity is the only rule to follow, and in that kind of charity of love I work through souls in many ways. At times this may seem contradictory to the mind of men, but this is because they do not understand heritage, its customs and traditions from one tribe of people to the other. Love each other. I do not govern all souls alike, nor do I lead them through the same paths and virtues to the hall of My Kingdom, which is not of this world.

"Mary, take Rachel as your companion. She will go with you to your desert cave, which I have shown you in vision-knowledge. There, with you, she will live a life of penance for Gestas and for any other soul whom I wish to share with her."

Shocked, Rachel asked, "Where is the cave?"

"Deep in the Arabian desert," Mary answered. "A man named Saul will take up his retreat there first, to find Jesus through prayer. We will arrive shortly after he leaves for Jerusalem. In the cave we will discover many of his hand-written scrolls on methods of prayer. Jesus has asked me to follow them as my rule for I, too, have a mission of penance to perform until death. I am glad, Rachel, that you are going with me. We will encounter great difficulties before we finally reach our destination, however, and at one time we will be lost at sea. We will even live for a time on foreign soil."

While the two women talked, Jesus smiled tenderly at His mother, who was brushing flies away from His open wounds. John, known as the one the Master loved, held a canvas strip over her head as a sunshade. He was her protector.

Jesus said, "Mother, behold thy son. And behold thy daughters, Mary and Rachel. Counsel them on kindness and love. And Mother, give Mary the pearl I gave you when we talked in the desert of Bethesda."

Mary of Magdala stood up slowly, looking at Mother Mary and at the pearl in her hand. Could this be the same one that had rolled from John's lips at Capernaum?

Jesus answered, although she had not spoken aloud, "Yes, Mary, it is the same pearl. It is also the one Rachel gave John before his beheading. Mother will tell you how I came to have it in My possession."

Turning to Rachel, He continued, "Give Mary the pearls you have and she will add this one to them. Teach her the science of meditation. Open My life to her as you recall the stable scene."

Quietly, Rachel described that night of nights. They all heard the low tones of Heaven's music as if it came from the pearls. At the end, she breathed a vow that she would become an ascetical reparation-maker for the love of God.

Looking tenderly at the crowd before Him, Jesus suddenly cried aloud in anguish from physical torture and soul-sorrow, "I thirst! I thirst for Gestas!"

Peter heard these words, standing in his tent holding tightly to the door flap, and could hardly restrain himself from running boldly to the Master. Instead, however, he turned and sent one of his disciples to Veronica who stood alone at her husband's cross, requesting her to come to him. Quietly, and without question, she obeyed, her twin son in her arms.

Greeting her kindly, Peter said, "I am the ambassador of the Messiah. Go back quickly to your husband and tell him how much I admire his courage. He is a blessed man. Ask him to remember me when he is in Paradise with Jesus. I beg never to be forgotten. Here, take my handkerchief and touch it to the Master's feet, and return with it to me. This will be the nearest way I can touch the cross and behold His most Precious Blood while He is dying. I cannot go to Him. Whisper to Him that Peter is near, but tell no one else."

Veronica nodded silently, and then caught her breath as she heard Peter say, patting her boy's chubby hand: "This little child will someday be one of my successors. He will make many laws for earth."

Leaving the boy with Peter, she hastened out of the tent and knelt quietly beside Mary of Magdala and Rachel, who were silent now in their quiet waiting. Touching the handkerchief to the Master's feet and to the bloody wood that held them, she hurried back to the big fisherman.

Bowing down to earth, Peter wept as he venerated the drops of blood on the linen. Picking up her son, Veronica returned to her husband's cross. He was in great anguish, and in such pain that he could hardly speak. His mind was so fogged that he could no longer express himself coherently.

Then all was very still and Jesus cried out in a loud voice: "Father, into Thy hands I commend My Spirit!"

As His words died away, Veronica was astonished to hear Dismas whisper to her, no trace of suffering or fumbling now in his tones: "Jesus is dead. Go now, Veronica, and allow me the privilege of being a lone vigil-keeper with Him in my sufferings. Go home. Don't turn back lest temptation for me overtake you. I must follow God alone. Goodbye, and never forget that heaven's Refugee lived and died with us!"

BOOK SIX

The Resurrection

CHAPTER 1

Fear

THREE WOODEN CROSSES ornamented with death stood silhouetted against the sky on the hill of Golgotha, where they cast long, giant shadows over the people as they huddled near the Messiah. Jerusalem was quiet, desolate, and dim as the cloudy haze of night cast its first shades of gray across the earth, as if to erase the events of a dreadful day from both the world and the minds of men. Thousands of tired people turned homeward, exhausted from the noise and the nerve-racking scenes of brutality they had witnessed.

In general, they were afraid even though they had watched crucifixions before. This day left them with a feeling of dread and regret, which they could not explain. Questions were everywhere, "Do you think this crucified Jesus was the Messiah? If so, what is to become of us? Suppose He proves the tomb cannot resist His powers? Will you consider then that He was God?"

What else?

"If this Jesus rises from the tomb we *must* admit it. He is the Anointed One!"

A groan rose from hundreds of lips, and many hurried home to hide their faces in their hands and mourn in silence and fear. Others stood about in the streets in large groups. Questions, always questions. "Was Jesus the Christ, or an impostor?" Onlookers simply listened and were swayed this way and that by the tides of opinion that broke against the untouched stone of their hearts. Still others relived the mystifying orations of Dismas. Those holding high city positions tried to scatter the crowds, which were becoming angrier and angrier as the discussion grew more and more heated. They were afraid they would lose their prestige and power should the people rise in sudden, flaring revolt. It is estimated three million souls lived in Jerusalem at that time, and such numbers could be vastly dangerous if they chose.

A group of twenty high priests watched the seething crowds in the streets from the windows of an upper room, their minds busy with the mystery of why a conversion had taken place in the soul of Dismas. Why had he wanted to die with Jesus rather than be taken down from the cross? They could not help but marvel at the strange power Jesus had over men. One high priest said gravely that certainly Dismas had believed Him to be the Anointed One since He had cured his own son. What else could he have thought?

It was evident from the silence that followed and from the priests' awed expressions that they, too, were afraid. Was it possible they had made the mistake of all time?

Suddenly an uproar broke out beneath their windows. Angry voices shouted, "High priests, you have crucified your God! Because of your worldliness and little learning of the times, you led us to help you. Come down and we'll crucify you now! We must crucify you, for you teach error. You are sinners and hypocrites to the law of Moses. Come down and fight for your lives—we know you are hidden in that room!"

Before any of the terrified priests could move, a servant entered and recounted the miracle of Veronica's veil. Immediately slaves were sent into the streets to verify it. Dismayed and frightened, the high priests paced the floor, wringing their hands and pleading for divine guidance.

The slaves returned with the news that the rumor was absolutely true and that all priests in the city were in danger of crucifixion, for mob violence was growing steadily. The priests wept and shook their heads. For the first time they realized they did not have an answer for the angry people. They cursed Jesus and His unseen power. A few suddenly admitted their belief in Him, only to be violently scoffed at by the others.

One priest asked, "How can it happen that we are the butt of this crucifixion? Why do people blame only us, for surely they must realize that many scholars from the Houses of David also condemned this Man to death? They are the most bitter of all people against impostors, for have they not denied themselves the pleasures and rights of the flesh in order that the Messiah might be born through their lineage? Let us turn the people on them—they are the ones who really are to blame. They are the scriptural scholars. Why should we take the first blame when the people of David know the prophecies? They should have guided us. They knew a New Jerusalem would be born and that she would be a virgin and the mother of all men, as well as the mother of God. Now only today we learn that this Jesus has a mother who is a virgin educated in the House of David. She was a firstborn. She took the vows of virginity. Were any of us acquainted with these facts before the crucifixion? I demand an answer!"

One elderly priest said sadly, "No, this news was not brought to our attention. Let us question what sort of a trial was held for this Man. Was it just? As we see it now, it was nothing but a miscarriage of law. What was the matter with Caiphas and Annas that they allowed this? They knew the prophecies and should have heeded the important issue of the virgin mother. Could they have crucified this Man without having learned of His lineage? I do not consider myself guilty in the least because I did not know all the facts."

Another priest answered, "Nor do I. And while we are on the subject, have any of you ever thought about the strangeness of the crucifixion hour? There was the most severe earthquake of the century and it made no impression on the people. Their whole concern and fear is over this Jesus. What a mystery! He holds first place even over acts of nature and the death of loved ones. What kind of Man was He? Do you think the tumbling of the earth could have signified the wrath of God toward those who crucified Him?"

A door burst open and a distraught newcomer, also a high priest, entered and fell to his knees in exhaustion. "I have heard," he gasped, "that the graves opened when Jesus died and that the dead are walking the streets frightening people into hysteria and heart attacks![24] Many of them have been identified by their relations but will not answer a question nor allow anyone to touch them—they seem to vaporize.

24 This took place until the Resurrection.

All they will say is, 'Where is the Living Bread that came down from Heaven? We have risen only to receive it, for which we longed before the death of life overcame us.[25]

"'We learned of the God-Man's gift through the ancient prophecy. We have walked and talked to Him as did Isaiah of old. He, the God-Man, told us, through prayer, that we would rise and receive the Living Bread before actual death, which must be for us before we enter into the Kingdom of Kingdoms. We were never considered among the dead, for we were only sleeping in God's embrace until this hour."[26]

"They also talk about God's mercy rather than His justice. Many of them are said to be queer and crude and are amazed at the progress of this generation!"

A priest, who stood in one corner of the room, answered in a blustery manner, "This is nothing but witchcraft. Be sensible. How can it be anything else but a lie—the result of mass hysteria? Shake yourselves and listen to reason. The dead cannot live again!"

One of his servants entered headlong at that moment with the news that his mother was dead from shock, for his father was one of those who had come back from the grave. Even then he was outside that room. He had seen him!

None of the priests could talk for a moment. Quickly they closed and bolted the door. They did not want to see the dead nor hear him speak.

Presently an elderly priest asked in a subdued voice, "What will we do if this Jesus rises like the others? Do you suppose this is what He meant when He said He would rebuild the temple in three days? Does He mean that His body is the temple? We know an earthquake could never reawaken the dead and give life back to them. Only God could have such power. If He can give life to the newborn, then He can certainly stir the dead to move among us once more. What are we going to do?"

No one had an answer. Suddenly the silence was broken by a loud cheer from the street—as though a thousand voices were responsible for it. Hurrying to the windows they saw a great procession marching by, and as it went they heard various voices calling, "Where is Peter Simon? Where is Peter, the friend of Jesus? We want Peter—we want

25 Sleep.
26 Ecstasy.

Peter! Peter is the head of the Kingdom of Jesus—the head of the New Law. Away with the old. Away with our priests of the Old Law of Moses. Peter, Peter, come to us. We are your subjects!"

A few of the braver high priests moved to a nearby balcony from where they might better view the procession, and were astonished to see hundreds of people carrying the huge temple veil, which had been torn in two in a mysterious manner at the very hour Jesus died. Behind them came another group carrying Veronica's veil, and among them was Veronica's mother with her cured grandson. Men, women, and children pressed forward to venerate the scarf and many walked away cured, throwing their staffs, or canes, aside. Their screams and shouts of joy were breathtaking.

The priests on the balcony knelt slowly in prayer and begged God to forgive them for their crime. Thousands of other people were converted, too, as the procession passed. These took up torches and became torchbearers in their search for Peter. Loudly they chanted, "Peter, Peter, come to us. We want you. Come, do not fear!"

Soldiers appeared and struggled to disperse the growing throng. They were pushed aside, their orders and threats completely disregarded. The joyful people shouted all the louder of their belief in the New Law of Jesus, and were not brought under control until new numbers of determined soldiers swept down upon them.

Meanwhile, on Calvary, Peter and a few of his apostles still knelt in silent adoration in their tent, waiting for darkness to cover them before they dared venture nearer the cross of Jesus. Although tears glistened in the big fisherman's eyes, there was a smile upon his lips for he had just learned that within the last hour Caiphas, Annas, and a few other high priests had been forced into hiding, for the people had turned against them when, according to prophecy, the temple veil had been rent. That event was a symbolical truth to the Jews, and great was their mourning and sorrow because they finally realized they had crucified the Messiah. Hundreds took the tearing of the veil as proof that the Old Law was no more.

Then to add to their sorrow, Caiphas and Annas learned that Turan had died of shock when the veil had been rent as she bowed beside it in prayer.

Peter's eyes moved to Veronica as she knelt before her husband's cross. A tall, stately man of great culture and learning approached her and said, "I have learned through the mystery of prayer that you know where Simon Peter is hiding. Please take me to him. I am Joseph of Arimathea and I have often been in the company of Jesus and Peter. I would like to see Simon in regard to the burial of the Messiah's body."

Drying her tears as she kissed Dismas' feet, Veronica arose, and nodded with a smile to Joseph. Quietly he followed her down the jagged, rocky path to Peter's tent.

A moment later he knelt at Simon's feet. In holy submission to authority he said, "Peter, I have come to beg your permission to take the body of Jesus down. Just last week I finished hewing a new sepulcher that I made especially for Him, for He told me of His approaching death. In my home I have linen wrappings, linen lint, and spices, all prepared by my wife, Mary, and myself for the proper burial."

Peter, embarrassed at the honor given him, was at the same time enthralled with Joseph's thoughtfulness. He answered, "First it will be necessary for you to hurry to Pilate and ask for the body. If he will grant you this favor I will give you permission to take it to your sepulcher. Since I must exercise prudence, please do not mention my name. I will wait here until you return."

Joseph, bowing to the dust, kissed Peter's feet saying, "Power of God indwelling within you, Peter, do you realize that thousands of people in the city have been converted within the last hour through the discourses of Dismas, and the miracle of his child? All of them are subject to you, and they are calling for you. They even search every avenue and house and are determined to find and parade you through the streets. Your power will be greater than Caiphas'. During the earthquake the temple veil was rent and this has caused a great number of people to believe, at last, that this Jesus is the Messiah.

"It is also rumored that many graves were opened during the quake and the dead arose—they are alive and roaming through the city talking to their friends. They claim they have risen from sleep, not death, in order to receive the Living Bread, which Jesus gave you permission to give to the world until the end of time through your priests. I gained this information of the Living Bread from Andrew, who is not far from here. Peter, please allow me to receive it, too. Teach me how to make myself worthy—all of this is such a shock to the mind—it seems impossible that we are living the age the ancients only dreamed about!

"I wish you could see the city at this hour. It is indeed a strange Jerusalem. The risen dead are jubilant, and the living are afraid and mourning. It is an unforgettable hour of joy and sorrow. People die as the dead speak of God's mercy. Wild chaos is on every side at these happenings and the people call for you. Only you can still their fears. Will you not please send them a word of comfort?"

Joseph's words gave Peter great joy even though he felt the loss of Jesus more and more. His heart was heavy, for he could not tell the Master about the joys and the strange bits of news he had just learned. Quietly he prayed, "God, Thou are extravagant with us! O, the mystery of Your suffering is indeed the knowledge of mercy. Your cross, the key of salvation, has slowly turned in its setting and has unlocked the dead in, and on the earth. Jesus, You are wonderful! You are wonderful!"

Turning to Joseph he continued, "Take these apostles with you. They will console the frightened people. There is only one thing to do—lead them in prayer. I must stay here with the body of Jesus and embrace Him before He is taken down. I must also keep constant watch, and I will pray for your success with Pilate. Jesus must have a proper burial."

It was a long wait for Peter. Shuddering in the quietness of thought, he remembered how the soldiers had pierced the Master's side. At the same time, others had come with hammers to break the knees of the two thieves in order to end life if any were left in their poor bodies. He shivered as he recalled their screams as they died of shock.

In a vision of the water and blood coming forth from the Master's side, he was caught up into ecstasy. He saw the holy cross holding the body of Jesus, encircled with a magnificent arch of many-colored rainbows, standing in a crystal stream of water that had a moment before come from the Messiah's heart. Fired drops of blood appeared as rubies on this crystal stream and were tossed here and there upon the crest of each rippling wave as it spread like a mighty fan over the earth. Beneath that surging sea stood a million priests, representing the priests of time, all with chalices uplifted to catch each drop of blood. Having captured them, they poured them out upon the earth, where they found repose in individual human hearts.

The colloquy of Peter's thoughts was, "O, Flames of Everlasting Glory, O, Fires of the Beatific Vision before us, cleanse our lips through the Holy Love Feast that You have given us!"

Peter stayed in his immovable silent prayer of adoration, after the vision ended, until nearly ten o'clock, when he was awakened by the sound of approaching footsteps. Looking up he saw three men walking side by side, carrying lanterns that cast black shadows across their path, even though the sky shimmered in its depths of blue-blackness set with God's ornamentations of silver clouds, stars, and moon. As they drew nearer he saw they were Joseph, one of his slaves, and his friend, Nicodemus.

On his part, Joseph was alarmed, for he could discern figures moving in the darkness near Jesus' cross. Fear tugged at his heart. Were Jesus' enemies stealing His body from them?

Running toward Peter's tent, and raising his lantern, he called, "Simon, Simon, come! I have permission to bury the Messiah's body!"

CHAPTER 2

Jesus Is Taken down from the Cross

DISCOVERING PETER SAFE IN HIS TENT, Joseph hurried toward Jesus' cross. The figures he had seen in the darkness turned out to be three soldiers who had been left on guard. They were tired and only too happy to ride away after reading the burial permit. Two others were too drunk to be aroused. Seeing that they were harmless, and that all others who stood about near the cross were friendly, Joseph sent word for Peter to come. Smiles were mixed with tears as he greeted Mother Mary, Mary of Magdala, Rachel, and Mary the mother of James.

A sound in the night caused them to look up uneasily. It was the familiar plodding jolt of a camel and the human shuffling of tired feet. Nicodemus raised and swung his lantern as he called, "Who are you? The road ends here. Are you lost?"

An aged woman's voice answered: "We are searching for Jesus."

Mother Mary, recognizing the tired old voice at once called back, "Granny Mary, it is I, the mother of Jesus. Come!"

Peter darted through the darkness, and embracing Granny sobbed, "It is too late to visit with the Master. He is dead."

"He said He was the Resurrection," Granny answered, "and that the tomb would not keep Him prisoner for more than three days. He will speak again. He knows I have come to see Him and He will greet me. Take me to His body."

Arm in arm, she and Peter walked to the cross while the friends who had come with her from Galilee followed.

Mary of Magdala moved away, for the first time, from the foot of the cross to allow Peter and Granny to kneel and embrace the chilled feet of their Master. Peter's strong, trembling arms encircled the real crucifix for the first time while his tears bathed Jesus' feet.

Mother Mary asked, "Did Pilate say we can take His body down?"

"He belongs to us now," Joseph answered quietly.

Grief-stricken, Granny turned to Mother Mary and was taken into her gentle embrace. Sobbing, she said, "Our Jesus died before I got here. We hurried, but I was too late. The mountain passes were so crowded with people leaving Jerusalem that we could hardly get through. I gathered from their conversation and sorrow that Jesus was crucified. Other people were joyous and told us to turn back. I didn't tell them I was Jesus' grandmother. We hurried on to help and console you, Mother Mary, but I am sad that I didn't get to say goodbye to Him."

Mother Mary beckoned to Mary of Magdala and introduced her to the old lady. Then sadness was turned to joy as Rachel recognized her. They hurriedly exchanged stories about their first meeting and how the pearls had been a fond expression of memory for each other the past years. Mary of Magdala was awed at the two holy women and knelt at their feet as she listened to their words of wisdom and interest.

When Granny Mary learned that Rachel still heard music, as though from the pearls, she was amazed. Here was the answer to the question she had wondered about for so long. But this was the first she had heard about the mystery of meditation and miracles. Eagerly, she begged Rachel to teach her the art of meditation at once.

Sitting side by side, Rachel said, "Granny, in our thoughts let us return to my stable in Bethlehem. You remember the cave-stable, and the darkness, and the sound of the oxen's heavy breathing?"

"Of course I do," Granny answered. "It is so real I could be there now, instead of at this terrible place of death."

Mary of Magdala handed her the ten pearls. Overcome with joy, the little old lady fondled them and told the story of how Joseph had given them to her in a necklace so many years ago. Removing the original strand, which she still wore about her neck, she tied the ten beads to them and then held the long circlet up toward her Grandson. Even though He was dead she wanted to share her joys with Him.

At the same time, Rachel quietly retold the story of the Messiah's birth. Soft music filled the night air. Granny smiled and said gently, "It is the same heavenly chords we heard coming from Mother Mary's heart when she told us the little Jesus was to be born into the world."

Tears streamed down her cheeks as the meditation story ended. Without taking her eyes from the stilled form on the cross, she handed the strand of pearls to Mary of Magdala, saying, "Here, Mary of His Heart, take His pearls and use them as your prayer stones in your travels of life. He will always be with you. I am sure Joseph would want me to give them to you for remember, they are his pearls, too."

Meanwhile, Nicodemus and Joseph steadied a short ladder against the back of the cross. Standing on the bottom rungs, they braced themselves as they tied a rolled linen sheet, rope fashion, around the body of Jesus, circling it under His arms and tying the ends up and around the crossbeams. Thus, it would act as a lever in lowering His body after the nails were removed.

Peter, who was short in stature, rolled a large rock beneath the outstretched left hand of the Master. Standing on it he shuddered as he touched the cold, stiffened fingers and prayed for the courage to accomplish the terrible task he had set for himself.

Pulling on the nail he found he could not dislodge it. Nor would it yield when he used pincers, or jarred it with blows from a wooden mallet. After several futile attempts, he suggested reluctantly that Nicodemus and Joseph prepare to lift the Sacred Body slightly.

He shuddered again, but after a brief prayer, he calmly studied the situation. At a given signal to Nicodemus and Joseph to lift, his strong hands pulled and yanked the Master's wrist free of the nail that held it. Moving the rock to the right hand, he repeated the procedure. The Master's body now slumped forward onto the rope-twisted sheet, which was held securely by Joseph.

Peter stepped quickly from the rock, and lifting Jesus' feet he pulled them off the one large remaining nail. Thus, all six nails that had been used in the crucifixion were left in the cross.

With slow, careful guidance the Sacred Body was lowered into the embrace of Peter's arms. Holding Him, Peter beckoned Mother Mary to come and embrace Him, too. Kneeling in the dust she held her Son tenderly against her knee. Gently she patted His sacred face and tried to remove the thorns that clung stubbornly in His matted hair. With Granny Mary's help she smoothed away His furrowed frown caused by His anguish at the moment of death. Last of all, she bent His stiff fingers into a graceful gesture of blessing.

"O, my poor Jesus," Granny Mary whispered as she kissed His cold hands. "I will miss Your visits to me in Galilee. No more will I count the days and the hours until You come again. No more will I watch You at play, or listen in the dead of night for Your footstep and cheerful hail. How well I remember how You used to stop at the gate and call: 'Granny Mary, did you bake cookies today?'

"O, my Jesus, how I long to hear Your voice as I heard it when You were a little boy. You used to sleep beside me and whisper: 'Granny, I want a drink of water.'

"But, that which I am most grateful for is Your promise to give the world the Living Manna from Heaven. Jesus, how You have suffered!"

Falling across His body, she wept uncontrollably. Peter lifted her to her feet, and for a moment they stood together in silence, their minds busy with wonderful recollections. Her tears bathing Jesus' face, Peter watched Nicodemus and Joseph place Jesus' body on an improvised stretcher, which they had made from two poles and the linen sheet that had served as a lowering rope.

Giving the old lady into Mother Mary's care, Peter removed his outside toga and covered the body of his Master with it. He, Joseph, Nicodemus, and his slave, picked up the stretcher and the procession to the sepulcher began. Behind them walked John, later known as the Beloved, with Mother Mary and Granny. Then Mary of Magdala, and Mary, the wife of Joseph followed. Last of all came the group of Granny's friends from Galilee.

The procession moved slowly through a world that seemed unusually quiet. Granny's weak voice was heard as she told John the Beloved and Mother Mary how she happened to come to Jerusalem at this particular time. Jesus and two of His disciples had visited her a month ago, and one evening at dusk, after her Grandson had been out swimming with His friends in Lake Galilee, He had pulled Himself out of the water and onto the rock where she was standing. They sat down side by side and He ate the cookies she had brought for Him, while she wrapped herself in a tapestry shawl and snuggled close to His side. It was then that He said, "Granny, do you remember the prophecy that I told you years ago, about the day when I would give the world the Living Manna, and then would be crucified for the sins of man?"

Her delicate face had paled as she nodded. Jesus then told her this would be His last visit. He would not swim again in the lake He loved, nor eat cookies with her. His hour was near.

Granny remembered how she had pleaded, "When, Jesus, when will this happen?"

Jesus had taken her into His arms and answered, "Soon, but do not worry, Granny, for I know your heart will be with Me, and I know you would spare Me suffering if you could, but the prophecies must be fulfilled. I have come into the world to die, to pay the debt man owes to God."

"Did He tell you the exact day of His crucifixion?" John asked.

Granny shook her head. "He wanted to spare me that anxiety, John. However, He did say He was going to return to Jerusalem and there give the Living Manna to His chosen ones. Never until the end of time would the world then be without it. And those who would eat it would live forever in His Father's Kingdom.

"He said they would instantly be clothed invisibly in beautiful spiritual gowns of ravishing fire, which could only be seen and understood in Heaven. The light of these gowns from within would match the Light of the Bridegroom, His Father's Light.

"He also said that He loved a certain man by the name of Simon, and would choose him to be His successor. To this Simon He would give the power to change ordinary bread into the Living Manna."

Granny's faltering voice sank to a whisper. "While I am here I would like to meet that wonderful man whom Jesus loved."

John answered, "You have already met him, Granny. He is the man whom you were introduced to as Peter."

Granny caught her breath and smiled. "Jesus promised," she said, "to tell one of His chosen men, many of whom He would elect in Jerusalem, to find me and allow me to receive the Bread of Heaven before He called me in death.

"I worried continually, John, that the man who was to search for me might lose his way, or forget the Messiah's orders. I was afraid I'd miss the opportunity of receiving the Sacred Gift and so I planned this trip with my friends."

Her tired, old voice continued to waver through the night as they proceeded slowly. She had thought it only proper for one of Joseph's family to be represented with Mary at the cross. As for her friends, they, too, believed her Jesus to be the Messiah and wished to receive the Living Bread. How they had hoped to arrive in time to embrace Him before He took up His cross. But, then they had been disappointed—the trip had been filled with many hindrances—and the little caravan of eight women and three men arrived only at sundown, in time to stand in mourning beneath the stilled holy cross.

At length they reached the sepulcher and Granny Mary asked in almost a whisper, "How long did He suffer? Do you think He was in much pain? Were the torments as bad as tradition has taught us? I have never seen a crucifixion. Mary, did Jesus tell you of His promise to me, that I was to receive the Living Bread?"

Mother Mary nodded. "Granny," she answered, "Jesus was always happy when He made you happy." Her voice trembled. "He suffered three hours of terrible agony."

Granny turned to John. "Do you think I will have the privilege of beholding the Living Bread while I am here, so soon after His death? I have to start back tomorrow, for we borrowed the camels and they must be returned as soon as possible."

John answered, "I am sure you will."

Happy, the old lady turned back to her daughter-in-law. "Mary," she asked, "have you seen it? What does it look like? And how is it possible for Simon Peter to reach with his earthly hands into the Kingdom of God and continually bring it to earth for us? It is such a mystery and I have so many questions. Forgive me if I ask too many."

Mary embraced her tenderly. "You could never do that," she answered softly. "I love you so much, and your childlike simplicity and courage. Come with me and I'll speak to Simon Peter."

Granny Mary was awed as Peter lowered the stretcher and bowed his head toward Mother Mary.

"Simon," she said, "in honor of and to the majesty of the power that you hold in the office of successor to my Son, I beg of you to allow Granny Mary the privilege of receiving the Promised Bread tomorrow."

"She may kneel at the breaking of Bread this very night," the big fisherman answered. "Tell John to give her the Gift of God, and at the same time to give it to those other people who journeyed with her. This will be our first way of pleasing Jesus since He died. To please Him now is to honor and respect His friends."

CHAPTER 3

The Burial

THE FOUR MEN LOWERED THE STRETCHER carefully to the ground and the carrying poles were cast aside. The Master's body rested now only upon the linen sheet. For a moment Joseph studied the sepulcher entrance, which was tunnel-like and about two feet wide by four feet in length. Clearly Jesus' shoulders were too broad to allow Him to be carried inside face upward so, as a consequence, He was rolled onto His side. Joseph and his slave pulled Him forward.

The sepulcher was an improved natural cave hewn from solid rock in the side of a low mountain. Its entrance led into a room that measured approximately nine by ten feet and had a low ceiling of only seven. Directly across from the entrance was a shelf of rock, roughly three feet in width and three feet from the floor. On this Joseph had skillfully cemented smooth, flat stones into a low, oblong rock basin, coffin fashion. For days he had worked tirelessly with his chisel in this hot, humid room, hoping to finish before the death of the Messiah. His wish had been fulfilled.

Before Jesus was lifted onto the shelf, Peter pulled the sheet from beneath Him and used it to line the rock basin coffin. About fourteen feet in length and seven in width, it was known as a "winding sheet," so named because its length enabled one to employ it both as a cover and as an under-sheet at the same time.

Jesus was placed reverently into this coffin, and Peter took the portion of the sheet that hung down over the end and arranged it to cover the Master's body. He stepped back and each person in the little procession came forward, venerated the sacred brow, and retired silently from the cave. When the last one had gone, Peter pulled the sheet up and over Jesus' face.

Mother Mary, Granny, Mary of Magdala, John, and the visitors from Galilee went at once to a tent that had been given them by a friend, and which had been set up a short distance from the sepulcher. Joseph, his wife, Nicodemus, and the slave left to get linen wrappings, spices, aloes, myrrh, and linen lint for the coming embalming, as well as a peculiar sap resembling pitch, which came from the Pinus Picea tree. This particular sap was favored above all others for its preserving qualities. The long process, customary with the rich, took two days.

In the sepulcher, Peter lay prostrate across the form of Jesus while the dim, dancing light of the flickering lantern cast long shadows on the wall. Peter, the sepulcher-keeper, was weeping and feeling the weight of his unutterable loneliness for the living Man Jesus. Also, he was afraid of the great task ahead as the Messiah's successor. How glad he would be when the promised Paraclete would come to help him. His sighs were heavy as he turned down the sheet and bent to kiss his Master's closed eyes.

With great affection he then tucked the sheet once more into place. With lantern in hand he turned and walked toward the entrance. But as the cool night air from the outside touched him he was overcome with grief and returned quickly to the Master's side. He could not part with Him. He would just have to have another glimpse of that wonderful face!

Holding the lantern above his head, he stood transfixed, for there on the sheet was a clear likeness, a complete outline of the Master!

Peter touched it carefully and then examined it. He could scarcely believe his eyes, for it was a picture, a true image of the Master in His tomb, as though it had been painted by an artist. Every detail was reproduced clearly.

Although nearly numb with astonishment, Peter nevertheless felt strangely calm and peaceful. Could this be the Master's way of consoling his loneliness? He smiled and nodded. Jesus always found a way. All fear left him in regard to the government of the Church. Now he was confident that with the Master he would be able to teach discipline and love.

Once more, with great trepidation, he touched the sheet. It was damp and a sweet fragrance of fresh roses effused from it. Now that he was no longer fearful, he was conscious of a strong desire to learn why this strange event had taken place. He had never heard of anything like it, and he had helped embalm many bodies. He wanted to make absolutely certain that it was a miracle.

Touching the Sacred Body, he found it dripping wet as if from perspiration. He could discover no reason for this, for it had been perfectly dry when they placed it into the shallow basin. Of course, the room itself was very hot and humid and his own body and clothes were damp, but not to such a degree as the Master's, and certainly his clothing did not bear the likeness of his flesh imprinted upon it. Again he examined the sheet. Yes, he could clearly see the distinct image of Jesus. Leaning against the sepulcher wall he studied the linen from a distance, and the longer he looked the more vivid the picture became.

As patiently as he could he waited for Joseph and Nicodemus to return. Thoughts swarmed through his mind and he began to think of family treasures and heirlooms. How wonderful to have this linen in his own particular possession. He knew that Rosa, too, would want it. But how should he approach the subject to Joseph? Most certainly he would desire the picture-image also when he saw it.

With a start, Peter suddenly remembered the office he held. It was his right to keep the sheet if he wished, if for no other purpose than to use it for further investigation and study. Surely the Messiah's picture was the property of His new institution.

The heat and humidity finally drove him outside, and he knelt to pray in a grove that was within twenty feet of the tomb's entrance. From there he could keep his eyes on the holy sepulcher as well as think about what had taken place.

Approximately an hour later he heard steady, rhythmical footsteps approaching. Getting to his feet he stepped into the path to see who it might be. In the brightness of the full moon it was easy to recognize Joseph bearing a large sack upon his back. Behind him came Nicodemus, walking carefully, so as not to spill the liquid sap, which he carried in two clay pitchers balanced on his shoulders.

Surprised at seeing Nicodemus, Peter exclaimed, "I didn't expect you back. The hour is late and you must be very tired. Here, let me carry the pitchers."

Transferring them to his own shoulders, Peter led the way toward the sepulcher. Nicodemus said, "It was my wish to return, for I want to help Joseph. I have done so many times during the years and I know each preparation. Be at peace, Peter. In case you don't know, I am a disciple of Jesus."

With some concern Peter answered, "Be a good disciple then, Nicodemus. It is worth any trial to please Him."

Nicodemus nodded quietly. "Joseph tells me Jesus appointed you to succeed Him. If this is true, then in the presence of the Messiah's power and dignity vested in you, allow me to honor you by venerating the hem of your toga." He dropped to his knees and kissed the big fisherman's hem and sandals.

Peter was more than startled. This sort of veneration awed him. Who was he to allow such a man of culture, wealth, and wisdom to kneel before him? Perhaps he should not allow it. He must remember that he, Peter, was a man of weakness and many faults. Joseph came and knelt beside Nicodemus in the dust and pleaded also for his blessing. Remembering the duties of his enthronement, Peter slowly complied.

Quietly he said, "Your faith is astonishing. And now, Joseph, since you know more about embalming than either Nicodemus or I, please allow me to help you."

Joseph and Nicodemus answered as one, "We are honored. Please come with us."

In spite of protest, Peter lifted the sack of embalming equipment, which Joseph had brought, to his own back. In single file, with Joseph leading the way and holding high his flickering lantern, they quietly sang a psalm of praise, as they once more went toward the tomb entrance.

Within a few minutes they were back inside the damp sepulcher. Peter lowered the embalming equipment to the floor and crossed directly to the shelf-coffin. As Joseph began to unpack the articles from the sack, the fisherman asked, "I presume the sheet in which Jesus is wrapped is yours? If so may I buy it? Or perhaps you would allow me to exchange one of Rosa's for it. I would like to have this one as a keepsake. God alone knows the sentiments for which I value it."

Joseph was pleased with the request and made Peter a present of the sheet at once. Quickly, and without saying a word about the miraculous image imprinted upon it, Simon removed it, folded it, and placed it upon a rock across the room.

The embalming began. Peter helped Joseph lift Jesus' arms while Nicodemus applied bandages to them as if they were swaddling clothes.

It was then that Peter looked up aghast. "Joseph, do you know the Master is going to rise on the third day?" he asked. "Why then should we encumber Him with these wrappings? And why should we care about preserving His body? This is a mockery! Don't you remember how Lazarus looked when he walked from the tomb? The bandages had to be unwound and some even chipped from him for they were like stone. It was a horrible ordeal. Not only that, he looked awful and was terribly embarrassed.

"Think how the Master will feel. You may be sure He will reprimand us, thinking we did not believe He would rise as He said. Let's just bathe Him with clove water and place a clean sheet over Him."

Joseph glanced questioningly at Nicodemus and then answered, "He didn't tell me He would rise in this same body. Perhaps we will only see His spirit. I don't believe it will rise and live among us and make itself manifest in many ways concerning faith. But if things take place as you expect, how do you think we will feel if we allow His body to decay because we haven't embalmed it? I cannot take that risk."

Nicodemus added, "I think you have reasoned well, Joseph, and according to law we had better go ahead." He turned to the fisherman. "We must not forget, Peter, that Joseph is a man of great learning and once held the title of Wiseman. It is possible we may only see the Messiah's spirit, which could in some way resemble this body—or, perhaps we will only hear His voice. Anyway, I am sure we will know Him in any form He chooses to manifest Himself."

Peter was bewildered.

Joseph frowned and asked, "Did you understand Jesus to say He would actually rise in this body? Did He say precisely that He would make this body breathe, and talk, and walk?"

Poor Peter, his heart grieving, answered, "He said that in three days He would rebuild the temple, and that temple is His body. I beg you to believe His words!"

After a few minutes of deep thought, Joseph said, "That's a broad statement, Peter, and the words could be interpreted many ways. Perhaps in your heart and in your great love for Him you have allowed yourself to become over-zealous. Now, just for instance, His spirit could rise and dwell as a great cloud in the temple where the veil was rent. That to me would be the logical way of expecting His appearance again.

"Apparently He meant that He would rebuild the temple in the degree that the veil was destroyed. His spirit dwelling there would accomplish that end and He would have a palace worthy to live in.

"I believe He figuratively meant that He would rebuild the Old Laws into the new beautiful truths that He taught. No longer must we believe an eye for an eye, and a tooth for a tooth. His way is of love and kindness.

"And, Peter, I promised Pilate I would embalm His body."

"You are wrong!" Peter answered sternly, righteous indignation in his voice. "He said He would rise again in this same body, which lies here. I know He will! I believe His words! His way of speaking was not figurative. He meant exactly what He said.

"I beg of you to cease with this embalming. How will you feel, and what will you say about the pain you will cause Him when you help strip Him of this cocoon? Remember, it was days before Lazarus soaked the linen bark from his body.

"If you insist on going ahead I, as Christ's successor, will order you to help remove all this from Him when the time comes! Follow your own consciences and judgment. I shall simply sit by and watch you. I refuse to have any part in it."

The tomb became very quiet. Joseph and Nicodemus were both ashamed and perplexed at not having listened with closer attention when Jesus talked about His death. Also, they felt guilty of impudence because of the way they had just answered Peter. For a moment they had forgotten whom he represented. Not daring to look at him, they knew they did not want to hear his voice again for fear of another reprimand. But go ahead with the embalming they must.

Peter sat down on the rock ledge beside the folded sheet and bowed his head in his hands and wept. Tears trickled down through his fingers.

Quietly Joseph washed the Messiah's body with perfumed clove and cinnamon water. Then, with Nicodemus helping, he wrapped linen bandages, about four inches wide, around the Sacred Body and legs. When all of these were in place, they wound still wider linen strips about the body until it was encased in a shell approximately three inches thick. The arms were then folded across the chest and covered.

Tying one end of a narrow bandage to a piece of linen wrapped about one of the Master's wrists, they brought the bandage up and around the back of His neck and down to the other wrist. Back and forth this winding, or weaving, continued until His head lay in a deep shell. They left only a small portion of His face uncovered, for somehow they did not have the courage to conceal it all.

"Come, Peter," Nicodemus said quietly, "would you like to look upon the Sacred Face for the last time before we cover it?"

Peter boosted himself from the ledge, and bending over Jesus said sadly, "O, my poor Jesus, what have they done to You? This will be the last time I shall see Your face until You rise on the third day, and three days seem such an eternity! And, O my Jesus, how are You ever going to get out of all these rags?"

Backing away, he adored His silent Master and wept more bitterly than ever. Shuddering, he watched as Joseph poured the mixture of liquid aloes and myrrh over the bandages. How he dreaded having a covering placed over the Master's face.

As Nicodemus was about to lay a square piece of cloth over the Sacred Countenance, Peter said suddenly, "May I place my handkerchief over it, instead?"

Both Joseph and Nicodemus nodded their approval, and Peter unfolded a brown, linen handkerchief that Rosa had made for him. In one corner was embroidered a red ship, which symbolized his fishing fleet, and was one of the same set that he had used to cover the Baptizer's face in the Garden of Gethsemane.

Gently he smoothed it over the holy countenance. Nicodemus poured the brown, syrupy mixture over it. With great tenderness Peter patted the wet cloth into place, pushing it close to the eyes and around the nose.

Then, unable to stand what he had done, he tore the handkerchief away. Overcome with grief he fell across the body. Weeping, he sobbed, "I cannot part with You, Jesus!"

Nicodemus touched his arm. "Come now, Peter," he said kindly, "you must not be so overcome with sorrow. Why do you weep? Didn't you say He will rise on the third day? That is not long to wait. You will see Him again."

Peter answered angrily, "Leave His face uncovered. Why encumber

Him with these things? Think how He, a King, will look, and we will be the cause of His embarrassment. The way you are cementing these bandages He will never find a way out!"[27]

Without answering, Nicodemus began to pour the spicy liquid over the Master's uncovered face, hoping Peter would have a change of heart and replace the handkerchief.

Peter, suddenly recollected, yet angry, did as Nicodemus hoped. Once more he tucked the cloth gently into place. As he did so he looked with wide eyes at Joseph. "I cannot part with Him!" he said broken-heartedly.

Again he started to remove the handkerchief, only to find it now adhered to the Sacred Flesh and to the linens near the neck and forehead.

He walked slowly back to the rock ledge and said in a stunned manner, "Why must you do this to Him? Why must you be so disbelieving? Why retard the hour of the Resurrection because of your unbelief? Can't you see these bandages show plainly you do not believe He will rise again? Pilate would never know whether you embalmed Him or not." Turning to Jesus he said brokenly, "Lord, Lord, how are You going to get out of these wrappings?"

Nicodemus removed great handfuls of linen lint from the sack on the floor beside him and patted them onto the wet linens to another depth of two inches around Jesus' complete body.

By this time Peter was on his knees. Leaning his head against the rock he prayed, "Lord, forgive us, forgive us. We know You will rise, for You have said You are the Resurrection and the Life. But Lord, I have heard about the burial shells Joseph makes. It is said nothing can enter them and nothing can leave. Lord, what will You do?"

Nicodemus and Joseph now sewed a large sheet about the Messiah's body and over that the last large linen strips were wrapped. The Master looked as though He was encased in a huge linen mask. With a sigh, the two men poured a pitch-like cement over Him, which hardened almost immediately as though it were varnish.

Joseph said, "This hardening syrup must be applied about every two

---

27 Not having received the gifts of the Holy Spirit, Peter questioned how the risen Jesus could undress from the bandages. He could not visualize the Master's gifts of infinite power and how those rags would fall at His least command.

hours all during the night. Perhaps the women will help. I'll ask my wife."

Joseph and Nicodemus then left the sepulcher, for the difficult task of embalming was over, except for the two-hour application that Joseph had mentioned.

Peter drew near to the Master once more. As he touched the thick, varnished shell he said angrily, "Forgive us, Lord. Will You take a whip to us as You did to the money changers in the temple? Lord, we are worthy of a greater reprimand. These varnished rags cannot be removed by human hands, for each bandage seems to have sunk into the one beneath it and become like hard cement. And now Joseph has ordered that this jail of Yours be made even stronger. God forgive us!"

He stumbled through the entrance opening into the night air. Breathing deeply, he looked around for Joseph. Not finding him, he returned to the tomb. Frantically he tried to remove the embalming shell from Jesus, but meeting only with defeat, he fell across the jewel case of the Master and wept tears of frustration.

CHAPTER 4

The First Love Feast: The Sealing of the Sepulcher

BEFORE THE FIRST PUBLIC MASS, known as the Divine Love Feast, was to begin, and while John the Beloved, the celebrant, was in his prayer of preparation, Mother Mary, Granny, Mary of Magdala, and the other friends from Galilee hurriedly returned to the sepulcher. They were hoping for another privilege to venerate the Body of Jesus.

Mother Mary, looking into the darkness of the sepulcher through the tunnel entrance, whispered, "Is there anyone in the tomb? We have come to see the Body of Jesus."

"Yes, Mother Mary, come."

After the little group of friends had offered a prayer of adoration, they entered the tomb one by one and in turn kissed the cocoon wrappings that encased their Jesus. No one spoke—they were shocked, for they had fully expected to see His Body. Then hurrying to John, sorrowful yet happy, for this gift of the Love Feast was a wondrous occasion, Granny Mary and her friends were to receive their first Holy Communion.

Within the same hour, Mary of Magdala quickly left the scene of the Love Feast and hurried toward the sepulcher. On the way she met

Mary, the wife of Joseph, who was also on her way to the tomb with a pitcher of spicy water, with which she was going to moisten the cocoon shell. Together they entered the sepulcher.

Mary of Magdala touched Peter's shoulder as he stood in deep mourning beside the Sacred Body. She whispered, "Peter, I have sad news for you. John asked me to find you and give you this message that while Granny Mary received the Bread of Heaven, she swooned away in death."

Startled at such unexpected news, Peter questioned, "How is Mother Mary? Surely her heart must be pierced, for she loved Granny."

With great courage, forcing a firmness of voice, Mary of Magdala answered, "Peter, she is sad but joyous. She said when Granny died in her arms, 'Jesus would have it no other way. He and His Granny were inseparable.'"

Mary of Magdala continued, "Peter, they are making plans to return with her body to Galilee at daybreak. Mother Mary requests, if you have time, to come and give your blessing to those who mourn and to her body."

Peter gave a sigh of relief when he had learned that all was well with Mother Mary. He left the tomb and walked to the grove where Nicodemus and Joseph were resting and taking turns watching the path to the sepulcher. After he had given them the news of her death, they recalled with smiles and tears the few hours they had had with the lovely lady from Galilee. This sudden death was hard for them to realize, for it seemed like moments when she had knelt before the real crucifix—His real body—and now she was with Him in death.

Peter suggested that Nicodemus and Joseph take her body to their home and prepare it with a good embalming, for the journey to Galilee would be hot and difficult—therefore it would be necessary for her encasement to be stiff and firm. They agreed they would go immediately for her body after Peter returned from giving the blessing. Within a few minutes Peter was back. He could not yet bear to leave the Body of Jesus. The wife of Joseph had just finished pouring the last spicy water over the varnished-like case of Jesus and she, with Peter, left the tomb. Joseph and Nicodemus, using poles as levers, rolled a huge boulder into the tunnel entrance of the tomb. They bid Peter goodnight as he stood in stunned silence looking at the boulder—he was blocked from even touching the wrappings on Jesus.

Nicodemus, Joseph, and his wife hurried to the tent where the body of Granny was mourned.

Peter was alone. He wanted to be alone with his thoughts. He knelt in silent reverence beside the boulder—it was now his prie-dieu, and then in a moment of complete forgetfulness of self and time, he seemed to have the gift of intuitive knowledge pertaining to the knowledge of the Divinity. In the cloud of that particular grace of ecstasy, Peter whispered aloud, "Oh Lord, if I could only remove those linen strips. Perhaps if I find a way—Nicodemus and Joseph might know of a method—You would rise earlier than You prophesied because of Granny Mary's death."

The little flight of ecstasy was over. Then rising to his feet, he thought aloud, "How I wish I could console Jesus. I know of the great love He had for Granny. He must be sorrowing." Then quickly, as if he had awakened to reality, he realized that no longer could Jesus feel sorrow. And happiness was the Master's, for Granny was with Him. Peering through the narrow opening above the boulder, Peter standing on tiptoe whispered to his silent Jesus, "Lord, forgive me for such trivial thoughts and earthly concerns. I am glad you took Granny home. But You know Jesus, if you were alive I would be the first to console You. I have seen You weep over death. I am glad You will never weep again."

In that moment, Peter unmistakably heard within the depths of his heart the voice of His Master saying, "Do not weep. Because you would console Me, I have come to console you."

Peter was dazed—he stumbled from the boulder and sat down. He was trembling; he was not yet acquainted with all the ways of ecstasy. This was in likeness to his experience during the Paschal dinner and the first receiving of the Gift of Heaven. He did hear the voice of Jesus as clearly now as then. Then hurrying to the boulder he looked into the tunnel of darkness and called, "Lord, have You risen? I heard You speak. Because of Granny Mary I would not be surprised if You changed Your plans. Lord, have You risen?"

After Joseph had finished embalming the lovely body of Granny, he was concerned about Peter being alone at the sepulcher. Hurriedly he returned to the tomb. Peter was still gazing into the opening. No doubt he was listening for the Master to say that He had risen.

Joseph questioned, "Peter, do you think I should close this open space above the boulder and make the sepulcher more secure?"

"Don't bother me, Joseph," growled Peter. "Can't you see I am listening; it would not surprise me to hear Jesus call for assistance when He finds Himself cocooned. Why did you do it, Joseph? No, don't fill in this narrow space, for I intend to stay here all night watching and listening."

Then Peter realized that he had been severely quick with Joseph, for he had retreated to the grove. Peter followed him and apologized, saying, "I am sorry, Joseph. Forgive my sudden impatience. I desire to stay here near the tomb all night. This will be a new kind of venture with Jesus. Many times we have prayed together in Gethsemane and for all night vigils, too, but this will be the first experience of a one-sided conversation in prayer vigil that we have kept. Even though He sleeps in death, I do not consider Him dead as we know silent death. (Peter knew he had heard the Master's voice.) Joseph, I am not afraid to be here alone, and there is no reason why you should not return to your home and take your rest. Please leave us alone."

Joseph rose from his position of prayer as Peter had found him, and together they walked down the path that would lead to the city. Joseph, hoping that he could coax Peter to his home, questioned, "Aren't you tired? I beg of you to come to my home for at least an hour's rest. I am sure Rosa is greatly concerned and wondering whether or not the great crowds on parade have found you. She will be grateful if she knows you will take rest."

Peter answered, "No, I must go back to the sepulcher. I am sure Rosa will not be disturbed at my absence, for she is well aware of my allegiance to Jesus."

Within the half hour he had returned to his niche beside the boulder. Sitting in the dust and leaning against the huge rock, he toyed with a stick in his hand, and in the sand he wrote these words, "Jesus, my friends think You are dead, but I know You are alive—Spirit cannot die. And this night You have spoken to me in such a way that I have never experienced with the natural ear. Would that I could die for this truth that I have heard You tonight! How can I thank You?"

Then gazing into the night Peter said aloud, "Lord, I weep when I think about Your generosity! Truly You will not be outdone in generosity . . . this You have promised me in one of our conversations. And now, when I would want the most to console You because of Your Granny's death, You consoled me with Your invisible nearness. Jesus, in You there is no death—already You have given me Your Voice from the tomb."

Rising quickly to his feet, Peter peered again into the dark passageway above the boulder, saying, "Lord, have You risen yet?"

Not hearing an answer, he knelt in prayer facing the boulder. He brushed away his writing in the dust and prayed aloud to his silent Jesus. "Tell me, Lord, how to begin this new life of our silences? You are the Messiah and therefore know our least thought and desire. Are You going to speak often to us from the darkness of silence in the coming ages? I have heard Your Voice and I know You are listening. I miss You, Jesus. Oh, I miss You. Come closer to my interior self and just let us talk."

Continuing as he stood again at the boulder and peering through the opening, he said, "See, Jesus, I have removed my swords. You know I am trying to obey Your least command, and I have put them away. Never will I use them again. They caused quite a stir, didn't they? You know I love the touch of fine steel, and I love a skillful fight, but You have willed that I fight with silent prayer—I'll try, Lord. How I miss Your favorite reprimand. I can almost hear You say, 'My impetuous Peter.' Remember, Lord, how I knelt at Your knee and fought my will about using the two swords on Judas? You helped me then win over my stupid self when You reached for the ear of Malchus and performed a miracle to save my life. I'll never forget that, Jesus. Anything, Lord, let me suffer anything just to hear Your voice again. I would welcome Your reprimand tonight, Jesus. Pour Your scolding words again into my soul, for I am fighting an interior anger every time I think about the struggle You are going to have when You try getting out of those rags Joseph wrapped You in. How are You going to get out of them? Or, are You going to appear in those linen bandages as another proof of Your humility, which You have never failed to teach us? My, how I wish I could unwrap Your Body this instant, but the linens have adhered to Your Flesh, and it can't be done. And You know, I did not want to cover Your Face. Lord, forgive the stupidity of man."

Leaning close to the boulder and standing on tiptoe, better to gaze into the darkness of the tomb, Peter could see the outline of the Master's Body in the basin-shelf. No, Peter realized, Jesus had not moved. Peter whispered aloud into the deathlike stillness, "Lord, if You were only with me as You were last week, I would ask You a thousand questions. I think I would begin by asking, 'What would You have us do to please You most as the Silent Jesus and especially when we hold You in the Living Bread at the breaking of Bread?'"

While Peter mused on these thoughts, he knelt in the dust and toyed again with a stick. Suddenly his hand seemed to move by an invisible force and he read his own writing, which read, "Seek My love. Let Me hear your voice in all things. I am the Good Shepherd. Keep Me alive in yourself."

At the first break of dawn, Peter was still keeping his vigil with his silent Master. At least a hundred times during the night Peter's heart had asked, "Lord, have You risen yet?"

Peter felt new life and encouragement in the phenomena of loving his silent Master. Awakening from his beautiful prayer of quiet, Peter retired to the grove to rest, pray and wait for the hour of the Resurrection. He wanted to be near if Jesus should call for assistance to remove the rags.

Peter was tired, yet he kept his eyes on the sepulcher. It was early morning, and the city of Jerusalem was still in a state of turmoil. All through the night thousands of sudden conversions had been made through the miracle of Veronica's scarf and the temple veil, as they were paraded through the streets for public veneration.

The cry "Peter" was on the tongues of thousands of people as cure after cure took place in the streets. People clung to the veils and venerated them as if they were their banners of salvation. (They venerated them as we admire and venerate the sign of the cross.) To one another they retold the magnificent story of Dismas and his crippled child, who had suddenly been cured, and of how Dismas had preached from his cross as if it were a pulpit.

As these veils were being paraded through the streets, it was rumored that the body of Dismas was also being carried in solemn procession in another part of the city by converts to the New Law. Cries and loud cheering arose, attesting that many new cures were being attributed to the venerating of his body. All through the city intensified riots were taking place between the new converts and those who zealously clung to the belief of the Old Law.

Because of the general unrest in the city, the shouting, cures, parades, and rioting during the night, Annas and Caiphas had hatefully forfeited their rest. They stayed hidden behind locked doors, for they were afraid as they debated as to their next move and how they should oppose the philosophers of both the Old and New Law. They realized that the numbers of Jesus' followers had grown very great during the night, but Caiphas hoped the zealousness would soon calm as the day broke. However, even at this hour the noise of the shouting people could be heard through the great stone walls of Caiphas' courts. And through the stone floors from the dungeons below could be heard the joyful cries of the prisoners, who were raising their voices in belief that they would be liberated when Jesus rose from the dead.

Caiphas and Annas could hear them shout, "Jesus is the Messiah! Jesus is our liberator! Jesus, Jesus, Jesus, come and save us."

Even though Caiphas issued orders for quiet, neither the people nor the prisoners would be quieted. Nothing could stop them, and Caiphas wondered whether or not this rioting was going to last three days. The noise was terrible and he was sick from it all. Threats of death from the soldiers only met with scoff and delight, for the people were joyous that they, too, could die with Jesus as Dismas had.

Annas asked Caiphas and a few other friends who had hidden with them, "What kind of philosophy is this that makes people welcome death? What is this martyr ideology? Hear them; they say that Dismas was a martyr and true friend of God. We should crucify all the followers of the impostor Jesus. My, what power He has over them! What is it all about?"

Caiphas merely shook his head. He, too, could not imagine what had come over the majority of the people of Jerusalem. Annas and Caiphas were afraid of losing their judicial voice if these conditions persisted. They did not have time to lose in bringing about city order. They were too frightened even to break down and mourn the death of Turan. They were afraid to question each other about the miraculous roses, and the cure, which it was claimed the roses had produced when they touched her eye. They would not believe her death was caused by the wrath of God manifesting Himself in the rending of the temple veil as Turan knelt in prayer beside it.

They were also fearful to learn how much Turan might have told her servants about this Jesus, and the cure. Annas had ordered her to keep her eye bandaged and not speak, but seeing how the people rebelled at order, he wondered if Turan had disobeyed in her zeal for this

Jesus. Caiphas and Annas were afraid of ridicule, and now they were wondering if Turan's servants were spreading the news among the people, which kept the turmoil at fever pitch. They feared the thought of violence that would be brought to their own doors. They knew the common people loved Turan, and that they would even uphold her ideals against those of her own father if they should prove she admired Jesus and His philosophy.

Caiphas said, "I hope all this quiets down before the people learn of her death if they do not already know." To this hour her death had been kept a secret even from Pilate and Claudentia, his wife.

Now that it was daylight, Annas and Caiphas shuddered at the realization that they would have to give orders for Turan's body to be given a light form of embalming, which would last until the great feast days were over. They would have to notify Pilate because Claudentia and Turan had been raised together as sisters—Turan was the adopted child of the family.

With all these questions and thoughts confronting them, Annas and Caiphas discussed the possibility as to whether or not this Jesus was the Messiah. And, if He were the Christ, then what would become of them? They trembled as they talked over many scriptural passages, which could point a proving finger that this Nazarene was the long looked-for Messiah. They wondered why they had been so stubborn about the prophecies and their intricate design in regard to time and the Messiah's coming to earth. Quickly they put these questions and other disturbing thoughts from their minds, as they concluded there was only one thing left for them to do, and that was to make sure this Jesus did not rise from the tomb as He had predicted.

They would hurry to Pilate and inform him of Turan's death, and ask him to place guards around the tomb of Jesus. Then they questioned each other whether or not they could arrest a man for rising from the dead? And who would capture and imprison a man who rose from the dead? And if they should catch Him, to whom would they take Him for further judgment? Could the Sanhedrin prove it was a sin to rise from the dead? Could they be bribed in this cause? And, if they arrested Jesus, they would also have to arrest all the people who rose from the tombs when Jesus was crucified. The last notice of events that Caiphas had heard was that new tombs were hourly breaking open and the dead rising. Caiphas and Annas were nearly in a state of shock as they were faced with such unanswerable questions.

They resolved with an oath to each other that they would ask Pilate to arrest Jesus immediately if He should break through the tomb. At least, until after the third day, they realized they would have every reason to fear this Jesus because of the people's actions. Well they knew that if He arose they would lose their prestige as men of wisdom, and perhaps the priestly robes would be removed from Annas.

As they left the building in company of a few Pharisees who would accompany them as a bodyguard to Pilate, an elderly beggar woman in the streets, pointing her long, thin finger at them, scoffed accusingly, "A servant of Pilate has just informed me that Jesus, the Son of God, told Pilate that you, Annas and Caiphas, had betrayed Him to Pilate; and that, therefore, your guilt is greater than Pilate's even though he did order the crucifixion by the voice of the Jews."

The mystifying way of truth that the woman spoke to Caiphas and Annas overwhelmed them with fear. Trembling, they hurried to Pilate.

As they entered upon the pavilion steps to wait for the servants to say when they could enter into the room with Pilate, they overheard Claudentia plead and cry in bitter anguish as she knelt at the feet of Pilate. She was saying, "I tell you, Pilate, you have killed the Son of God! I reminded you in plenty of time about this horrible crime—you could have prevented it by following Him. What is your wealth and position going to mean to you in eternal life? How can you deny the miracle on Turan's eye? You saw it as well as I, and you will have to admit only God could perform that cure. And, even though you know of the truths of my dream [ecstasy], for you have followed my advice before in matters of state because God allowed me to know through the gift of prayer, you still followed the wiles of greed and position. You crucified God because people cheered. You knew I believed in Jesus, and now because of my belief you have severed our peace and friendship. Pilate, please confess to the people that you have made a grave mistake and come with me as a follower. True, we will be disgraced and face poverty, but just think, we will be the beginners of people in high positions to live the New Law. Just think, Pilate, with our influence we would convert thousands of our friends and in this way you could repair the damage you have done."

Sternly Pilate answered, "Claudentia, I was inclined to believe the miracles as divine truths a few days ago and, until this, your last divine slumber prayer, I have believed in you, but since talking to Herod I have changed my mind. I want the greater position he offers, and I must make it clear to him that I am convinced that your Jesus was an impostor. By following the will of Herod, I will be given a greater governing power over the people. Now that your Jesus is dead, I prefer to hear no more about Him, and I intend that you obey me. I forbid you to speak of this Man to anyone. Leave the room; I have other business to attend."

Weeping, Claudentia left the column-clustered pavilion. Pilate watched her as anger swept through his soul, and yet he was troubled and touched with her words of truth. They burned deeply into his soul. He wished he had never spoken to Herod. Thoughtfully, he recalled many words Jesus had spoken to him. Pilate liked Jesus and yet he feared His philosophy. Down in his heart Pilate hoped Jesus would not rise from the tomb. But, if He did, how would he as governor explain away this ponderous phenomena?

Before Pilate allowed Caiphas and Annas to enter the room, he sat musing about Jesus. He tried to recapture a certain scene and the words of Jesus before the crucifixion. Jesus had said to him, "Everyone who is of the truth hears My voice."

Pilate remembered he had answered, "What is truth?"

Then Jesus answered, "Truth is what you have both seen and heard. Remember, Pilate, Turan came to you with the roses and showed you the cure on her eye. You admitted then in you heart that only God could have performed that miracle. You admitted then in your heart that I was the Messiah even though you did not speak of it. That is why I asked you, 'Dost thou say this of thyself that I am a King, or have others told thee of Me?'"

Jesus had continued, "Pilate, I asked you this because I wanted you to show yourself as a humble man and admit the truth in your heart, for I knew that Turan had told you I was the King of the Jews and you respected her wisdom and you saw the miracle. It was then you turned a deaf ear to the grace of truth and, because a servant was near, you made a question to distract your servant by saying, 'Am I a Jew?' Then to oblige you, Pilate, and keep you from further embarrassment, I continued telling you about My Kingdom, which was not of this world."

Pilate rolled his head in his hands and groaned. Could he be wrong? If Jesus was the Messiah then Jesus was the Romans' God, too, for there was certainly only one God. All these questions and answers pierced the soul of Pilate as Claudentia disappeared toward the great stairway.

Caiphas and Annas smiled to each other; now their anguish of soul was over. They had nothing to fear on how to explain to Pilate about their desires that a guard should be placed at the tomb. They knew Pilate was worried.

The servant bid them enter. With expressions of mock grief on their faces, they slowly approached Pilate. Then, in a feigned manner of gentle composure, Annas spoke, "Your Honor, we have remembered how that deceiver, Jesus, said while He was yet alive, 'After three days I will rise again.' Your Honor, since we know the rioting chaos in the city, we have come to plead that you place a guard to stand watch at the sepulcher for at least three days, or we fear the people whom Jesus taught might steal His Body away and then say to the people, 'He is risen from the dead.' Pilate, if this happens, the last impostor will be worse than the first.

"And we have further news that is of a sad nature—Turan is dead, and we must now see to it that she is embalmed and buried. We, too, are alarmed about the so-called miracle on her eye and we understand your worry and how Claudentia feels toward you in regard to Jesus and the crucifixion. Allow us to remind you that we are with you in your decisions."

Pilate, grief-stricken, stood and faced the two men, saying, "No, Turan can't be dead! Tell me you are only guessing."

Caiphas knelt at Pilate's feet and broke into tears and assured Pilate they were not mistaken. Then Pilate heard the mystery of the veils and how Turan's death made their plans all the more difficult. Still standing, Pilate recalled the truths Jesus had talked about and how He had said, "My Way is the way of everlasting life and joy in the Kingdom of My Father."

The thought of death frightened Pilate, for well he understood he could not escape death—everybody died. Surely in justice there must be another life, he mused, for he did not want Turan to be forgotten as useless dust—there just had to be a Kingdom of the heavenly Father, the Creator of the universe. His skin turned pale as he thought of the possibility that, at the moment of his own death, he might be confronted with this Jesus whom he had ordered crucified. Was He God? This was almost too much to think about. No, it could not be true that he had put to death the Son of God. Quickly he remembered the appalling opportunities Herod had offered him. He could not pass them by.

In newborn anger and pride, Pilate ordered Annas and Caiphas to leave the hall at once and to take their own guards to watch the tomb. Pilate staggered from his chair and made his way to the stairs—he was afraid and ill and grief-stricken about Turan. He wanted to tell Claudentia.

CHAPTER 5

The Resurrection: Inside the Sepulcher

AFTER RETURNING TO HIS OWN COURTS, Caiphas, with Annas, angrily chose thirty of their own guards to stand watch at the sepulcher. In his anger, Caiphas had not chosen wisely, for many of the guards had seen the miracle of the ear after Peter had severed it with his sword, and two others had seen the conversion of the prisoners in the dungeon below, which had been ascribed to hysteria. With some trepidation and fear because of the miracles, the guards assembled in the line formation, ready for their march to the sepulcher of Jesus.

Hoping to foster a degree of courage, even though they doubted their own reason against miracles, they boisterously scoffed at any thought of fear in regard to the supernatural as they marched through the narrow streets of Jerusalem. As they approached the tomb, their loud manner of talking and laughing, along with the clanking of their swords in their scabbards, awakened Peter from his light slumber as he watched and prayed.

Quickly he got to his feet—only to watch the soldiers peer through the opening above the boulder in the passageway to the tomb. He overheard one guard say as he turned to the others, "He is here all right. His disciples have not taken His Body away as Annas feared they would do."

Another guard exclaimed with great surprise as he looked into the tunnel entrance, "Can you imagine! They have Him wrapped as a King for burial. And smell those spices! If I am not mistaken, they are the best in all the world. I ask you, where did His poor disciples get the money for such expensive spices and wrappings? Who did the embalming? We should have him arrested. And this looks like a new sepulcher—the Body is alone. No living person could be in there with Him because of this boulder being in the way. Come, let us fill in the entrance and cover the boulder with a heavy layer of earth so that it will look like part of the mountainside. It is the only safe way to carry out Caiphas' order to seal the tomb."

The guard laughed as he continued, saying, "Then, too, we will know that this Jesus will not be able to carry out His prophecy that He will rise on the third day. Come, men, let us cover the sepulcher."

He was answered by a guard who laughed as he said, "Caiphas is actually afraid that this dead Man will arise or he would not order us here. Can you imagine that of the fearless Caiphas?"

All the soldiers roared with laughter as they jested about Caiphas and Annas. Then the soldier who had been speaking continued, "I know he is afraid because he paid me well to be sure that the sealing of the tomb was done in the right manner for security. Here, help me lift these logs and willows to the front of the boulder before we shovel the dirt and shale."

When the task was finished, the soldier who gave the orders leaned on his shovel and laughing said, "I would like to see this Jesus dig Himself through this tangled mess. And, if He should find a way, I will arrest Him immediately. Won't He be a sight trying to loosen Himself from the embalming bandages? Won't He be surprised to find us waiting for Him? I'll wager He never bargained for a bodyguard when He made that prophecy. If Caiphas had only known that He was embalmed, he would not bother having us here, for that Body is sealed within the shell of linens."

Peter smiled, yet tears were in his eyes as he thought about the stupidity of man. He was also sad to think he could no longer peer through the opening to see the Body of Jesus. As Peter remained hidden waiting for the day to pass, he mused about the events that would take place at the Resurrection. The anticipation of that hour was nearly beyond Peter's powers of patience—time was slow. The very word, Resurrection, was new to him and it was hard to visualize the scope of its meaning. He wondered again whether or not Jesus would need anyone to help Him? And, if He should call, how would he, Peter, gain entrance to the tomb? Would Jesus call on His legions of heavenly soldiers—He had spoken of them? My how Peter would enjoy seeing them. He shook himself from the thought, for well he knew if that phenomena took place he would be frightened and perhaps die from shock.

Smiling, he mused as to how the soldiers at the tomb would react to the swords of the heavenly arms. Peter could be heard saying in a low tone of voice, "It would be just like Jesus to scare them to death with His army. He was always surprising us." Sadly, he shook his head as he thought about the stiffened linens. And then he wondered why he had not insisted that Jesus be buried in His toga. He was angry with himself.

These passing questions of mind-musings having been ended, Peter resolved to stay near the tomb just in case Jesus suddenly called to him. Toward evening, the soldiers found Peter and they forced him to leave the grove. With a heavy heart he returned to his home, and from there he and Andrew hurried to the synagogue to pray. Prayer at this hour was their only consolation. Their grief and feeling of loss were very great. Miraculously they seemed to be hidden from the crowds on the streets and also from the eyes of the people in the synagogue.

At dusk the soldiers had set their torches and lamps around the new mound of earth, with which they had covered the sepulcher entrance. As the night grew silent and the sky's adornments made their appearance, the guards rested and many fell asleep. The night was uneventful.

Late on the second night of the Messiah's death, Peter and Andrew knelt again side by side in the quiet of the synagogue. They realized that their only means of helping Jesus now in His rising from the tomb was through prayer. They wanted to have some fellowship in helping with the greatest event on earth—the Resurrection.

In this mood of deep prayer and desire, they were suddenly lifted to the extreme of contemplative, intuitive knowledge and wisdom. Then Peter alone was instantly transported in body, though invisibly in the gift of bilocation, *into* the sepulcher. Peter found himself standing near and gazing upon the linen encasement that held the still Body of Jesus. In the gift of bilocation and not knowing fear within its intellectual knowledge, Peter basked with delight in the effable riches of

Heaven's Light, which came nearer as from the heavens to the sepulcher. That great Light reminded him of the earthly sun descending slowly toward him inch by inch—it was delightful and beautiful! As he watched that mystifying magnificence, it seemed that the heavens' atmospheres divided into countless arched bows around the golden Light. Then suddenly through these arches of astonishing design and size, he could see thousands of angels in assumed forms of young men adoring the hidden, stilled Body of Jesus.

The inside of the tomb was now aglow with this royal gown of glory—every niche seemed to be painted in gold. And, as if silhouetted against that beautiful wonderment, the tomb, Peter watched angels going out over the earth as if on missions to stand at the place or places on earth where the Master had touched His foot while He lived on earth. They, the angels, would stay at that hallowed place in thanksgiving for time. And everyone who touched or passed by would receive a blessing from the sacramental of hallowed ground.

Peter sighed aloud, "Oh what a benediction to earth!"

The hour of triumph was here at last—death and sin would be channeled to new ways and means of hope for the peoples of the earth. Suddenly the golden Light seemed to condense into a column in the tomb. And from out of this column walked the glorious assumed form of John the Baptizer. He bowed to Peter and beckoned for him to come nearer to the Body of Jesus.

Peter fell to the earth floor as if to venerate the feet of John, but John lifted him again to his feet and said, "We have assembled here, Peter, to be near the Messiah in His hour of glory. Peter, with your permission, for you are the director of souls on earth and in Heaven, we will call His Name. He will hear us and rise from the dead."

Even in these ecstasy gifts of bilocation, Peter was stunned; he could not answer. Suddenly, with new light and understanding he understood the prophetic truths about himself and the office that he held. Yes, he was the Successor Christ and could act in His name. Silently and with great awe he just looked at John and nodded his head that John could speak.

John quietly called, "Jesus."

Then their eyes fell upon the stilled form of the Master. Peter smiled. His worries over the stiffened linens were at an end. As they had reached to touch them, the linens suddenly shone with the luster of radiant pearl, and all discoloration from the spice and pitch were gone. The linens seemed to bend away from the Master's Body with ease, as if they were rose petals unfolding from a bud.

One by one Peter and John folded the linens and placed them on the rock ledge, where to Peter's astonishment he noticed his own brown handkerchief. It was neatly folded on the shelf. "How could this be?" he questioned himself, for he could yet see the handkerchief over the Master's face. He reached for it, handled it and found that it was his. He could identify it because of the embroidered red ship in the corner. Yet he felt sure it was the same handkerchief he had used to cover the Master's face with during the embalming. With the handkerchief in his hand he gazed in a bewildered way toward the Body of Jesus, then to the shelf, and then to John. Then he asked, "How could this be possible?"

In answer to Peter's questioning gaze, John replied, "I had this handkerchief brought from my own burial place. I deeply appreciate your covering my face with linen, but I prefer you to keep this set of linens unbroken; for, since they have been so close to the King and especially this one having been touched by Him when He uncovered my body in Gethsemane for you to view, gives them a supernatural quality as gifts (sacramentals) from God. Many people who are ill will be cured by touching them. Remove your other handkerchief from the Master's face."

Gently, Peter removed the linen mask. It seemed to roll away—it did not adhere to the Holy Face. Peter gasped aloud, "Why, His countenance is glowing! He is alive! He is warm!" Peter fell across the Sacred Body and whispered acts of thanksgiving. Then rising to a standing position, he found himself suddenly recollected, and without any particular thought he placed the second folded handkerchief on top of the first one on the shelf.

John addressed him, "Peter, give me permission to awaken Jesus. Remember, you hold the keys of power to both Heaven and earth."

Quietly and with some hesitancy, Peter answered, "Why, yes, awaken Him."

Bending over the King of Kings, John whispered as he touched His shoulder, "Jesus, it is now the hour for You to rise. The world is waiting for the news of Your Resurrection. This is Your hour of triumph over death."

Jesus smiled and sat up. And it seemed to Peter that He was clothed in a gown of golden light. Many angels, all in assumed forms as young men, for Peter's benefit, placed a crown on the Master's head and handed Him a huge crosier, which He steadied against the sepulcher wall.

With the angels, John and Peter first worshipped the risen King. Peter, in great admiration, glanced toward the magnificent crosier—it was near the rock shelf where the handkerchiefs lay, and for a fleeting second he caught sight of them again. Peter marveled at the goodness of God and how He thought of everything, and even at this hour to think He would think of the simple little things that would later be known as sacramentals.

The Master addressed Peter, saying, "Peter, do you love Me?"

Startled at the question and as deeply moved, as he had been when Jesus had asked him the same question before the crucifixion, Peter found it impossible to answer. He just bowed in deep adoration before his King. Rising and backing away, Peter noticed the magnificent crosier in John's hand as he stood beside Jesus. Handing the crosier to Peter, John gestured that it should be given to the Master. Peter took it, and as he handed it to Jesus he said, "Lord, You know of my love."

Jesus smiled. Could it be possible that He needed that token of love from a creature to begin His reign of the Resurrection?

Slightly bowing before Peter the Master said, "Fear not about that which I will ask of you during the next few weeks. I want you to accompany Me in the sublime invisible gifts of bilocation into this city as well as neighboring cities during My life of the Resurrection. And at other times you will see Me and be with Me outside the vision-life and its joys. When I call you in that gift of bilocation I will also summon John."

Suddenly, all was very still and Jesus bowed. Peter looked around, and there inside the sepulcher stood Mother Mary—she, too, had been gifted with the gifts of bilocation into the tomb. She remained silent as Jesus, Peter, and John enjoyed the gifts of silence. Then Jesus embraced His mother, and that which was spoken between them no mortal man would dare interpret. Then Jesus discussed the coming events according to hours and days.

Outside the tomb, the guards who kept watch were suddenly frozen from fright as they noticed tiny streams of golden Light trickle, as if they were water, through the mound of earth outside the tomb.

They were watching the hour of earth's real dawn. This was the Light of the resurrected Jesus. Within minutes the outside of the sepulcher appeared as a sieve, with streaming light coming out in all directions.

Calming themselves and gathering their strength, they backed away from the unearthly sight. All was silent—no one cared to speak. Without any noise, just using their hands, they quietly awakened the other guards and pointed to the Light. As if in a daze they all walked back to the sepulcher entrance. They wanted to run, but they were afraid of the laws of Caiphas—they were sent there to watch and keep order.

After half an hour of intense watching, and finding no harm had come to them, they began to move about and whisper to one another about the sieve-like streams of light.

Through the mercy of God, the guards were in a partial state of rapture, which was necessary for them to have to withstand such a sight without harm to their mind and body, yet the guards did not realize the gift of God to them. In this state of a sense of intuitive knowledge, which does not neglect the human sense of touch, they heard human voices that seemed to come from the inner depths of the sepulcher. Terrified, they grabbed their shovels and tried to cover the streams of Light, or the tiny pinholes in the soft earth through which they streamed. It was not long before they realized this task was utterly impossible to accomplish.

The sound of human voices continued. A few of the most courageous guards put their heads close to the earth over the boulder and listened. Their facial expressions told of their shock. They could hardly speak as they mumbled, "Why, it is Peter's voice."

One other guard asked, "How did he get in the tomb? We have kept a close watch and we sent him away. He could not enter without passing here and there is no other entrance."

Quickly, a few of the other guards leaned their heads toward the dirt-covered entrance to listen. Trembling and shocked they exclaimed, "It is Peter's voice! And the answering voice sounds like John the Baptizer. We would know his voice anywhere. But he was beheaded in Capernaum. Men, are we dreaming?"

Another one answered in angry protest, "Get away from the entrance, all of you. I want to listen alone. You are all mad. Who ever heard of such nonsense! I know he is dead! Why, my brother in Capernaum helped behead that baptizer! I know he is dead! Anyway, he didn't say he would rise again. Move back and let me listen. All this hysteria and imagination! Come, let us uncover the tomb and find out from where the voices are coming!"

He reached for his shovel, and as he pushed it into the earth near the boulder he fell dead.

CHAPTER 6

The Resurrection: Jesus Comes through the Sepulcher

BY THE MOMENT, the guards at the sepulcher entrance were losing their nerve, and their actions would indicate such fear that they might desert their post. The soldier in charge noticed the unrest and he began to talk to the men by saying, "Come now, men, let us try reasoning this strange event and see if we can come to a conclusion as to what we should do. We must avoid panic among ourselves lest we become a laughing jest among the people. Does anyone here think it is possible that the Man in the tomb was the Son of God?"

No one answered, but their silence told that they were doubtful as to any conviction.

The commanding officer continued, "Do you think it is possible that this Light that we cannot cover over means that Jesus is rising from the dead as he predicted? If He is rising then to whom is He speaking? He was not the type of man to talk to Himself. As I stand here I swear that I am hearing voices coming out from within the tomb. And I swear that one voice resembles that of John the Baptizer. Do you men think that he, too, has risen as Lazarus did? I have it on good authority that Lazarus was dead and that he was called by Jesus to arise."

One of the trembling soldiers answered, "I have talked to Lazarus; he doesn't live far from my home, and to this minute I did not believe the story he tells nor what I have heard, but these events make me change my mind. I wish I knew what to believe. I did not believe that this Jesus was the Messiah, but now I am doubtful of my former decisions. God help me! What a terrible thing for us if He rises from the dead and proves that He is the Messiah—that would be the final proof if He came through the sepulcher.

"Just think, men, we have kept watch at the Messiah's tomb, if He is God, hoping to prevent His rising. If He is God then we are guilty of fighting the will of God because He said He would resurrect. Why, at this very moment we have hatred and malice in our hearts, whereas we should bow down in this dust and adore Him in the sepulcher. God forgive us!"

Another soldier said, "We have all heard the ancient prophecies, and there is no reason why we did not investigate this Man's miracles. If His miracles were true rather than just talk, it is proof that He was trying to show us He was the Messiah. What fools we have been!"

One other man said, "If He is the Messiah we are guilty in some measure for His death. Will there be any hope for us? I am afraid of His scorn; He had a powerful voice and I trembled when I heard Him speak."

A quick, blustery, unbelieving guard answered, "He can't be the Messiah! Don't make fools of yourselves. Don't believe your reasoning—it is enough to drive us mad, and more so because of our positions as guards and coworkers to such an evil death. I don't believe He is the Messiah!"

Frightened, another guard answered, "It seems to me the scribes have taught us that we, in this generation, would see the real Messiah. If the Light coming from out of the tomb continues, I am afraid I will have to admit that the Man entombed is the Messiah. Light can only mean glory—the Light of God, which cannot be hidden. Remember He said He and the Father were One."

As he gave his answer several guards laughed scornfully, while others knelt in great fear, for the Light was getting brighter and brighter.

Quickly the officer ordered his swiftest runner to go in search of Peter, whom they had sent out of the grove as he had lingered near the tomb. The officer wanted proof as to whether or not Peter was at home, or the possibility that he had found a way into the sepulcher, which would prove that he had recognized his voice through the mound of dirt and shale, which they had shoveled over the entrance.

Within the hour the runner returned with the news that a friend of his had told him that he had just seen Peter with his brother Andrew praying in the synagogue.

Breathless, the runner told the news to the other men, and then laughingly chided them that the voices were nothing more than their imaginations and hysteria. And the mystery of light from the tomb was nothing more than self-hypnotism, since they were looking for something to happen in regard to the prophecy of the third day. He scolded the men for being traitors to the cause of good sense and that they should abolish the thought that this buried Man was the Messiah.

Chuckling aloud with the feeling of great interior pride, for hadn't he been the means, so he thought, of stilling their fears? But suddenly he came to a standstill. Sheepishly he looked around to the men as he silently questioned himself as to how his answers would prove that the guard who had plunged his shovel into the beams of light had suddenly died, as if from shock, if there wasn't something to this mystery. Was this soldier's death from a natural cause? Or was it from fear? Could he have been frightened to death thinking he had heard Peter's voice? Perhaps the men would say that the wrath of God was upon him as it was upon men of old who dared touch the Ark of the Covenant.

Trying to control his voice, which betrayed his calm, he tried to convince the men that the dead guard had died from over-exertion and fear, and that it was not too uncommon for men to die suddenly under physical and mental strain. And he continued to say that possibly the golden light coming from the sepulcher was some sort of witchcraft made possible by this Jesus' disciples in order to frighten the guards.

Regardless of what he said, expressions of terror were etched on their faces—the Light was brighter. No longer were they thin, threading beams of gold-like incense smoke emitting through the earth, but now they seemed to condense into a cloud of golden fog.

The guards called to the commanding officer, "Let us go back to Caiphas in a body. We are afraid. It is not safe here. Caiphas should come and see this himself. He will never believe us. What are we going to do?"

The officer answered, "To return now would make us guilty of desertion while on a field of duty. We must stay regardless of what happens. I don't want to face imprisonment, and therefore I command you to stay where you are. This buried Jesus cannot rise, nor must we be alarmed of what His disciples may do to frighten us."

The guard who had gone in search of Peter shouted to the men who were weeping and showing signs of revolt, "Men, I tell you Peter is praying in the synagogue. How could he be here in the tomb? I looked in the tomb before we covered it, and I am sure no one was with the Body of Jesus."

Then the voices from within the tomb grew louder and the guards could not deny they heard. Quickly the men seized the guard who had gone in search of Peter and pushed him to the wall and held him there to listen. They asked him in a demanding voice, "Now do you hear anything? Whose voice is it? We dare you to deny that you hear human voices." Terrified he answered them, "Yes, I hear voices, and one who speaks now is Peter."

Shuddering, he fell to his knees and begged God's mercy on his sinful soul. Then hysterically he cried to the men, "I believe this Jesus is the Messiah! Confess, men, before it is too late. He is the Son of God! This is His day to rise! He is no longer dead—He is alive and this Light is His glory brought from Heaven. This is the Resurrection!"

The officer in charge vigorously shook the weeping guard and demanded him to answer how he could suddenly change his opinions as to where Peter was. Cuffing him on the head as he threw him to the ground the officer said, "How is this possible that you suddenly believe that this Jesus is the Messiah? Take back this terrible conviction or admit that you lied to us about knowing that Peter was in the synagogue praying."

Before he could answer, the earth trembled and the Light from the tomb grew intensely bright; all the air was filled with Heaven's music. Several of the guards fell to the ground in fear and fainting, while others, especially those who had openly professed belief in Jesus, were miraculously gifted with sudden rapture, wherein they learned the deeper knowledge and mystery about the Son of God on earth.

Immediately they became ardent believers in Jesus as they awakened from the divine slumber of rapture.

The men who had fainted, after being revived, waited on one another and then crawled into hidden paths of nearby shrubbery, where they huddled together and decided that they should hurry to Caiphas and tell him about the other guards' desertion through conversion, and in this way of reporting they hoped to save themselves from prison and perhaps death.

Later, and when they had finished telling Caiphas the false story with some of its mysteries of truth, Caiphas bribed them with large sums of money to go through the city and tell the people that the body of Jesus had been stolen during the night by the disciples while the guards slept. He would give them the word when to go about their false mission as soon as any word should be voiced through the city that Jesus had risen.

During the solemn moments of the Resurrection, the guards who had been caught up into rapture, and having the appearance of being dead, actually witnessed the miracle of Jesus coming through the huge boulder, which had been rolled into the entrance, as if it were not there. At that moment, another terrible earthquake, in the intensity of the one at the crucifixion, shook the earth and the boulder rolled to one side. And then, through the tunnel entrance Mother Mary walked out into the world in her gifts of bilocation and smiled upon the guards. They knew they had seen her. When the rapturous slumber released them, they fled to the hills, there to hide until they could flee into other countries. Their one aim was to preach Christ crucified and the truths about the Resurrection, which they had both seen and heard.

Peter, too, had seen all these events in his ecstasy of bilocation as he actually knelt in his true body beside Andrew as they prayed together in the synagogue. Rising from his divine slumber, Peter looked at Andrew and beckoned that it was time to leave.

Peter was filled with great joy, wonderment, and peace and he was about to speak when the ground trembled from a terrible earthquake. (He was still in the lingering gifts of ecstasy's intuitive knowledge and he seemed to know what was happening; all was present knowledge with God.) He knew this was the moment of the Messiah's triumphal rising, or going forth from the tomb to the people of the world.

Suddenly Peter was himself again. His first impulse was to return to the sepulcher, but he remembered the guards had threatened him with arrest if he so much as dared to venture near the tomb. As they hurried through the streets they met James and John the Beloved. They, too, were frightened and amazed at the sudden upheaval of the earth. The city was unusually quiet—the people were afraid—this was the third day. James asked, "Peter, do you think the earthquake has any significance to the prophecy regarding the Resurrection that is now upon us?"

Peter hurried them to a quiet corner, and there in great exuberance he related to them the happenings of the night, and how he had been bilocated with Mother Mary into the sepulcher and had seen the real moment of the Resurrection while the guards had kept watch. Peter also told them the confusion the guards had been in. John the Beloved and James chuckled and said, "Jesus is wonderful!" They were then awed into silence as Peter told them about the glorified John they had known as the Baptizer. And Peter was breathless as he told them the mysterious events about the two handkerchiefs on the stone ledge in the tomb, and of the prophecy that in the near future miracles would be attributed to them and their use according to faith and the glory it would give to God.

For a few minutes they were silent—they were awed into a state of quiet. It was good just to gaze into space and marvel at the extravagance of God. When conversation broke the beautiful silence, Peter said that he felt that he should go and uncover the grave of John and see for himself whether the gifts of the handkerchiefs were only a mystery of ecstasy, or did they actually exist in the place on the shelf?

Smiling, John the Beloved answered, "Peter, I feel sure you will be acting wisely if you uncover the grave of John. Let us go there now and see for ourselves whether or not this is an actual happening along with the knowledge."

With all these suggestions and thoughts of his own, Peter was baffled, but after a few minutes of quiet thought, John the Beloved broke the silence, saying, "Peter, have you already forgotten the promise Jesus gave you? Remember, you are our leader and decision maker. You are the successor to Jesus and therefore you have power and authority to make laws as if you were the Master Himself. You are the

Ambassador. You have every right to open John's grave. You have a right to know the answer to the question you seek. If the handkerchief is missing, well, then the miracle would be all the more profound. Also, I think it would be a holy act of faith and guidance of wisdom to venerate the sacred body of John at this hour of the Resurrection."

But Peter's answer was still wavering in decision as he answered, "I wonder what Jesus is doing? I would like to know where He is at this moment. Why didn't I ask Him before He was crucified where we should meet Him? Now that He is not here I realize how stupid I was not to have asked Him His will for this hour. I have been so neglectful. I feel so helpless. However, I cannot help but wonder if He needs our assistance in assembling the apostles together in a general meeting room."

John the Beloved was still persistent with his trend of thought in regard to John's tomb, and he questioned again, "Peter, if you decide to uncover John's body, may I accompany you?"

In deep humility and aware of his nothingness and that perhaps he should not be in such holy company of Christ's successor, Andrew withdrew himself from the group and walked into the semi-darkness.

With a quick move of his hands, Peter readjusted the handkerchief scarf around his head, which helped keep his unruly hair out of his eyes, and he answered, "I have made up my mind. Come, this very hour we will open the grave."

Turning to invite Andrew, and not seeing him, he called, "Where are you, Andrew?"

Andrew, all smiles when he heard Peter's voice, quickly returned to the group. It was not long before they were in the garden of Gethsemane kneeling beside the grave. With great reverence and silence they removed the earth from the top part of John's body. That which they saw stunned them—the handkerchief was not there. This scene before them was an actual miracle given to them through the kindness of John. No doubt he, too, wanted to give an added proof of the Resurrection and that nothing was impossible with the Messiah's help. John the Baptizer's face shone with a luster of pearl light, and a heavenly fragrance of roses issued from the open grave.

Bending low to venerate the brow of John, they could not help seeing the Messiah's chalice clasped in his folded hands. James could not hold back the tears as he quietly tore a strip of linen from his own toga and placed it over the face of John before they filled in the open grave. While they gently pushed the earth over his face, James said, "Peter, this is indeed a solemn occasion. Just think, this is the first tomb that has been opened by permission of the world's first most holy successor to Jesus. You have opened the way for all time as an example that we should venerate the dead. It is in keeping with the Master's wish; remember He prayed here. And we must not forget these heavenly fragrances! Peter, how can we thank you? May it please the Eternal Father to permit your successors to follow in your footsteps in this your way of honoring the dead."

CHAPTER 7

Jesus Appears in the Dungeon

AFTER THE BURIAL PLACE of John the Baptizer was covered, Peter and his friends who had accompanied him to Gethsemane stood in silence, offering their prayers of thanksgiving for the miracle they had just witnessed—the missing handkerchief of Peter and the heavenly fragrance of roses that came from John's body and the grave.

Peter's low, clear voice broke the silence as he began telling them again the events at the sepulcher during his bilocation ecstasy into the tomb. With great enthusiasm he told them about the amazing beauty of Light that had appeared around the Master's body a few minutes before He arose and greeted them. And Peter chuckled as he told them how quickly the stiffened, embalming rags had dropped from Jesus with the ease as if they were dry leaves falling from a tree.

Andrew asked, "Did His resurrected Body actually pass through the boulder in the sepulcher entrance?"

"Yes," answered Peter, "He came through the rock with as much ease and silence as sunlight through the rippling water of a creek. It was at that moment that the divine ecstasy left me and I found myself kneeling in prayer in the synagogue."

To this moment Peter did not know that the boulder had actually been rolled to one side by the tumbling earthquake as Jesus appeared just outside the tomb. In his gifts of bilocation Peter had not noticed the earthquake damage. Nor did he know that two angels, in assumed forms of young men dressed in white, had talked to the two guards, who had been converted to Christ within the hour through the amazing mystery of Light that had permeated through the walls of the sepulcher. They had been requested by the angels to quickly make their way into the city of Galilee, and from there Jesus Himself would direct them into their fields of mission work.

Immediately the guards recognized the great privilege that was theirs, and they hurried to Galilee after they had placed their swords on the boulder that had been in the tomb entrance. This gesture was an outward sign of their pledge of loyalty to Jesus—He was now their refuge and strength.

When Caiphas and Annas heard the news from the other guards who had returned to them, they were amazed and frightened. Quickly they sent searchers out to find the guards who had escaped.

Within the hour after Peter and his men had left Gethsemane, Mary of Magdala found Peter and told him that the Messiah's tomb was empty. Without answering he hurried to the sepulcher, hoping that Jesus had left a message of some sort that would tell them where they would meet. Naturally, Peter had assumed that Jesus would linger in or near the tomb—somehow Peter had failed to give this hour and conditions much thought. How he wished that he had asked Jesus about future instructions and directions as to where they should meet and when.

Arriving at the sepulcher, out of breath from running uphill, Peter leaned against the tunnel wall and peered into what he thought would be depths of darkness, but he was surprised, for the tomb was not dark; it was aglow with a heavenly Light that seemed to come from the two angels as they sat on the stone shelf upon which Jesus had been laid to rest in death.

Peter did not show any emotion or gesture that he was afraid of the angels. Slowly he bowed to them and they disappeared. The tomb was dark again. Into that darkness Peter found his way to the rock ledge, and falling across it he wept and venerated the stones upon which Jesus had rested—were they not great sacramentals? As he wept silent tears he recalled how just a few hours before this time he had cried over the Body of Jesus as He lay stilled in death. When his eyes had accustomed themselves to the darkness, he searched for the handkerchiefs. He touched them—there they were on the rock shelf exactly as he had seen them in his bilocation experience. Venerating them, he folded them into the folds of his toga and hurried out of the sepulcher.

For several days, the prisoners in the dungeon to whom Jesus had promised that He would return and give to them the Living Manna, continued with their songs to His praise and promises, and at intervals they would shout aloud their belief that He would rise from the sepulcher. All current events of the Resurrection had been kept from them until a soldier, who had been secretly converted because of Veronica's veil, told them that the Messiah must have risen because His Body was not in the tomb and neither could it be found.

The prisoners were jubilant. Loudly they called through the window, "Jesus, Jesus, Jesus." And in unison they prayed for Him to hurry, for they realized as the hours passed that they could be condemned to death for their belief and unruly conduct. They realized they had angered Caiphas and he could take his revenge out on them.

As they were praying, a night guard made his way into the darkened dungeon to place a lighted pitch torch in its niche for the night. Cursing the prisoners, he commanded them to be quiet or Caiphas would order them put to death. But all the louder they prayed and sang for the love of the Messiah.

Then suddenly the men were quiet—they were breathless as they watched a Light, as if it were coming from nowhere, appear in the dungeon. The room's dark, damp wall disappeared into the vapor mists of night, and in its stead appeared unnumbered arches of colored hues—each higher than the other until the whole Light gave the appearance of a huge funnel with it entrance inside the dungeon. Through this hall of rainbows, Jesus and many of His angels, who had assumed the appearance of young men, walked toward the happy but startled prisoners. And at the left side of Jesus walked John the Baptizer in his assumed body (a gift which the dead can use), and beside him walked Peter in his bilocation gift and knowledge.

Many of the prisoners recognizing John called to him—they were not afraid. John was smiling. His smile had broken the august stillness, which such an apparition would give to anyone, for here were two distinct miracles, the resurrected Jesus and bilocation.

To the prisoners, Jesus was robed as a King in all the pomp of ceremonial magnificence that gold could give. He blessed each one by lowering His crosier toward each man. They were so overcome with joy they could only gasp from astonishment. They were amazed at the size and beauty of His crosier, and they could hardly keep their eyes from it.

Walking to the side of the table from where He had once arranged the roses for Turan, Jesus addressed them, saying, "Men, do you remember Turan and how kind she was to you?"

They answered as one, "Yes, Lord, how could we forget her? Where is she? We have not seen her the last two days. We miss her gifts of food."

The Master answered, "I will tell you about her. At the moment of My death on the cross, and when My Father's hand of justice struck the earth with an earthquake and tore the temple veil in two, Turan was at that moment kneeling beside the veil in the temple and shock caused her to die in My Father's love.

"She was known to My Father as a victim soul of charity. Even though she never heard Me ask My friends to be their brother's keeper, she lived and worked that ideal in life. Because of this she merited, as an atonement, enough grace for the tombs of the saints to be opened at the moment of My death. Many are still rising and they will wander over the earth until they have received the Living Bread that I have also promised you.

"The rising of the dead is a figure of the first Resurrection, but you my friends may taste of its fruits while you breathe the breath of life. When you receive the Bread of Heaven you may consider your bodies undergoing a wonderful change, which is another form of a Resurrection given to you through the merits of My death. When you understand my indwelling is by means of the Living Bread, you will put on transfiguration in many different degrees of grace. When I indwell in you, and since I cannot have corruption in death neither shall you, even though your body crumbles into ashes, for the dust of you is most sacred and holy and as bright as the noonday sun because of being nurtured on Me. When death does come and you crumble to ashes, each speck of you will scatter across the world as acting, invisible missionaries to bless and do good to the world and cause evil to scatter. The new era and progress of nations will merit much from the dead and their invisible way of blessing. With Me there is no death. I am the Way and the Resurrection and your dust will live until the end of time.

"Friends, I have remembered My promise to you. I have come to give you the Living Manna. Before we begin the Feast, invite Turan to join you; she is waiting in the Light of this dungeon. She is one of the chosen ones and she will never taste of death, and now after she, too, receives the Living Manna, her dust will brighten and have power to bless the world until the end of time. The dust of saints is one of My greatest gifts to man."

The prisoners gasped! They looked in amazement at one another, then answering they said, "Jesus, Son of God, bring her here. Only You can invite the dead to live. Lord, if we only had our freedom we would serve and follow You and make You known throughout the world. Jesus, save us that we may serve You. It is said that we will die by the sword tomorrow. Help us that we may live to serve Your Kingdom on earth."

Another prisoner questioned before Jesus could answer, "Lord, we are so overcome with joy that we do not remember whether or not You promised us freedom of body and soul or of soul only. Please liberate us and allow us to defend Your followers as Turan defended us with food and drink."

Pleading, another prisoner said, "Jesus, I am guilty of my sin and deserving to be here, but many of these other men are innocent and deserve freedom. I beg of You to take them through these walls of Light when You leave, but let me stay here to live out the sentences of each man. Would that be unjust?"

Jesus answered, "Your charity is very great. You will be granted your desire. However, My plan is different than the one you suggest. The promise of My Father's Kingdom will be very great for you when I come to take you in death."

Jesus handed His crosier to Peter, better that He might have freedom to lift the kneeling prisoner to his feet and embrace him. He said to the prisoner, "Young man, your charity above the thought of self is so meritorious as to bring about the immediate freedom of all your friends."

At that moment all eyes were attracted to a woman walking toward them in the dungeon through the bows of Light. It was Turan! And beside her walked the risen Dismas!

The prisoners were so astonished that they could not utter a cheering tone of joy. They just looked. The two night guards who took their rest a little above the dungeon room in a shelf-like room, were aroused from their sleep by the strange Light and utter silence that permeated the halls and dungeon.

Quietly, they hurried to the dungeon depths. Startled upon seeing Jesus, they backed to the door for support for they were trembling. Then anger swept over them and they remembered their promise to Caiphas and the threat to their lives if they did not carry out his orders; all this made them lunge forward in order to grab Jesus as He stood at the head of the table. As they uttered words of success about arresting Him and as they touched Him, they fell dead at His feet. Without any further notice about the dead guards, Jesus continued talking to the prisoners and the necessity of baptism before they could receive the Living Manna.

After a short discourse, He asked, "Do you men desire to be baptized? This outward sign of actual baptism will not be necessary for Turan and Dismas because they died in the baptism of martyrdom and also under the laws of the Old Law."

All the men answered, "Yes, but how can this be accomplished here? We cannot get out of here to go into a river. The dungeon doors above are too well guarded for us to make an escape."

Turning to John, Jesus asked him to baptize the prisoners. Taking water from a bucket, he sprinkled water across and over each man's head and pronounced the words of baptism. Then in turn, in procession style, with Turan and Dismas leading, they approached the table and Jesus gave them the Living Bread.

Later when the morning watch of guards checked through the dungeon, they found only one prisoner—the brave man who had asked to stay when Jesus had invisibly bilocated the other men to other lands where they would preach Christ crucified.

Terrified upon seeing the dead guards and no avenue open through which the prisoners could have used as an escape, the guards tried forcing the one last man to tell how the escape had been accomplished. His silence brought about a quick martyrdom by the rough treatment given to him by the guards. Now they were frightened because they had no right to take the life of a prisoner. Kneeling in the mud, they prayed, asking God to have mercy on them, and then they acknowledged that they believed this Jesus must have been the Messiah. Fearfully they wept. And, as they made their way to the top of the stairs, they ran for their freedom through the huge doors into the streets and were soon lost in the milling crowds.

The End

EPILOGUE

How is it that a faithful Catholic would have the willingness to write a story that gives new voice to the life and experiences of Jesus Christ? The important question here is motivation. Cora Evans felt compelled by our Lord to write and at the same time felt wholly unqualified to take on such a task. Due to childhood illnesses, she never completed a full schedule of elementary school, and with less than two years of high school her education was rudimentary at best. Add to that, she was thirty years old before she had any exposure to the Catholic faith and she passed away at age fifty-six. It is what transpired during the years following her conversion that is truly remarkable.

A mystic and a visionary, Cora was called up into the deepest state of prayer known as ecstasy and rapture, but what our Lord preferred to have known as *Divine Slumber.* It is a pure gift from God and the source of all private revelation. Because the revelation is private there is no burden of belief on Catholics to accept it.

Cora's diary reveals that our Lord entrusted her with the responsibility to write. She suffered greatly for the privilege. After an experience of ecstasy, which might last for many hours, Cora would sit at the typewriter and attempt to capture the stories revealed to her.

Prior to writing this book, Cora Evans expressed her gratitude to our Lord: "I knelt in prayer to thank Jesus for His gift of knowledge and for the gift of writing He had given me, better to describe His life and infinite love into our world."

Cora prayed about the graces bestowed on her, the craft of writing, and the responsibility of accurately conveying our Lord's wishes: "My soul gives Thee thanks for this great trust, and in that trust I believe Thou will help me write the knowledge for souls to use as a stepping-stone to love Thee more.

"God's gifts were so clearly caught up into my soul, there to write them for His glory for souls on earth. To begin such a task is only to lose myself in the mystery of time and pretend that I am a citizen of Jerusalem taking notes from the Master's lips. I am just the reporter and of myself filled with many imperfections." She continued: "To understand, Beloved, the path of my mission would be to say with deepest sincerity, *not my will be done, but Thine.*" She always positioned writing as "an act of continuous praise for the glory of God."

A Remarkable Story

Saints are known by their stories. Their lives were given freely to the Lord in response to the circumstances at the time, and for the good of the whole Church. They did not ask for or expect to be in the situations in which they found themselves. These men and women radiated the holiness of God dwelling within them. It is the story of their lives, how they responded to grace, their impact on others, combined with God's proof by miracles in their name that led the pope to declare, "We know for certain this person is with God in Heaven."

Only God can make a saint. At this stage there is no certainty that Cora Evans will become a canonized saint. Today, she is a Servant of God[28], and her cause is under way in the Diocese of Monterey, California.

Cora Evans was born July 9, 1904, and she passed away March 30, 1957. Her first mystical experience, an apparition of the Blessed Mother, took place when she was three years old. It was an event she could not fully comprehend and would never forget. Many years would pass before she understood the vision and the message.

Cora was raised a Mormon and was married to Maclellan Evans in the well-known Mormon Temple in Salt Lake City, Utah. That event was the turning point in her life. She left the secret ceremony disillusioned and disappointed with Mormonism, especially the doctrine that placed manmade gods above the God of Abraham. "I was without a God and religion but had gained a very wonderful husband. As I looked at him and learned to love him more and more, I resolved to help find a God for him. After ten years of searching, we found the One True God in the Roman Catholic Church."

During the ten years that followed the marriage ceremony, Cora and Mack had three children. They suffered the loss of a child, Bobby, when he was ten months old. Cora investigated many religions, but believed it would be a waste of time to even inquire about Catholicism. Although she no longer considered herself a Mormon, she held on to pervasive anti-Catholic warnings she learned growing up in Utah.

---

28 "A Catholic whose cause of beatification and canonization has been initiated is called Servant of God." *Sanctorum Mater*, Congregation for the Causes of Saints, Title II, Article 4, February 22, 2007.

On December 9, 1934, Cora was quite ill. The family lived in Ogden, Utah, at the time. Cora was in bed and the radio was on the other side of the room. No one was home and she was too sick to get out of bed to change the station when the Catholic Hour began broadcasting. Despite her aversion to Catholicism, Cora was forced to listen to Monsignor Duane Hunt[29] talk about the Blessed Mother and the teachings of the Catholic faith. His message conflicted with the negative stories Cora had been told about Catholics. As soon as she recovered, Cora went to nearby Saint Joseph Catholic Church to inquire about the faith and have her questions answered. This was a courageous move for a former Mormon. A series of meetings followed, including debates in her home between the parish priest, Father Edward Vaughn, and several Mormon bishops. Cora quickly became aware of the truth of Christianity and the obvious false stories told about Catholics. She appreciated Father Vaughn's demeanor and the clarity of his responses to questions about Catholic doctrine. Cora was baptized March 30, 1935, and received her first Holy Communion the next day. Mack and their daughters, LaVonne and Dorothy, followed her lead a few months later.

Cora influenced many Mormons to visit Saint Joseph's, inviting them to open house gatherings. Years later, Father Vaughn wrote a letter confirming that through Cora's evangelization efforts there were hundreds of conversions of Mormons to the Catholic faith.

Vow Day for a Mystic

In July 1938, she had a profound mystical experience. Cora wrote about this event in the autobiography of her mystical life, titled "Captain of the Ship." During this deep ecstasy Cora made the choice to serve God for the rest of her life. She described the state of her soul as being intimately united to God, and referred to this as her *vow day:* "It was necessary for me to live my chosen vocation with Him as my companion. By loaning Jesus my humanity for Him to govern as well as dwell within, would make my life a living prayer for He was life,

29 Most Reverend Duane G. Hunt (1884-1960), consecrated Bishop of the Diocese of Salt Lake City, October 28, 1937. Bishop Hunt visited Cora in her home in Boulder Creek, California, shortly before she passed away in 1957.

living life within me, and my body now dead to me was His living cross, His cross to take to Calvary, Calvary, the door to eternal life."

The Move to Southern California and Spiritual Guidance

Due to religious and cultural prejudices, it was virtually impossible for Cora's husband, also a convert, to hold down a job. In 1941 the family moved to Southern California. In retrospect, I recognize this as God's plan. Cora began having mystical experiences with much greater frequency. In response to her search for spiritual guidance, on February 20, 1945, Father Frank Parrish, S.J.[30] was appointed her confessor and spiritual director by the Provincial[31] of the Society of Jesus (Jesuits). The meeting took place at Loyola High School in Los Angeles.

On December 24, 1946, Jesus revealed the mission entrusted to Cora. She learned that she was to promulgate the Mystical Humanity of Christ, a way of prayer that encourages people to live with a heightened awareness of the indwelling presence of Jesus in their daily lives. It is Eucharistic spirituality, and Jesus promised to foster the devotion.

Father Frank served as the spiritual guide of Cora's soul for the rest of her life. His written account of events is testimony to Cora's heroic virtues and her reputation of sanctity.

Cora is considered a hidden mystic, and although there were many friends, including priests and religious, she was not known publicly. There are many examples of visionaries who where unknown at the time of their death, including Saints Margaret Mary (devotion to the Sacred Heart of Jesus), Catherine Laboure (Miraculous Medal), and Sister Faustina (Divine Mercy). Like these women, there was never any publicity about Cora's private revelation.

The life story of Cora Evans, wife and mother, is that of a remarkable woman who practiced Christian virtues and earned a reputation for holiness. She became a daily communicant and one of her favorite devotions was the Stations of the Cross. At times she would say the

30 Fr. Frank Parrish, S.J. (1911-2003) is best known in Catholic circles for his blessing of terminally ill Fr. John A. Houle, S.J. with the relic of Blessed Claude la Colombiere on February 23, 1990. This led to a miraculous cure—a first class miracle. Colombiere, who had been the spiritual director of Saint Margaret Mary, was declared a saint and canonized by Pope John Paul II, May 31, 1992.

31 Fr. Joseph J. King, S.J. (1900-1986) served as provincial from January 1943 to August 1948. The geographic area served in 1945 included California, Arizona, Nevada and Utah.

stations in reverse, mirroring the way the Blessed Mother saw them as she walked home from the crucifixion.

Cora's gifts of mysticism (suffering the wounds of Christ, known as the stigmata; the phenomena of bilocation associated with deep insight, a mystical gift not fully understood; the fragrance of roses associated with her presence, known as the odor of sanctity; visionary experiences, known as ecstasy; and profound writings far beyond her education level) are not in and of themselves sufficient grounds for the declaration of sainthood. It is the story of her life with the proof of heroic virtues that places everything else in context.

The Vatican granted *nihil obstat*[32] for the cause for Beatification and Canonization of the Servant of God, Cora Evans. The Diocese of Monterey, California, is proceeding with the investigation of her life and writings.

Prayer for the Intercession of Cora Evans

Cora prayed that she would be given the same gift as Saint Therese of Lisieux, the Little Flower, spending her heaven on earth doing good, and promised to pray for all who asked for her intercession after first visiting the Blessed Sacrament. The Archbishop of San Francisco granted the Imprimatur[33] for the intercessory prayer, written by Father Frank Parrish, S.J.

Dear Jesus, You blessed Cora Evans with many supernatural mystical gifts as a means of drawing us to a deeper and more intimate union with your Sacred Heart through Your Divine Indwelling, Your Mystical Humanity. I ask You through her intercession to help me in my special request (name the favor) and my efforts to do Your will here on earth and be with You, Your Blessed Mother, Saint Joseph and the whole Court of Heaven forever.

Say three times: the Our Father, Hail Mary, Glory Be to the Father.

---

32 Nihil obstat (Latin "Nothing stand in the way") is a term used for the approval for a given process to proceed. Granted by Angelo Cardinal Amato, S.D.B., Prefect, *Congregation for the Causes of Saints*, Rome, Italy. Letter March 29, 2012.

33 Imprimatur (Latin "it may be printed") approval to publish given by diocesan bishop provides assurance that the published text conforms to Church teaching. Granted Most Reverend George Niederauer, Archbishop of San Francisco. Letter February 18, 2011.

Profound Questions

There is new, never before revealed, information in this book. Many questions arise and remain unanswered at this point in time. Will the swaddling clothes be uncovered? Will the place of prayer built by John the Baptist be found? Is the body of John the Baptist incorrupt? Does this book lend support for the Shroud of Turin? And the most profound revelation of all: Will the Church finally locate the Holy Grail? Cora provides new details of historical and archaeological significance. And what are we to make of Cora's interpretation of the words spoken by Jesus, Mary, the apostles, and others? My answer: to the degree that you come closer to Christ, it is good. If anything causes doubt or concern, rely on Sacred Scripture.

Cora prayed, "Please give me the grace to remember the vision and understanding in Thy wisdom to better relate to friends Thy hidden mystery of love for them . . . help me, Jesus, to write them as You would like them written for Thy glory to be better known among men." The purpose of her life, the suffering she endured, and her writings inspire us to live with awareness of the presence of Jesus. When you practice this way of prayer, known as the Mystical Humanity of Christ, you take Jesus with you wherever you go.

Your comments are welcome and encouraged.

Michael McDevitt
Custodian for the Writings of Cora Evans
MysticalHumanity@aol.com
CoraEvans.com